Real Geometries

Real Geometries

by
Walter Benz
Professor of Mathematics
University of Hamburg

Wissenschaftsverlag
Mannheim · Leipzig · Wien · Zürich

Die Deutsche Bibliothek – CIP-Einheitsaufnahme

Benz, Walter:
Real geometries / Walter Benz.
– Mannheim; Leipzig; Wien;
Zürich: BI-Wiss.-Verl., 1994
    ISBN 3-411-16941-9

Printed on acid-free paper
Supported in part by the Hamburgische Wissenschaftliche Stiftung

© Bibliographisches Institut & F.A. Brockhaus AG, Mannheim 1994
Printed by Progressdruck GmbH, Speyer
Bound by Ludwig Fleischmann, Fulda
Printed in Germany
ISBN 3-411-16941-9

Preface

A mapping f of $\mathbb{R}^n$, $n \geq 3$, into itself such that $f(x), f(y), f(z)$ are the vertices of a triangle of area 1 whenever x, y, z are the vertices of a triangle of area 1, must be a euclidean isometry of $\mathbb{R}^n$. This is a theorem of June Lester [5] (for a proof see section 5.1.2). A mapping f of the set M^n of all lines of $\mathbb{R}^n$, $n \geq 3$, into itself such that $f(x), f(y), f(z)$ are the sides of a triangle of area 1 whenever x, y, z are the sides of a triangle of area 1, must be induced by a euclidean isometry g of $\mathbb{R}^n$, i.e. the action of g on M^n is equal to the mapping f. This is a theorem of Wen–ling Huang [1] (for a proof see section 6.4.2). These and other theorems of a similar spirit will be presented in this book. This means that a young and active geometrical discipline called *characterizations of geometrical mappings under mild hypotheses* will play an important role in the book. This discipline started almost at the same time that the fundamental theorems of A.D. Alexandrov (see section 5.9) and F.S. Beckman, D.A. Quarles (see section 5.1.1) appeared. I would like to emphasize that no regularity assumptions (like differentiability or continuity) are required in the theorems of that discipline in question.

However, this book is designed mainly as a modern text on several geometries which were developed since the beginning of the 19. century. This means especially that I tried to present newer results whenever possible, and it means also that I tried to include newer geometries like Einstein's cylinder universe, de Sitter's world (which both appear sometimes as shadows even in popular books) and for instance the proportion geometries or the real chain geometries. The reader will find affine geometry over a real vector space S of arbitrary (even infinite) dimension ≥ 2. In section 5.4.3 the theorem is proved that the set of parabolas is a *defining notion* (see section 1.2) of that specific geometry: if γ is a bijection of S such that the image $\gamma(p)$ of every parabola p of S is contained in a parabola, then the mapping $x \to \gamma(x) - \gamma(0)$ is a linear mapping of S. Of course, the set of lines is also a defining notion of affine geometry (see section 5.4.1). The reader will find projective geometry over a real vector space S of arbitrary (even infinite) dimension ≥ 2. In the case $\dim S \geq 3$ the theorem is proved (see section 5.6.3) that the set of lines is a defining notion of projective geometry. In section 5.6.5 all 4–point–invariants of 1–dimensional real projective geometry are determined (see Theorem 35). In the same section 1–dimensional projective geometry over a real algebra is considered and all harmonic mappings are determined (Theorem 36) in this general case. Section 5.6.6 contributes to the following problem. How to describe geometrical mappings which are not defined for every point of a geometry? The reader will find some non–euclidean geometry: in section 5.7.3 for instance the theorem is proved that the volume of an h–bounded and closed subset M of n–dimensional hyperbolic geometry is given by the Lebesgue integral

$$\mu(M) = \int\limits_{M} \frac{dx}{x_{n+1}}$$

which is written in Weierstrass coordinates.

In chapter 1 it is my intention to present precise definitions of certain notions which are fundamental in the theory of geometries and which are sometimes given in the literature in the form of examples. I think of notions like *invariant notion, invariant (function), notion of a set S, function of a set S, Übertragungsprinzip*, among others. Three main possibilities to define a geometry are fundamental in this book, namely the definition of a geometry

(1) *as geometry of a transformation group* (see section 1.1),

(2) *as geometry of a notion or a function* (see section 1.2),

(3) *as a substructure of a geometry* (see section 1.3).

With respect to the first possibility I refer to Felix Klein who wrote in his Erlangen programme (see section 1.5): *Es ist eine Mannigfaltigkeit und in derselben eine Transformationsgruppe gegeben. Man entwickle die auf die Gruppe bezügliche Invariantentheorie.* With respect to the term *Invariantentheorie* the following remark of Felix Klein in his collected works (New York, 1973, Volume 1, p. 464) might be mentioned: *Bei diesem Term ist hier und in der Folge keineswegs an die Frage der jeweiligen rationalen ganzen Invarianten irgendwelcher vorgelegter Formen bzw. der zwischen ihnen bestehenden rationalen, ganzen Syzygien gedacht. Diese Frage war mir 1872, entsprechend meinem Verkehr mit Clebsch (der erst 1871 seine Theorie der binären Formen herausgegeben hatte) selbstverständlich durchaus geläufig. Trotzdem fühlte ich mich an sie keineswegs gebunden. Ich verstand unter der Invariantentheorie einer Gruppe schlechtweg die Lehre von den bei der Gruppe unverändert bleibenden Beziehungen irgendwelcher vorgelegter Gebilde.*

Functional equations are fundamental in geometry (see section 1.6). They occur at many places of this book. If one tries for instance to find all 3–point–invariants f of a geometry (S, G), one has to solve the functional equation

$$\forall_{x,y,z \in S} \quad \forall_{\varphi \in G} \; f(x,y,z) = f(\varphi(x), \varphi(y), \varphi(z))$$

where the unknown functions f are mappings from $S \times S \times S$ into abstract sets $W \neq \emptyset$. However, all results which are needed with respect to functional equations, are proved in the book.

Five sections of chapter 2 deal with 1–dimensional hyperbolic geometry. It seems to be convenient, to get acquainted in the framework of such a simple geometry with important notions like *n–point–invariant, distance, Weierstrass coordinates*, and with important results about special functional equations, which play a role at several places in the book. In section 2.6 the Weierstrass model of n–dimensional hyperbolic geometry is studied, Lorentz boosts are introduced and also a group of Lorentz matrices which acts sharply transitively on the set of points of the geometry in question.

Two n–dimensional real geometries are studied in chapters 3 and 4, namely Einstein's cylinder universe and de Sitter's world. The latter geometry is a so–called Einstein space since it satisfies the equation $R_{ij} = \lambda g_{ij}$ where λ is a scalar and where R_{ij} and g_{ij} are the Ricci tensor and the fundamental tensor, respectively. Einstein's cylinder universe is not an Einstein space, but a solution of Einstein's law of gravitation (see A.S. Eddington, The Mathematical Theory of Relativity, New York 1965, 159 f). In Theorem 3 (chapter 3) I determine all 2–point–invariants of (C^n, M^n) (see section 3.1) and in Theorem 4 of the same chapter I prove that all solutions $\varphi : C^n \to C^n$ of

$$\forall_{x,y \in C^n} \quad f(x,y) = f\big(\varphi(x), \varphi(y)\big)$$

with $f(x,y) = (\arccos xy)^2 - (x_{n+1} - y_{n+1})^2$ are given by the mappings $\varphi \in M^n$. Here put $xy = x_1 y_1 + \ldots + x_n y_n$ and $\arccos xy \in [0, \pi]$. In Theorem 5 (see section 3.5) I characterize the notion of *distance* of Einstein's cylinder universe. In Theorem 15 (see section 3.8) all $f : C^n \to C^n$ ($n \geq 3$) are determined which preserve null–lines. Lie transformations are involved in this problem as are bijections between countable sets. In section 3.10 I define the notion of Einstein's cylinder universe over a ring. I think that such a definition makes sense, since one obtains in this way finite and hence combinatorial structures in the case that the ring is finite. Finite geometrical structures with nice groups (see Theorem 19), having nice transitivity properties, seem to be welcome in combinatorics. The highlights of chapter 4 on de Sitter's world are Theorems 12, 15, 16, 19, 20. In Theorem 12 I determine all 2–point–invariants of (S^n, Δ^n) which are additive on lines. In Theorem 15 I determine all bijections of de Sitter's plane (up to motions as factors) such that images and pre–images of null–lines are null–lines. In Theorem 16 I prove that all bijections of the set of points of de Sitter's plane such that images and pre–images of null–lines are null–lines, and such that images of open lines are open lines, are motions of (S^2, Δ^2). In Theorem 19 I prove that S^n, $n \geq 3$, together with the parallel classes of null–lines can be mapped bijectively onto the set L^{n-1} of all Lie cycles of $(n-1)$–dimensional Lie geometry such that the objects x, y are on a common null–line if and only if their images are in the position of contact. Theorem 20 is a theorem of June Lester: every bijection of S^n, $n \geq 3$, such that images and pre–images of null–lines are null–lines, must be in Δ^n. I reduce the proof of this theorem to the Fundamental Theorem of Lie geometry. A proof of this important theorem can be found in my book Geometrische Transformationen (W. Benz [1]). I did not repeat in the present book proofs of some main theorems of different geometries which can be found in my book Geometrische Transformationen. Several groups of the present book on real geometries are, of course, *r–parameter Lie groups* for some finite r. An r–parameter Lie group is a group G which is at the same time an r–dimensional analytic manifold such that the mapping

$$\mu : G \times G \to G$$

with $\mu(g_1, g_2) := g_1 \, g_2^{-1}$ is analytic. The group M^n of Einstein's cylinder universe is a $\left[\binom{n}{2} + 1 \right]$–parameter group and the group Δ^n of de Sitter's world is for instance a $\binom{n+1}{2}$–parameter group which is easy to check by counting the essential parameters.

I already mentioned several topics which are studied in chapters 5 and 6. A bijection of $\mathbb{R}^n$, $n \geq 2$, such that euclidean circles are mapped into euclidean circles, is a similarity transformation (Theorem 8, section 5.2.1). This seems to be really a beautiful characterization of similarity transformations. Of course, 3–point–invariants in euclidean geometry have something to do with *congruent triangles* (see section 5.1.4) and 2–line–invariants in the geometry of similarity transformations have something to do with *angles* (see section 5.2.2). For a Cremona geometry (see section 6.1) $\mathbb{R}^n$ must be extended to a set $\overline{\mathbb{R}^n} \supset \mathbb{R}^n$ such that a group of birational transformations acts as a group of bijections on $\overline{\mathbb{R}^n}$. Chain geometries, circle geometries, sphere geometries, among others, are Cremona geometries. The notion of a Cremona geometry is hence one of the fundamental notions in geometry which certainly deserves attention in a book on real geometries. Proportions play an important role in arts and in architecture. Generalizations of proportions may also be used in these fields. The reader might get a better impression of this statement if he looks to the *rectangle patterns* in section 6.5.7 constructed by Detlef Gronau. Proportion polynomials (see section 6.5.5) are involved here.

This is a book on real geometries despite the fact that sometimes generalizations even to the ring case are possible (see sections 3.10, 4.7). Of course, in the case of some geometries (S, G) of this book, $\mathbb{R}$ may be replaced by any field. Think of affine and projective geometry, of chain geometries and of some other Cremona geometries. At other places, generalizations still might cause difficult problems: a general version, for instance, of the theorem of Beckman and Quarles (see section 5.1.1) for the field case is not known. Partial results in this context can be found in F. Radó [3], [4]. The reason that I restricted this book to the real case is simply that this case is the most prominent and important one, and that it is of interest also for mathematicians of other disciplines.

As far as the prerequisites which are necessary for a fruitful use of the book are concerned, I would like to say that most parts of the book can be read at the sophomore level, after mastering general and linear algebra, calculus, and basic geometry of $\mathbb{R}^2$ and $\mathbb{R}^3$.

It is a pleasant task for an author to thank those who have helped him. I must chiefly give my thanks to Alice Günther, June Lester, and Hans–Joachim Samaga, who provided me with many valuable suggestions on the preparation of the final version of this book. I wish to express my gratitude to Roland Höfer, who read some chapters saving me from error more than once, and to Wen–ling Huang, who gave me her assistence on matters relating to the manuscript. I wish also to acknowledge the fine work of Detlef Gronau, Graz, already mentioned. Finally, I would like to express my thanks to the BI Wissenschaftsverlag and especially to Hermann Engesser for their conscientious work and helpful cooperation.

My book owes so much to ideas of Felix Klein that its preface should also contain the following private reminiscence. When my PhD–supervisor Robert Furch (1894–1967) after having finished his doctoral exam in Tübingen went to Göttingen in 1920, he became one of seven young mathematicians who Felix Klein (1849–1925) invited to attend his private lectures in his house. (The official retirement of Klein already took place in 1913.) As I know from many conversations with my dear teacher, these lectures had a dominating influence on his life as a geometer. Shortly before 1920 Felix Klein wrote his important paper in which Einstein's cylinder universe and de Sitter's world play the central role (see F. Klein [2]). I am deeply thankful to have had the opportunity to receive a geometrical education with this background.

Königsberg, September 1993,
and Hamburg, January 1994   Walter Benz

uxori bene consulenti

Contents

Chapter 1

GEOMETRIES
GENERAL THEORY

1.1 Geometry of a transformation group

Let $S \neq \emptyset$ be a set and let G be a group of bijections of S with the usual multiplication

$$\forall_{x \in S} \ (fg)(x) := f\big(g(x)\big)$$

for $f, g \in G$. Suppose that $N \neq \emptyset$ is a set and that

$$\varphi : G \times N \to N$$

is a mapping satisfying

(i) $\varphi(fg, l) = \varphi\big(f, \varphi(g, l)\big)$,

(ii) $\varphi(e, l) = l$

for all $f, g \in G$ and $l \in N$ where e denotes the neutral element of G. We then call (N, φ) an *invariant notion* of (S, G). Instead of $\varphi(f, l)$ we often shall write only $f(l)$. Let (N, φ) be an invariant notion of (S, G) and let W be a set. A function

$$h : N \to W$$

is called an *invariant* (or an *invariant function*) of (S, G) iff

$$\forall_{f \in G} \ \forall_{l \in N} \ h\big(f(l)\big) = h(l) \tag{1}$$

holds true.

If we put $N := S$ and if we define $\varphi(f, x)$ as the image of $x \in S$ under $f \in G$, we get an example (N, φ) of an invariant notion. The function

$$h : S \rightarrow \{1\}$$

is obviously an example of an invariant of (S, G). If we define

$$\varphi(f, (x_1, \ldots, x_n)) := (f(x_1), \ldots, f(x_n)) \tag{2}$$

for $f \in G$ and $x_1, \ldots, x_n \in S$, then

$$(S \times \ldots \times S, \varphi)$$

is also an invariant notion of (S, G).

The structure (S, G) will be called a *geometry*. A fundamental problem of the theory of geometries is to study invariants and invariant notions of structures (S, G). Another important problem in geometry is the characterization of structures (S, G) of a certain type. Many results are known concerning both problems as we will see later on.

We now would like to present an example of a structure (S, G). Define $S := \mathbb{C}$ and moreover G as the group of all bijections

$$z \rightarrow \gamma(z) = az + b$$

of $\mathbb{C}$ with $a, b \in \mathbb{C}$ and $|a| = 1$. If we identify $(x, y) \in \mathbb{R}^2$ with $x + iy \in \mathbb{C}$, then the mapping γ is a translation of $\mathbb{R}^2$ whenever $a = 1$

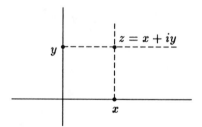

and a rotation about

$$p := \frac{b}{1 - a}$$

in the case $a \neq 1$ in view of $\gamma(p) = p$ and

$$(\gamma(z) - p) = a \cdot (z - p).$$

The mappings γ are hence of a simple nature and it is therefore immediately clear that the set $\mathbb{C}$ of *points*, the set L of *lines*, the set C of *euclidean circles*, the set of *parabolas* (and many other sets) must be invariant notions of $(\mathbb{C}, G)$. Of course, $\gamma(l)$ is defined here as the image of the point set l under γ. Scarcely more complicated than the previous examples is the invariant notion N of all 3–circles of $\mathbb{C}$: By a 3–circle we mean three circles c_1, c_2, c_3 which have the property that c_i and c_j intersect in exactly one point for all $i, j \in \{1, 2, 3\}$ with $i \neq j$. (Observe that the points $c_i \cap c_j$ may coincide.)

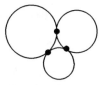

Here also $\gamma(l)$ denotes the image of the point set l under the mapping γ. An example of an invariant notion (N, φ) such that N is not a subset of $S = \mathbb{C}$ is given by

$$N := \{(z, r) \in \mathbb{C} \times \mathbb{R} \mid r > 0\}$$

and

$$\varphi(\gamma, (z, r)) := (\gamma(z), |a| \cdot r)$$

for $\gamma(z) = az + b$ with $a \neq 0$. (In the case of our present group G, we have to put $|a| = 1$.) This notion has an important geometrical meaning: (z, r) might be considered as coordinates of the circle with center z and radius r. Then $\gamma(z, r)$ are the coordinates of the image circle of (z, r) under γ.

A well–known invariant of $(\mathbb{C}, G)$ is the distance function

$$d : \mathbb{C} \times \mathbb{C} \to \mathbb{R}$$

which is defined by

$$d(x_1 + ix_2, y_1 + iy_2) := \sqrt{(x_1 - y_1)^2 + (x_2 - y_2)^2},$$

i.e. by

$$d(z, w) := |z - w|.$$

Several times we have already spoken of an invariant notion N instead of the invariant notion (N, φ). We will do this also in future whenever the definition of φ is clear from the context. Obviously,

$$(l_1, l_2) \in L \times L$$

is such a case: here of course (see (2)) we put

$$\varphi(\gamma, (l_1, l_2)) := (\gamma(l_1), \gamma(l_2)).$$

The invariant notion

$$M = \{(l_1, l_2) \in L \times L \mid l_1 \cap l_2 \neq \emptyset\}$$

is called the set of *oriented angles* modulo π.

With a fixed orientation of $\mathbb{R}^2$ (we identify $(x_1, x_2) \in \mathbb{R}^2$ as before with $x_1 + ix_2 \in \mathbb{C}$) we may define an *angle measure* modulo π,

$$\psi : M \rightarrow [0, \pi[,$$

as follows. Put $\psi(l, l) = 0$. In the case $l_1 \neq l_2$ denote by c the oriented circle in $\mathbb{C}$ with center $l_1 \cap l_2$, radius 1 and the orientation of $\mathbb{R}^2$.

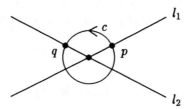

Let p be a point of $c \cap l_1$. Now go along c in the direction of its orientation from p on, up to the first point q of $c \cap l_2$. Define $\psi(l_1, l_2)$ to be the length of the arc from p to q.

Obviously, the angle measure ψ is an invariant of $(\mathbb{C}, G)$.

Let N be the set of all bounded subsets F of $\mathbb{R}^2$ such that the Riemann integral

$$\mu(F) := \iint\limits_{\mathbb{R}^2} \chi_F(x, y)\, dx\, dy$$

exists where χ_F denotes the characteristic function

$$\chi_F(x, y) = \begin{cases} 1 & (x, y) \in F \\ & \text{for} \\ 0 & (x, y) \in \mathbb{R}^2 \backslash F \end{cases}$$

of F. The set N is an invariant notion of $(\mathbb{C}, G)$ and $\mu : N \rightarrow \mathbb{R}$ must be an invariant.

1.2   Geometry of a notion or a function

Geometries often are not defined by means of a transformation group G. Occasionally it is a certain notion or a certain function which leads to a geometry. Let for instance S be the set $\mathbb{R}^n$, n an integer ≥ 1, and let

$$d : S \times S \to \mathbb{R}$$

be the function

$$d(x, y) = \sqrt{\sum_{i=1}^{n}(x_i - y_i)^2}$$

for $x = (x_1, \ldots, x_n) \in \mathbb{R}^n$ and $y = (y_1, \ldots, y_n) \in \mathbb{R}^n$. We ask for the set G of all mappings

$$\gamma : S \to S$$

such that

$$d(x, y) = d(\gamma(x), \gamma(y)) \tag{3}$$

holds true for all $x, y \in S$.

PROPOSITION 1. *Let $\gamma : \mathbb{R}^n \to \mathbb{R}^n$, $n \geq 1$, be a mapping satisfying (3) for all $x, y \in \mathbb{R}^n$. Then there exists an orthogonal and real $n \times n$-matrix Q with*

$$\gamma(x) = xQ + \gamma(0) \tag{4}$$

for all $x \in \mathbb{R}^n$.

Proof. $g(x) := \gamma(x) - \gamma(0)$ also preserves d. By means of the scalar product

$$x \cdot y := \sum_{i=1}^{n} x_i y_i \tag{5}$$

we get $p^2 = [g(p)]^2$, $(p - q)^2 = [g(p) - g(q)]^2$, i.e.

$$pq = g(p)g(q) \tag{6}$$

for all $p, q \in \mathbb{R}^n$ as a consequence of

$$d(0, p) = d(0, g(p)) \text{ and } d(p, q) = d(g(p), g(q)).$$

$E_1 = (1, 0, \ldots, 0)$, $E_2 = (0, 1, 0, \ldots, 0), \ldots, E_n = (0, \ldots, 0, 1)$ is an orthonormal basis of $\mathbb{R}^n$ and hence so is $g(E_1), \ldots, g(E_n)$ in view of (6). Put

$$x =: \sum_{i=1}^{n} x_i E_i, \quad g(x) =: \sum_{i=1}^{n} \xi_i g(E_i).$$

Hence (6) implies

$$x_i = x E_i = g(x) g(E_i) = \xi_i$$

for $i = 1, \ldots, n$. Define

$$g(x) =: \sum_{i=1}^{n} x_i' E_i$$

and

$$g(E_i) =: \sum_{j=1}^{n} q_{ij} E_j, \quad i = 1, \ldots, n.$$

Hence

$$(x_1' \ldots x_n') = (x_1 \ldots x_n) \begin{pmatrix} q_{11} & \cdots & q_{1n} \\ \vdots & & \\ q_{n1} & \cdots & q_{nn} \end{pmatrix}.$$

The orthogonality of $Q := (q_{ij})$ is a straightforward consequence of the orthonormality of $g(E_1), \ldots, g(E_n)$.   □

The situation is now indeed as described: $S = \mathbb{R}^n$ together with the function $d : S \times S \to \mathbb{R}$ leads to the geometry (S, G). As an abstract framework of the present situation, *distance spaces* may be defined (see the book Geometrische Transformationen of the author, 33ff; from now on we shall refer to this book in form GT). A distance space (S, W, d) consists of sets $S \neq \emptyset$, W and of a function

$$d : S \times S \to W.$$

$d(x, y)$, $x, y \in S$, is called the *distance* of x, y (in this order). To S define the group G of all bijections γ of S satisfying

$$\forall_{x, y \in S} \; d(x, y) = d\big(\gamma(x), \gamma(y)\big).$$

We thus get a geometry (S, G) from (S, W, d). Since $S \times S$ is an invariant notion of (S, G),

$$d : S \times S \to W$$

must be an invariant of (S, G).

Let $S \neq \emptyset$ be a set and denote by Perm S the group of all bijections of S. Suppose that (Ω, φ) is an invariant notion of $(S, \text{Perm } S)$ and that $N \neq \emptyset$ is a subset of Ω. We then will call

$$(N, \; \varphi : [\text{ Perm } S] \times N \to \Omega) \tag{7}$$

a *notion* of S and a mapping

$$h : N \to W \tag{8}$$

a *function* of S where φ also denotes the restriction of

$$\varphi : [\text{ Perm } S] \times \Omega \to \Omega$$

on $[\text{Perm } S] \times N$ and where W is a set.

We shall now define the group $G(N)$ of a notion (7) of S and moreover the group $G(h)$ of a function h of S. Let $G(N)$ be the set of all $\gamma \in \text{Perm } S$ such that $\varphi(\gamma, l)$ and $\varphi(\gamma^{-1}, l)$ are in N for all $l \in N$. Let moreover $G(h)$ be the set of all $\gamma \in G(N)$ such that

$$h(\gamma(l)) = h(l)$$

holds true for all $l \in N$.

Observe that $\gamma^{-1} \in G(h)$ is a consequence of $\gamma \in G(h)$: since $\gamma \in G(N)$, γ^{-1} must also be an element of $G(N)$. Hence $\gamma^{-1}(l) \in N$ for $l \in N$ and thus

$$h(l) = h(\gamma[\gamma^{-1}(l)]) = h(\gamma^{-1}(l)).$$

We hence get geometries $(S, G(N))$, $(S, G(h))$, respectively, associated to a notion N or a function h of S. We shall call a notion N of S a *defining notion* of (S, G) iff $G = G(N)$. The function h of S will similarly be called a *defining function* of (S, G) iff $G = G(h)$. A system

$$h_1, \ldots, h_r, N_1, \ldots, N_s$$

of functions $h_1, \ldots, h_r$ and notions $N_1, \ldots, N_s$ of S is said to be a *defining* (or *complete*) *system* of functions and notions of (S, G) iff

$$G = G(h_1) \cap \ldots \cap G(h_r) \cap G(N_1) \cap \ldots \cap G(N_s).$$

The function d of $\mathbb{C}$ is not a defining function of the example $(\mathbb{C}, G)$ which we considered in section 1.1: there are elements in $G(d)$ which are not in G, for instance the mapping

$$x_1 + ix_2 \to x_1 - ix_2 \; (x_1, x_2 \in \mathbb{R}).$$

(Define the underlying invariant notion of $(\mathbb{C}, \mathrm{Perm}\ \mathbb{C})$ for d by $\Omega = \mathbb{C} \times \mathbb{C}$ and $\gamma(z, w) = (\gamma(z), \gamma(w))$ for $\gamma \in \mathrm{Perm}\ \mathbb{C}$.)

But according to Proposition 1

$$d : \mathbb{R}^n \times \mathbb{R}^n \to \mathbb{R}$$

is a defining function of $(\mathbb{R}^n, G)$ where G denotes the group of all mappings (4) with orthogonal and real $n \times n$–matrices Q.

In order to get an example for a geometry $(S, G(N))$, define N to be the set of all lines of $S := \mathbb{R}^2$. (Let Ω here be the set of all subsets of $\mathbb{R}^2$ and define $\varphi(\gamma, T)$ by

$$\gamma(T) := \{\gamma(t) \mid t \in T\}$$

for $T \subseteq \mathbb{R}^2$ and $\gamma \in \mathrm{Perm}\ \mathbb{R}^2$.)

PROPOSITION 2. *Suppose that $\gamma \in \mathrm{Perm}\ \mathbb{R}^2$ satisfies*

(∗)   *Whenever l is a line of $\mathbb{R}^2$, then so is $\gamma(l)$.*

Then there exist real numbers a_{ij}, a_k with $i, j, k \in \{1, 2\}$ such that

$$\gamma(x_1 x_2) = (x_1 x_2) \begin{pmatrix} a_{11} & a_{12} \\ a_{21} & a_{22} \end{pmatrix} + (a_1 a_2)$$

holds true for all $(x_1, x_2) \in \mathbb{R}^2$. Moreover

$$a_{11}\, a_{22} - a_{12}\, a_{21} \neq 0.$$

Proof.   A set $T \subseteq \mathbb{R}^2$ is called *collinear* iff there exists a line $l \supseteq T$.

(a) $\gamma(0,0)$, $\gamma(1,0)$, $\gamma(0,1)$ are not collinear. — In order to prove this statement assume that the line l contains the points in question. Let x be a point of $\mathbb{R}^2$ and let $g \ni x$ be a line which intersects

$$\overline{(0,0)(1,0)} \cup \overline{(1,0)(0,1)} \cup \overline{(0,1)(0,0)}$$

at least twice, where $\overline{yz}$ denotes the line through the points $y \neq z$. Hence

$$\gamma(x) \in \gamma(g) \subseteq l,$$

i.e. $\gamma(\mathbb{R}^2) \subseteq l$ which contradicts the fact that γ is a bijective mapping of $\mathbb{R}^2$.

(b)   Put

$$\gamma(0,0) =: (a_1, a_2), \ \gamma(1,0) =: (b_1, b_2), \ \gamma(0,1) =: (c_1, c_2)$$

and define
$$A := \begin{pmatrix} b_1 - a_1 & b_2 - a_2 \\ c_1 - a_1 & c_2 - a_2 \end{pmatrix}.$$

Observe that $\det A \neq 0$ because of (a). Put
$$\delta(x_1 x_2) := (x_1 x_2)A + (a_1 a_2)$$

and notice that δ is a bijective affine mapping of $\mathbb{R}^2$. Hence
$$\gamma_0 := \delta^{-1}\gamma$$

also satisfies (*). The points $(0,0)$, $(1,0)$, $(0,1)$ remain fixed under γ_0 and the lines $\overline{(0,0)(1,0)}$, $\overline{(1,0)(0,1)}$, $\overline{(0,1)(0,0)}$ are thus mapped onto themselves in view of (*).

Put
$$\gamma_0(x,0) =: (f(x),0) \text{ and } \gamma_0(0,y) =: (0,g(y)).$$
Obviously $f(0) = g(0) = 0$ and $f(1) = g(1) = 1$.

(c)   If l_1, l_2 are parallel lines of $\mathbb{R}^2$, then so are $\gamma_0(l_1), \gamma_0(l_2)$. — This is trivial if $l_1 = l_2$. Suppose that $l_1 \cap l_2 = \emptyset$. Assume $\gamma_0(l_1) \cap \gamma_0(l_2) \neq \emptyset$ and $p \in \gamma_0(l_1) \cap \gamma_0(l_2)$. Hence $\gamma_0^{-1}(p) \in l_1 \cap l_2$ which contradicts $l_1 \cap l_2 = \emptyset$.

(d) $f(x) = g(x)$ for all $x \in \mathbb{R}$. The lines $\overline{(1,0)(0,1)}$ and $\overline{(x,0)(0,x)}$ $(x \neq 0)$ are parallel and hence so are the lines $\overline{(1,0)(0,1)}$ and $\overline{(f(x),0)(0,g(x))}$.

(e) $\gamma_0(x_1, x_2) = (f(x_1), f(x_2))$ for all $(x_1, x_2) \in \mathbb{R}^2$. Let l_1 be the line through $(x_1, 0)$ and parallel to $\eta := \overline{(0,0)(0,1)}$ and let $l_2 \ni (0, x_2)$ be the line parallel to $\xi := \overline{(0,0)(1,0)}$. Observe that $(x_1, x_2) \in l_1 \cap l_2$. In view of (c) we get
$$\eta \parallel \gamma_0(l_1) \ni (f(x_1), 0),$$
$$\xi \parallel \gamma_0(l_2) \ni (0, g(x_2)) = (0, f(x_2)).$$

Hence
$$\gamma_0(x_1, x_2) \in \gamma_0(l_1) \cap \gamma_0(l_2) = \{(f(x_1), f(x_2))\}.$$

(f) $f(x+y) = f(x) + f(y)$ for all $x, y \in \mathbb{R}$.
$$\overline{(0,1)(x,0)} \parallel \overline{(y,1)(x+y,0)}$$

implies

$$\overline{(0,1)\big(f(x),0\big)} \parallel \overline{\big(f(y),1\big)\big(f(x+y),0\big)}.$$

(g) $f(xy) = f(x)f(y)$ for all $x, y \in \mathbb{R}$. This is trivial in the case $y = 0$. Suppose that $y \neq 0$. Hence $f(y) \neq 0$ because otherwise $\gamma_0(0,0) = \gamma_0(0,y)$. Now

$$\overline{(0,1)(x,0)} \parallel \overline{(0,y)(xy,0)}$$

implies

$$\overline{(0,1)\big(f(x),0\big)} \parallel \overline{\big(0,f(y)\big)\big(f(xy),0\big)}.$$

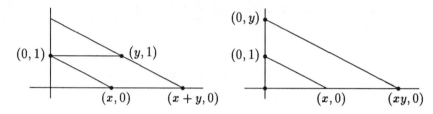

(h)   Because of (f), (g), and $f(y) \neq 0$ for $y \neq 0$ we get $f(x) = x$ for all $x \in \mathbb{R}$ in view of Proposition 3. Then (e) implies that γ_0 is the identity, id. Hence $\gamma = \delta$. $\square$

REMARK. In GT, 104 ff, a more general theorem than Proposition 2 is proved for dimension $n \geq 2$.

PROPOSITION 3. *Suppose that $f : \mathbb{R} \to \mathbb{R}$ is a function satisfying*

$$f(x+y) = f(x) + f(y) \ \ and \ \ f(xy) = f(x)f(y)$$

for all $x, y \in \mathbb{R}$. Then $f(t) = t$ for all $t \in \mathbb{R}$ or $f(t) = 0$ for all $t \in \mathbb{R}$.

Proof. $f(0) = f(0+0) = f(0) + f(0)$ implies $f(0) = 0$. If there exists a $y \neq 0$ in $\mathbb{R}$ with $f(y) = 0$, then

$$f(t) = f\left(y \cdot \frac{t}{y}\right) = f(y) \cdot f\left(\frac{t}{y}\right) = 0$$

for all $t \in \mathbb{R}$. So assume $f(t) \neq 0$ for all real $t \neq 0$. Hence $f(1) = f(1 \cdot 1) = f(1) \cdot f(1)$ implies $f(1) = 1$. By induction we get $f(n) = n$ for positive integers n and hence $f(g) = g$ for all integers g since $0 = f\big(n + (-n)\big) = n + f(-n)$. For integers g_1 and $g_2 \neq 0$ we obtain

$$f\left(\frac{g_1}{g_2}\right) = g_1 \cdot f\left(\frac{1}{g_2}\right) = \frac{g_1}{g_2}$$

since $1 = f\left(g_2 \cdot \frac{1}{g_2}\right) = g_2 \cdot f\left(\frac{1}{g_2}\right)$. Hence $f(r) = r$ for every rational number r. For a real number $t \geq 0$ we get $f(t) = f(\sqrt{t})f(\sqrt{t}) \geq 0$. Hence $a \leq b$ implies $f(a) \leq f(b)$ for real numbers a, b. For a real number t we take sequences α_ν, β_ν of rational numbers satisfying

$$\alpha_\nu \leq t \leq \beta_\nu$$

for all $\nu = 1, 2, \ldots$ and moreover

$$\lim_{\nu \to \infty} \alpha_\nu = t = \lim_{\nu \to \infty} \beta_\nu.$$

Hence $\alpha_\nu = f(\alpha_\nu) \leq f(t) \leq f(\beta_\nu) = \beta_\nu$ and thus

$$|f(t) - t| \leq \beta_\nu - \alpha_\nu$$

for all $\nu = 1, 2, \ldots$, i.e. $f(t) = t$. $\qquad\square$

1.3 Substructures of geometries (S, G)

Let (S, G) be a geometry and let $S_0 \neq \emptyset$ be a subset of S. Put

$$G_0 := \{g \in G \mid g(S_0) = S_0\}, \ N_0 := \{g \in G \mid g(s) = s \text{ for all } s \in S_0\}.$$

The geometry $(S_0, G_0/N_0)$ (or more generally (S_0, G_1) where G_1 is a subgroup of G_0/N_0) is then said to be a *substructure* of (S, G). Observe that every $g \in G_0$ leads to a bijection $s \to g(s)$ of S_0 and that elements $g, g' \in G_0$ lead to the same bijection of S_0 iff $g' \in gN_0$. At the beginning of section 5.6.5 $\#N_0 > 1$ will play a role. At other places $N_0 = \{e\}$ holds true. In this latter case we shall write (S_0, G_0) instead of $(S_0, G_0/N_0)$.

The procedure to introduce new geometries (S_0, G_0), $N_0 = \{e\}$, by means of a geometry (S, G) turns out to be fundamental in geometry. We shall apply this procedure in the sequel several times, for instance in the cases of hyperbolic geometry, of Einstein's Cylinder universe and of de Sitter's world. Here we would like to introduce *spherical geometry* via *euclidean geometry*. Define $S := \mathbb{R}^n$, $n \geq 1$, and moreover

$$d : \mathbb{R}^n \times \mathbb{R}^n \to \mathbb{R}$$

by means of

$$d(x, y) = \sqrt{\sum_{i=1}^n (x_i - y_i)^2}$$

for $x = (x_1, \ldots, x_n) \in \mathbb{R}^n$ and $y = (y_1, \ldots, y_n) \in \mathbb{R}^n$. We already know the group $G := G(d)$ of d: this is the set of all bijections

$$\gamma(x) = xQ + a \tag{9}$$

with real matrices

$$Q = \begin{pmatrix} q_{11} & \cdots & q_{1n} \\ \vdots & & \\ q_{n1} & \cdots & q_{nn} \end{pmatrix}$$

and $a = (a_1 \ldots a_n)$ such that $QQ^T = E$ holds true. Q^T denotes the transpose of Q, and E denotes the identity matrix

$$E = \begin{pmatrix} 1 & & 0 \\ & \ddots & \\ 0 & & 1 \end{pmatrix}$$

of n rows and n columns. — The structure $(\mathbb{R}^n, G)$ is called the *n–dimensional euclidean geometry*.

Let $\Sigma = (\mathbb{R}^{n+1}, G^{n+1})$ be the $(n+1)$–dimensional euclidean geometry (we write G^{n+1} for the group G in order to emphasize its dependence on $n+1$) and let S_0 be the set

$$S_0 := \{(x_1, \ldots, x_{n+1}) \in \mathbb{R}^{n+1} \mid x_1^2 + \ldots + x_{n+1}^2 = 1\}.$$

LEMMA 4. *The mapping* (9) *with $n+1$ instead of n and $QQ^T = E$ belongs to*

$$G_0 = \{\gamma \in G^{n+1} \mid \gamma(S_0) = S_0\}$$

if and only if,

$$a = 0.$$

Proof.   Since $xx^T = 1$ implies

$$1 = (xQ + a)(xQ + a)^T,$$

we obtain $0 = 2xQa^T + aa^T$. Apply this equation for x and $-x$. Hence $aa^T = 0$, i.e. $a = 0$. $\square$

The geometry (S_0, G_0) is called the *n–dimensional spherical geometry*.

PROPOSITION 5. *Let (S_0, G_0) be the n–dimensional spherical geometry. The function*

$$h \quad : \quad S_0 \times S_0 \to [0, \pi],$$

$$h(x, y) \quad := \quad \arccos xy$$

with

$$xy := x_1 y_1 + \ldots + x_{n+1} \, y_{n+1} \tag{10}$$

is then an invariant of (S_0, G_0) *and is moreover a defining function of this geometry.*

Proof. We do not distinguish between $(x_1, \ldots, x_{n+1})$ and the matrix $(x_1 \ldots x_{n+1})$. Writing (10) as a matrix equation, we obtain

$$xy^T = (xQ) \cdot (yQ)^T$$

and hence h is an invariant. In order to prove that h is a defining function of (S_0, G_0), we will show that

$$\gamma : S_0 \to S_0$$

belongs to G_0 whenever

$$h(x, y) = h\big(\gamma(x), \gamma(y)\big) \tag{11}$$

holds true for all $x, y \in S_0$. Put

$$E_1 = (1, 0, \ldots, 0), \ E_2 = (0, 1, 0, \ldots, 0), \ldots, E_{n+1} = (0, \ldots, 0, 1)$$

and $A_i := \gamma(E_i)$, $i = 1, \ldots, n+1$. All E_i are in S_0 and hence all A_i as well. This implies that $A_i^2 = 1$ for $i = 1, \ldots, n+1$. Moreover

$$0 = \cos h(E_i, E_j) = \cos h(A_i, A_j) = A_i A_j$$

for $i \neq j$. Define Q to be the matrix with rows $A_1, A_2, \ldots, A_{n+1}$. The mapping

$$f(x) := xQ$$

is hence an element of G_0. Observe that $f(E_i) = A_i$ for $i = 1, \ldots, n+1$. Put

$$\gamma_0 := f^{-1}\gamma.$$

Since (11) holds also true by replacing γ by γ_0, we obtain for $x \in S_0$

$$x_i = \cos h(x, E_i) = \cos h(y, E_i) = y_i,$$

$i = 1, \ldots, n+1$, by putting $y := \gamma_0(x)$ and observing $\gamma_0(E_i) = E_i$, $i = 1, \ldots, n+1$. Hence $\gamma_0 = \text{id}$ and thus $\gamma = f$. $\qquad\square$

REMARK. Let R be a commutative and associative ring with identity element 1 such that $1 + 1$ is not a zero divisor of R. Define R^n, $n \geq 1$ an integer, as the set of all ordered n–tuples

$$(x_1, \ldots, x_n)$$

with elements $x_i \in R$. Define moreover

$$(x_1, \ldots, x_n) + (y_1, \ldots, y_n) := (x_1 + y_1, \ldots, x_n + y_n),$$
$$\lambda \cdot (x_1, \ldots, x_n) := (\lambda x_1, \ldots, \lambda x_n) =: (x_1, \ldots, x_n) \cdot \lambda$$

for $x_i, y_i,\ \lambda \in R$. Then $(R^n, +)$ turns out to be an abelian group and the multiplication $\lambda \cdot x$ with $\lambda \in R$ and $x \in R^n$ satisfies usual rules:

$$
\begin{aligned}
\lambda \cdot (x + y) &= \lambda x + \lambda y \\
(\lambda + \mu) \cdot x &= \lambda x + \mu x \\
(\lambda \mu) \cdot x &= \lambda \cdot (\mu x) \\
1 \cdot x &= x
\end{aligned}
$$

for all $\lambda, \mu \in R$ and all $x, y \in R^n$. The *n–dimensional euclidean geometry* over R is defined as the geometry (R^n, G^n) with G^n as the group of all mappings

$$\gamma(x) = xQ + a \tag{12}$$

with matrices

$$
Q = \begin{pmatrix} q_{11} & \cdots & q_{1n} \\ \vdots & & \\ q_{n1} & \cdots & q_{nn} \end{pmatrix}
$$

and $a = (a_1 \ldots a_n)$ over R such that $QQ^T = E$ holds true. A defining invariant function is given by (GT, 58 ff)

$$d(x, y) = \sum_{i=1}^{n} (x_i - y_i)^2.$$

Let S_0 be the set

$$S_0 := \{(x_1, \ldots, x_{n+1} \in R^{n+1} \mid x_1^2 + \ldots + x_{n+1}^2 = 1\}.$$

Then also in this general case the result of Lemma 4, of course carried over to the present situation, remains true. We also have $aa^T = 0$. But now this need not imply $a = 0$. However,

$$0 = 2E_i Q a^T, \ i = 1, \ldots, n + 1,$$

leads to $Qa^T = 0$ since 2 is not a zero divisor in R, and $Qa^T = 0$ implies $a = 0$ in view of $QQ^T = E$. — As far as Proposition 5 is concerned in the general case, we need only replace $h(x, y)$ by $h_0(x, y) := xy$ with the product (10) to get a correct statement (GT 78 ff).

The proof of the following statement is obvious:

PROPOSITION 6. *Let (S_0, G_0) be a substructure of the geometry (S, G). Suppose that (N, φ) is an invariant notion of (S, G). Then (N, φ_0) with*

$$\varphi_0 := \varphi \mid G_0 \times N$$

must be an invariant notion of (S_0, G_0). Suppose that $h : N \to W$ is an invariant of (S, G) based on (N, φ). Then h is also an invariant of (S_0, G_0), now based on (N, φ_0).

1.4   Direct products of geometries

Let (S_i, G_i), $i = 1, 2$, be geometries. We then call

$$(S_1 \times S_2, G_1 \times G_2) \tag{13}$$

the *direct product* of the two geometries. In order to be sure that (13) is well–defined we must check that every element $(\gamma_1, \gamma_2) \in (G_1, G_2)$ is a bijection of the cartesian product $S_1 \times S_2$ of S_1, S_2. But this is obvious, since

$$(\gamma_1, \gamma_2)(s_1, s_2), \ s_i \in S_i (i = 1, 2),$$

is defined by

$$\big(\gamma_1(s_1), \gamma_2(s_2)\big).$$

As a prominent example of a direct product we would like to introduce *Einstein's cylinder universe.* Let (S_1, G_1) be the $(n - 1)$–dimensional spherical geometry, $n \geq 2$, and let (S_2, G_2) be the 1–dimensional euclidean geometry. The direct product (13) is then called the *n–dimensional cylinder geometry* or the *n–dimensional Einstein's cylinder universe.* In chapter 3 we will define this geometry as a substructure of a certain geometry (S, G). We emphasize that in the present case (13) could be based on geometries (S_i, G_i) over the reals but also more generally on a ring R as described in the Remark of section 1.3. Restricting ourselves to $\mathbb{R}$ we may write

$$S_1 \times S_2 = \{(x_1, \ldots, x_{n+1}) \in \mathbb{R}^{n+1} \mid x_1^2 + \ldots + x_n^2 = 1\}$$

and moreover $G_1 \times G_2$ as the set of mappings

$$(x_1, \ldots, x_n, x_{n+1}) \to ((x_1, \ldots, x_n) \, Q, \; cx_{n+1} + a)$$

with $QQ^T = E$ and $c^2 = 1$ where Q is a real $n \times n$–matrix and where c, a are elements of $\mathbb{R}$.

Geometries (S, G) and (S', G') are called *isomorphic* iff there exist bijections

$$\sigma : S \to S' \text{ and } \tau : G \to G'$$

such that the following equations hold true

$$\tau(g_1 g_2) \;\; = \;\; \tau(g_1)\tau(g_2), \tag{14}$$
$$\sigma\big(g(s)\big) \;\; = \;\; \tau(g)\big(\sigma(s)\big) \tag{15}$$

for all $s \in S$ and $g_1, g_2, g \in G$. The mapping τ is hence an isomorphism of the groups G, G'. If $(S, G), (S', G')$ are isomorphic, we shall write

$$(S, G) \simeq (S', G').$$

The relation $\simeq$ is reflexive, symmetric and transitive on every set of geometries (S, G). We call (S', G') a *homomorphic image* of (S, G) iff there exist surjective mappings

$$\sigma : S \to S' \text{ and } \tau : G \to G'$$

such that equations (14), (15) hold true. Its easy to verify that each of the geometries $(S_1, G_1), (S_2, G_2)$ is a homomorphic image of their direct product

$$(S_1 \times S_2, \; G_1 \times G_2):$$

in the case of (S_1, G_1), for instance, put

$$\sigma(s_1, s_2) := s_1 \text{ and } \tau(g_1, g_2) := g_1.$$

Isomorphic geometries (S, G) and (S', G') have, up to notation, the same invariant notions and the same invariants. Let (N, φ) be an invariant notion of (S, G), let N' be a set and let finally

$$\nu : N \to N'$$

be a bijection (for instance $N' = N$ and $\nu = \text{id}$). We then define an invariant notion (N', φ') of (S', G'). Put

$$\varphi'\big(\tau(g), \nu(l)\big) = \nu(l_1)$$

for $g \in G$ and $l, l_1 \in N$ iff

$$\varphi(g, l) = l_1$$

holds true, where $\tau : G \to G'$ is a bijection satisfying (14), (15). Obviously,

$$\varphi'(\tau(e), \nu(l)) = \nu(l)$$

since $\varphi(e, l) = l$. Put

$$\varphi(g_1 g_2, l) =: l_1 \text{ and } \varphi(g_2, l) =: l_2.$$

Then we get

$$\varphi'(\tau(g_1)\tau(g_2), \nu(l)) = \varphi'(\tau(g_1 g_2), \nu(l)) = \nu(l_1)$$

and

$$\varphi'\Big(\tau(g_1), \varphi'(\tau(g_2), \nu(l))\Big) = \varphi'(\tau(g_1), \nu(l_2)) = \nu(l_1),$$

i.e. (i) of section 1.1 for (N', φ'). Hence (N', φ') must be an invariant notion of (S', G').

Now let

$$h : N \to W$$

be an invariant of (S, G) based on the invariant notion (N, φ) of (S, G). We then would like to define an invariant

$$h' : N' \to W$$

of (S', G'). Put $h'(\nu(l)) := h(l)$ and

$$\varphi(g, l) =: l_1.$$

Then

$$\begin{aligned} h'\Big(\varphi'(\tau(g), \nu(l))\Big) &= h'(\nu(l_1)) = h(l_1) \\ &= h(\varphi(g, l)) = h(l) = h'(\nu(l)). \end{aligned}$$

h' is thus in fact an invariant of (S', G'). If we rewrite the definition of φ', namely

$$\varphi'(\tau(g), \nu(l)) = \nu[\varphi(g, l)],$$

by using the abbreviations

$$\varphi(g, l) =: g(l)$$

and

$$\varphi'(\tau(g), \nu(l)) =: \tau(g)(\nu(l)),$$

we get

$$\tau(g)(\nu(l)) = \nu(g(l))$$

for all $l \in N$ and $g \in G$. In the case that N is a set of subsets of S, or that it otherwise is based on S, the mapping ν might be taken equal to σ in view of (15), in order to construct the corresponding invariant notion of (N, φ) for (S', G') in terms of this latter geometry. Principally, however, the corresponding invariant notion of (N, φ) for (S', G') might be based on $(N, \varphi')(N' := N, \nu := \mathrm{id})$ with

$$\varphi'\big(\tau(g), l\big) := \varphi(g, l),$$

according to the proof above.

PROPOSITION 7. *Let (N_i, φ_i) be an invariant notion of the geometry (S_i, G_i), $i = 1, 2$. Then $(N_1 \times N_2, \varphi)$, with*

$$\varphi : (G_1 \times G_2) \times (N_1 \times N_2) \to N_1 \times N_2,$$

$$\varphi\big((\gamma_1, \gamma_2), (l_1, l_2)\big) := \big(\varphi_1(\gamma_1, l_1), \varphi_2(\gamma_2, l_2)\big)$$

for all $\gamma_i \in G_i$, $l_i \in N_i$, $i = 1, 2$, must be an invariant notion of the product

$$(S_1 \times S_2, \ G_1 \times G_2).$$

If $h_i : N_i \to W_i$, $i = 1, 2$, is an invariant of (S_i, G_i) based on the invariant notion (N_i, φ_i) and the abstract set W_i, then

$$h : N_1 \times N_2 \to W_1 \times W_2,$$

$$h(l_1, l_2) := \big(h_1(l_1), h_2(l_2)\big)$$

for all $l_i \in N_i$, $i = 1, 2$, is an invariant of the product based on the invariant notion $(N_1 \times N_2, \varphi)$.

Proof.   Denote the neutral element of G_i by ε_i, $i = 1, 2$. Then

$$\varphi\big((\varepsilon_1, \varepsilon_2), (l_1, l_2)\big) = \big(\varphi_1(\varepsilon_1, l_1), \varphi_2(\varepsilon_2, l_2)\big) = (l_1, l_2)$$

for all $l_i \in N_i$, $i = 1, 2$. For elements $\gamma_i, \delta_i \in G_i$ we get

$$\varphi\big((\delta_1, \delta_2)(\gamma_1, \gamma_2), (l_1, l_2)\big) = \big(\varphi_1(\delta_1\gamma_1, l_1), \varphi_2(\delta_2\gamma_2, l_2)\big)$$

and

$$
\begin{aligned}
\varphi\Big((\delta_1, \delta_2), \varphi\big((\gamma_1, \gamma_2), (l_1, l_2)\big)\Big) &= \varphi\Big((\delta_1, \delta_2), \big(\varphi_1(\gamma_1, l_1), \varphi_2(\gamma_2, l_2)\big)\Big) \\
&= \Big(\varphi_1\big(\delta_1, \varphi_1(\gamma_1, l_1)\big), \varphi_2\big(\delta_2, \varphi_2(\gamma_2, l_2)\big)\Big) \\
&= \big(\varphi_1(\delta_1\gamma_1, l_1), \varphi_2(\delta_2\gamma_2, l_2)\big).
\end{aligned}
$$

REMARKS.

1) In order to present an application of Proposition 7, we again would like to consider Einstein's cylinder universe. (S_1, G_1) is here the $(n-1)$–dimensional spherical geometry, $n \geq 2$, and (S_2, G_2) is the 1–dimensional euclidean geometry. Define $N_i = S_i \times S_i$, $i = 1, 2$, and

$$h_1\big((x_1, \ldots, x_n), (y_1, \ldots, y_n)\big) = \sum_{i=1}^{n} x_i y_i,$$

$$h_2(x_{n+1}, y_{n+1}) = |x_{n+1} - y_{n+1}|.$$

The invariant we get for the product of (S_1, G_1) and (S_2, G_2) according to Proposition 7 is then given by

$$h(x, y) = \left(\sum_{i=1}^{n} x_i y_i, |x_{n+1} - y_{n+1}| \right).$$

(Compare section 3.2.)

2) The isomorphism of geometries $(S, G), (S', G')$ was already playing an important role in geometry by the 19th century. At that time geometers spoke of so–called *Übertragungsprinzipe* which means that two geometries, based on different terminologies, could turn out to coincide from a structural point of view, by just following a vocabulary which associates to the objects of one geometry the objects of the other geometry. We would like to present an example, connecting Cayley–Klein–model and Poincaré–model of 1–dimensional hyperbolic geometry (compare section 2.1). Define

$$S = \,]-1, +1[\quad := \quad \{r \in \mathbb{R} \mid -1 < r < +1\},$$

$$S' = \,]0, \infty[\quad := \quad \{r \in \mathbb{R} \mid r > 0\}$$

and G, G', respectively, as the set of all bijections

$$\varphi_p(x) = \frac{x+p}{xp+1}, \quad \psi_q(x) = qx$$

of S, S', respectively, with $p \in S, q \in S'$. Put

$$\sigma(s) = \frac{1+s}{1-s}$$

for $s \in S$ and define $\tau(\varphi_p) = \psi_{\sigma(p)}$ for $p \in S$. The geometry (S, G) is called the Cayley–Klein–model of 1–dimensional hyperbolic geometry and (S', G') is said to be the Poincaré–model of that hyperbolic geometry. It is now easy to verify equation (14), i.e.

$$\tau(\varphi_p \varphi_q) = \tau(\varphi_p) \cdot \tau(\varphi_q)$$

for all $p, q \in S$. Since

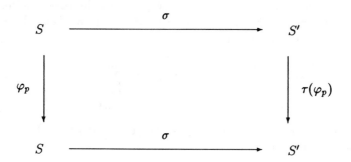

commutes, equation (15) also holds true. The mappings $\sigma : S \to S'$ and $\tau : G \to G'$ are moreover bijections. We thus established isomorphism (or an Übertragungsprinzip) between the geometries (S, G) and (S', G').

3) Homomorphic images of geometries have been known in geometry for a long time. We only need to think of projections in the usual sense. The following example might be presented. Define

$$S = \mathbb{R}^2, \ S' = \mathbb{R}$$

and G, G', respectively, as the set of bijections

$$
\begin{aligned}
\gamma(x_1 x_2) &= (x_1 x_2)A + (a_1 a_2), \\
\delta(x) &= ax + b,
\end{aligned}
$$

respectively, with

$$A = \left(\begin{array}{cc} a_{11} & a_{12} \\ a_{21} & a_{22} \end{array} \right), \det A \neq 0,$$

and $a_{ij}, a_k, a, b \in \mathbb{R}$, $a \neq 0$, $a_{21} = 0$. Set

$$\sigma(x_1, x_2) = x_1$$

and $\tau(\gamma) = \delta$ for $\delta(x) = a_{11}x_1 + a_1$ and

$$\gamma(x_1, x_2) = (a_{11}x_1 + a_1, \ a_{12}x_1 + a_{22}x_2 + a_2).$$

We again have to check that

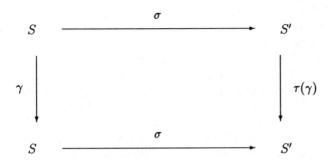

commutes, and that $\tau : G \to G'$ is a homomorphism. Observe also that σ and τ are surjective mappings.

4) Let (S, G) be a geometry and let H be a normal subgroup of G. For $s_1, s_2 \in S$ define
$$s_1 \sim s_2 \Leftrightarrow \exists_{h \in H} \; h(s_1) = s_2.$$
We hence get an equivalence relation. Denote by $S_\sim$ the set of all equivalence classes of S and by $[s]$ the class containing $s \in S$. Then by defining
$$(gH)([s]) := [g(s)],$$
$(S_\sim, G/H)$ must also be a geometry.

As an example we again consider the structure (S, G) of Remark 3. For H we will take the set of mappings
$$h(x_1, x_2) = (x_1 x_2) \begin{pmatrix} 1 & a_{12} \\ 0 & a_{22} \end{pmatrix} + (0 a_2)$$
with $a_{22} \neq 0$ which turns out to be a normal subgroup of G. Here
$$(x_1, x_2) \sim (y_1, y_2)$$
holds true iff $x_1 = y_1$. Hence
$$(S_\sim, G/H) \cong (S', G')$$
with S', G' as defined in Remark 3.

1.5   Klein's Erlangen programme

The so–called Erlangen programme of Felix Klein (1849–1925) is an inge-
nious and fundamental principle that allows us to distinguish between many
geometries which were developed.   It was published by Klein in 1872 under
the title *Vergleichende Betrachtungen über neuere geometrische Forschungen,
Programm zum Eintritt in die philosophische Facultät und den Senat der k.
Friedrich-Alexanders-Universität zu Erlangen (Verlag von Andreas Deichert,
Erlangen).*   In Volume 1 of the Collected Works of Klein (Verlag von Julius
Springer, Berlin, 1921) there are several additional remarks by Felix Klein con-
cerning his programme which are also of interest.   Julian Lowell Coolidge *(A
History of Geometrical Methods, At the Clarendon Press, Oxford, 1940)* calls
Klein *the greatest synthesist that geometry has ever known* and he says about
Klein's Erlangen programme that it *probably influenced geometrical thinking
more than any other work since the time of Euclid, with the exception of Gauß
and Riemann.*   Also, the following formulation of Coolidge, loc. cit., might be
repeated, since it expresses in an excellent way and in a few words the relation of geometry to transformation group as it was seen by Klein in his famous
programme:

A) *Here is a group of transformations. What numbers and what geometrical
relations are unaltered by the transformations of this group?*

B) *What group of transformations will keep this or that geometrical relation
unaltered?*

Of course, the reader realizes that it was our intention in previous sections to
give those questions a very precise meaning: see section 1.1 concerning question
A and compare section 1.2 concerning question B.   In section 1.1 we defined
the notion of an *invariant* (instead of *number* in question A) and that of an
invariant notion (instead of *geometrical relation*).   What we called *notion of S*
in section 1.2 generally replaces *geometrical relation* in question B.   What we
called *function of S* in section 1.2 replaces something which should be included
in question B.

With definitions of sections 1.1 and 1.2 we would now like to give questions
A and B the following form:

A*) *Find invariants and invariant notions of geometries (S, G).*

B*) *Find $G(N)$ and $G(h)$ to given notions N or functions h of a set $S \neq \emptyset$.
Find especially defining notions or defining functions of geometries (S, G).*

In a theory of a class of objects it is a prominent problem to determine all these objects in a satisfactory way. Concerning the class of commutative fields for instance, there exists such a classification: one starts with a prime–field, and what one has to do then is to go over to algebraic and transcendental extensions in order to get all commutative fields. Usually a class of objects is too general to be classified in a satisfactory way. Think for instance of the class of all groups. In those cases, however, one tries to classify subclasses. This is exactly the situation with the class of all geometries (S, G). It seems to be hopeless to find a satisfactory classification of this class. However, different classes of geometries (S, G) with additional properties were classified by many authors. To give just one reference, see R. Artzy [2].

1.6 Functional equations in geometry

There is a fundamental principle in geometry that leads to functional equations. To some extent it can be characterized as an inverse programme of Klein's Erlangen programme. The latter starts with a group G operating on a set S and it asks for the invariants and invariant notions of (S, G) and it also asks (compare B^*, section 1.5) for the groups of given notions or functions. The former starts conversely (as formulated in B^*) with a function h of S (distance between two points, angles between two intersecting lines, cross ratio of four points, tangential distance between two spheres, ...) or a notion N of S (line, plane, circle, orthogonality, order, ...) and tries to find *all* mappings

$$\gamma : S \to S$$

(and *not* only those in $G(h)$ or $G(N)$) preserving (or preserving partially) that function h, that notion N. We would like to emphasize this principle since it opens new vistas for further fruitful research and since it serves as a leading principle for organizing results under common points of view.

We now would like to formulate two functional equations problems derived from this general principle (others will occur in later sections). Since all functional equations problems in our book are stated explicitly, it is not really necessary for us to begin with a precise definition of what a functional equation could be. For our purposes it suffices to think of functional equations as of meaningful equations containing unknown mappings

$$f : A \to B.$$

In the case, for instance, that A and B are groups, we could ask for all homomorphisms f from A into B, thus getting the functional equation

$$\forall_{a_1,a_2 \in A} \ f(a_1 a_2) = f(a_1)f(a_2).$$

(See J. Aczél, J. Dhombres [1] for discussions conerning the notion of a functional equation.)

Let (S, W, d) be a distance space (see section 1.2) and let F be a fixed subset of $S \times S$. The Problem of Distance Preservance now asks, what are all functions

$$f : S \to S$$

such that the functional equation

$$d\big(f(x), f(y)\big) = d(x, y) \tag{16}$$

holds for all $(x, y) \in F$. In case $F = S \times S$ we call (16) *universal*. The following examples might be considered:

1) $S := \mathbb{R}^2$, $W := \mathbb{R}$,

$$d(x, y) := \sqrt{(x_1 - y_1)^2 + (x_2 - y_2)^2}$$

for $x = (x_1, x_2)$, $y = (y_1, y_2)$, and

$$F := \big\{(x, y) \in S \times S \mid d(x, y) = 1\big\}.$$

Put

$$f(x) =: \big(\varphi_1(x_1, x_2), \varphi_2(x_1, x_2)\big).$$

Then (16) becomes

$$\sum_{i=1}^{2} \big[\varphi_i(x_1 + \cos x_3, x_2 + \sin x_3) - \varphi_i(x_1, x_2)\big]^2 = 1 \tag{17}$$

for all $x_1, x_2, x_3 \in \mathbb{R}$. Its solutions

$$\varphi_1, \varphi_2 : \mathbb{R}^2 \to \mathbb{R}$$

are given by

$$\varphi_1(x_1, x_2) = x_1 \cos a - x_2 \sin a + b$$
$$\varphi_2(x_1, x_2) = x_1 \sin a + x_2 \cos a + c$$

and

$$\varphi_1(x_1, x_2) = x_1 \cos a + x_2 \sin a + b$$
$$\varphi_2(x_1, x_2) = x_1 \sin a - x_2 \cos a + c,$$

where a, b, c are real constants. This follows from a theorem of Beckman and Quarles (see Theorem 1 in section 5.1.1).

2) $S := \mathbb{R}^2$, $W := \mathbb{R}$ and

$$d(x,y) := (x_1 - y_1)(x_2 - y_2),$$
$$F := \{(x,y) \in S \times S \mid d(x,y) = 1\}.$$

The underlying notion of distance here is the Lorentz–Minkowski metric (see GT, section 6.15). The functional equation we get now is

$$\prod_{i=1}^{2} \left[\varphi_i \left(x_1 + x_3, x_2 + \frac{1}{x_3} \right) - \varphi_i(x_1, x_2) \right] = 1 \qquad (18)$$

for all $x_1, x_2, x_3 \in \mathbb{R}$ with $x_3 \neq 0$.

Its solutions

$$\varphi_1, \varphi_2 : \mathbb{R}^2 \to \mathbb{R}$$

are given by

$$\varphi_1(x_1, x_2) = ax_1 + b$$
$$\varphi_2(x_1, x_2) = \frac{1}{a}x_2 + c$$

and

$$\varphi_1(x_1, x_2) = ax_2 + b$$
$$\varphi_2(x_1, x_2) = \frac{1}{a}x_1 + c,$$

where a, b, c are real constants with $a \neq 0$. A more general equation of distance preservance was considered by W. Benz, F. Radó, and H. Schaeffer (see GT, loc. cit.).

Let $S \neq \emptyset$ and W be sets and let $\mathbb{F} \neq \emptyset$ be a set of non–empty subsets of S. Suppose that

$$\mu : \mathbb{F} \to W$$

is a mapping. We then call

$$(S, \mathbb{F}, W, \mu)$$

an *area (volume) space*. Let $\mathbb{F}_0$ be a fixed subset of $\mathbb{F}$.

The Problem of Area (Volume) Preservance now asks for all functions

$$f : S \to S$$

such that $f(F) \in \mathbb{F}$ and

$$\mu(f(F)) = \mu(F) \qquad (19)$$

hold for all $F \in \mathbb{F}_0$.

We consider the following example: $S := \mathbb{R}^3$, $W := \mathbb{R}$. Define

$$\mathbb{F} := \{T \subset \mathbb{R}^3 \mid 1 \leq \#T \leq 3\},$$

$\mu(T) = 0$ for $1 \leq \#T \leq 2$, and

$$\mu(T) := \text{ area of the triangle } x, y, z$$

whenever $T = \{x, y, z\}$ with $\#T = 3$. Finally, put

$$\mathbb{F}_0 := \{T \in \mathbb{F} \mid \mu(T) = 1\}.$$

Note that in our situation

$$f(F) \in \mathbb{F}$$

for $F \in \mathbb{F}$ is trivially satisfied for every $f : S \to S$. (Observe $f(F) := \{f(x) \mid x \in F\}$.) A consequence of a theorem of J. Lester implies that the solutions of (19) in the present case are given by the congruent mappings of $\mathbb{R}^3$ (see section 5.1.2). For more examples for equation (19) see sections 5.1.2 and 5.3.1. Concerning this section 1. 6, see also W. Benz [4].

Two distance spaces (S_i, W_i, d_i), $i = 1, 2$, are called *isomorphic* iff there exists a bijection

$$\varphi : S_1 \to S_2 \tag{20}$$

such that $d_1(a, b) = d_1(c, d)$ holds true iff

$$d_2\big(\varphi(a), \varphi(b)\big) = d_2\big(\varphi(c), \varphi(d)\big)$$

is satisfied for all $a, b, c, d \in S_1$. Isomorphic distance spaces have isomorphic groups of isometries (GT 35). The group of isometries of (S, W, d) is defined to be the subgroup

$$\big\{\gamma \in \text{ Perm } S \mid \forall_{a,b \in S} \ d(a, b) = d\big(\gamma(a), \gamma(b)\big)\big\}$$

of Perm S (see section 1.2).

PROPOSITION 8. *Let (S_i, W_i, d_i), $i = 1, 2$, be isomorphic distance spaces with the connecting bijection* (20). *Then there corresponds to every solution $f_1 : S_1 \to S_1$ of*

$$\forall_{x,y \in S_1} \ d_1\big(f_1(x), f_1(y)\big) = d_1(x, y) \tag{21}$$

a solution $f_2 : S_2 \to S_2$ of

$$\forall_{x,y \in S_2} \ d_2\big(f_2(x), f_2(y)\big) = d_2(x, y) \tag{22}$$

such that the diagram

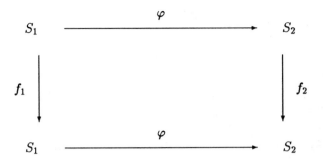

commutes, i.e. such that $f_2\varphi = \varphi f_1$ holds true.

Proof.   If $f_1 : S_1 \to S_2$ solves (21), then

$$f_2 := \varphi f_1 \varphi^{-1},$$

which is a mapping from S_2 into S_2, must be a solution of (22): let x, y be elements of S_2. Then

$$d_1\big(f_1\varphi^{-1}(x), f_1\varphi^{-1}(y)\big) = d_1\big(\varphi^{-1}(x), \varphi^{-1}(y)\big) \tag{23}$$

is a consequence of (21). Because of the isomorphism of the two spaces, (23) implies

$$d_2\big(\varphi f_1\varphi^{-1}(x), \varphi f_1\varphi^{-1}(y)\big) = d_2\big(\varphi\varphi^{-1}(x), \varphi\varphi^{-1}(y)\big).$$

But this yields

$$d_2\big(f_2(x), f_2(y)\big) = d_2(x, y). \qquad \Box$$

REMARKS.

1) By interchanging the distance spaces (S_1, W_1, d_1), (S_2, W_2, d_2) in Proposition 8, this Proposition also yields that to every solution

$$f_2 : S_2 \to S_2$$

of (22) there corresponds a solution $f_1 : S_1 \rightarrow S_1$ of (21) such that

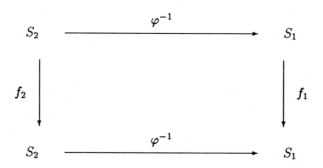

commutes. It therefore plays no role which of the two equations, (21) or (22), one solves, since the other equation is then also solved. We would like to present an example for this situation which shows that two completely different looking functional equations may arise from the same problem, but, formulated in two isomorphic distance spaces. Define

$$S_1 =]-1, +1[, \ \cosh d_1(x, y) = \frac{1 - xy}{\sqrt{(1 - x^2)(1 - y^2)}}$$

with $d_1 \geq 0$ and $x, y \in S_1$. (For the function cosh see section 1.2.) Set furthermore

$$S_2 =]0, \infty[, \ \cosh d_2(x, y) = \frac{1}{2}\left(\frac{x}{y} + \frac{y}{x}\right)$$

with $d_2 \geq 0$ and $x, y \in S_2$. The two distance spaces $(S_i, \mathbb{R}, d_i)$ (they are actually metric spaces) are isomorphic. Define

$$\varphi(x) = \sqrt{\frac{1 + x}{1 - x}}$$

for $x \in S_1$. The mapping $\varphi : S_1 \rightarrow S_2$ is then a bijection and it satisfies

$$d_1(a, b) = d_1(x, y)$$

for $a, b, x, y \in S_1$ if and only if,

$$d_2\big(\varphi(a), \varphi(b)\big) = d_2\big(\varphi(x), \varphi(y)\big)$$

holds true. This is consequence of

$$\cosh d_2\big(\varphi(a), \varphi(b)\big) = \cosh d_1(a, b)$$

for all $a, b \in S_1$. Equations (21), (22) may now be written in the following form. Find all $f_i : S_i \to S_i$, $i = 1, 2$, such that

$$\forall_{x,y \in S_1} \frac{1 - f_1(x)f_1(y)}{\sqrt{\left(1 - [f_1(x)]^2\right)\left(1 - [f_1(y)]^2\right)}} = \frac{1 - xy}{\sqrt{(1 - x^2)(1 - y^2)}},$$

$$\forall_{x,y \in S_2} \frac{f_2(x)}{f_2(y)} + \frac{f_2(y)}{f_2(x)} = \frac{x}{y} + \frac{y}{x}$$

hold true. All solutions f_1 of the first equation are determined in section 2.5. They are given by

$$\varphi_p(x) = \frac{x + p}{xp + 1} \text{ and } \varphi_p^-(x) = -\varphi_p(x)$$

for $p \in]-1, +1[$. All solutions f_2 of the second equation are hence given by

$$\psi_p(x) = px \text{ and } \psi_p^-(x) = \frac{p}{x}$$

for $p > 0$.

2) The notion of isomorphism of distance spaces is a special case of the notion of *equivalence* of invariants. Let (S_i, G_i), $i = 1, 2$, be geometries, let (N_i, φ_i) be an invariant notion of (S_i, G_i), $i = 1, 2$, and finally, let

$$h_i : N_i \to W_i$$

be an invariant of (S_i, G_i), $i = 1, 2$. The invariants h_1, h_2 are called *equivalent* iff there exists a bijection

$$\varrho : N_1 \to N_2$$

such that $h_1(l) = h_1(l')$ holds true for $l, l' \in N$ if, and only if,

$$h_2\big(\varrho(l)\big) = h_2\big(\varrho(l')\big)$$

is satisfied. For distance spaces (S_i, W_i, d_i), $i = 1, 2$, we have

$$N_i = S_i \times S_i$$

and $h_i = d_i$. Based on the isomorphism

$$\varphi : S_1 \to S_2,$$

$\varrho : N_1 \to N_2$ might be defined as

$$\varrho(x, y) := \big(\varphi(x), \varphi(y)\big)$$

for $x, y \in S_1$.

EXERCISES

1. Let G be the group of all bijections $x \to x' = ax + b$ of $\mathbb{R}$ where $a \neq 0$ and b are real numbers, and let N be the set of all open intervals $]\alpha, \beta[$ $(\alpha, \beta \in \mathbb{R}, \alpha < \beta)$ of $\mathbb{R}$. Define $\varphi(f, I) := \{f(x) \mid x \in I\}$ for $f \in G$ and $I \in N$. Show that (N, φ) is an invariant notion of $(\mathbb{R}, G)$.

2. For the same geometry $(\mathbb{R}, G)$ as above define

$$N := \{(x_1, x_2, x_3) \in \mathbb{R}^3 \mid x_1 < x_2 < x_3 \text{ or } x_1 > x_2 > x_3\} \qquad (24)$$

and $\varphi\big(f, (x_1, x_2, x_3)\big) := \big(f(x_1), f(x_2), f(x_3)\big)$. Show that (N, φ) is an invariant notion of $(\mathbb{R}, G)$ and that $h(x_1, x_2, x_3) := \left(\frac{x_2 - x_1}{x_3 - x_1}\right)^3$ is an invariant function $h : N \to \mathbb{R}$.

3. Define $\varphi\big(f, (x_1, x_2, x_3)\big) := \big(f(x_1), f(x_2), f(x_3)\big)$ for $(x_1, x_2, x_3) \in \mathbb{R}^3$ and $f \in \text{Perm } \mathbb{R}$. Obviously, $(\mathbb{R}^3, \varphi)$ is an invariant notion of $(\mathbb{R}, \text{Perm } \mathbb{R})$. Define N as in (24) and show that $G(N)$ consists exactly of all bijections f of $\mathbb{R}$ such that f and f^{-1} are continuous.

4. Define $\varphi\big(f, (x_1, x_2)\big) := \big(f(x_1), f(x_2)\big)$ for $(x_1, x_2) \in \mathbb{R}^2$ and $f \in \text{Perm } \mathbb{R}$. Then $(\mathbb{R}^2, \varphi)$ is an invariant notion of $(\mathbb{R}, \text{Perm } \mathbb{R})$. Put

$$N := \{(x_1, x_2) \in \mathbb{R}^2 \mid x_1 < x_2\}$$

and $h(x_1, x_2) := x_1 - x_2$. Show that $G(h)$ consists exactly of all bijections $x' = x + a$ $(a \in \mathbb{R})$ of $\mathbb{R}$.

5. Let Γ be the group of all bijections

$$\begin{aligned} x_1' &= x_1 a_{11} + x_2 a_{12} + a_{13} \\ x_2' &= x_1 a_{21} + x_2 a_{22} + a_{23} \end{aligned}$$

of $\mathbb{R}^2$ with real numbers a_{ij} such that $a_{11}a_{22} \neq a_{12}a_{21}$. Put

$$S_0 := \{(t, t^2) \mid t \in \mathbb{R}\}$$

and $\Gamma_0 := \{g \in \Gamma \mid g(S_0) = S_0\}$. Show that the substructure (S_0, Γ_0) of $(\mathbb{R}^2, \Gamma)$ is isomorphic to $(\mathbb{R}, G)$ where G denotes the group of exercise 1. Hint: Put $\sigma(t, t^2) := t$ and

$$\tau \begin{pmatrix} a & 2ab & 0 \\ 0 & a^2 & 0 \\ b & b^2 & 1 \end{pmatrix} := \begin{pmatrix} a & 0 \\ b & 1 \end{pmatrix}.$$

6. Show that Proposition 2 remains true if we replace (∗) by

(∘) To every line l of $\mathbb{R}^2$ there exists a line l' of $\mathbb{R}^2$ with $\gamma(l) \subseteq l'$.

Chapter 2

HYPERBOLIC GROUPS

2.1 The hyperbolic line

Let I be the interval

$$]-1,+1[:= \left\{ x \in \mathbb{R} \mid -1 < x < 1 \right\}$$

of $\mathbb{R}$ and suppose that

$$\varphi_p : I \to \mathbb{R}$$

is the mapping

$$\varphi_p(x) := \frac{x+p}{xp+1} \tag{1}$$

with $p \in I$. Then φ_p turns out to be a bijection of I. In order to verify this statement first notice that $xp + 1 > 0$ for $x, p \in I$. Furthermore, take into consideration the following lemma.

LEMMA 1. *Let x and p be elements of I. Then $\varphi_p(x)$ is in I as well.*

Proof.   This is a consequence of

$$(xp+1) - (x+p) = (1-x)(1-p) > 0$$

and

$$(xp+1) + (x+p) = (1+x)(1+p) > 0. \qquad \square$$

That $\varphi_p, p \in I$, is now a bijection of I follows finally from

$$\varphi_{-p}[\varphi_p(x)] = x \text{ and } \varphi_p[\varphi_{-p}(x)] = x \tag{2}$$

for all $x \in I$.

The set H^+ of bijections $\varphi_p, p \in I$, is a group with respect to the multiplication

$$(fg)(x) := f[g(x)].$$

Define $p * q := \dfrac{p+q}{pq+1}$ for $p, q \in I$. From $p * q = \varphi_p(q)$ and Lemma 1 we get $p * q \in I$ for $p, q \in I$, and we also get

$$\varphi_p \cdot \varphi_q = \varphi_{p*q}. \tag{3}$$

The groups $(I, *)$ and H^+ are thus isomorphic under the isomorphism

$$f : I \to H^+ \text{ with } f(p) := \varphi_p.$$

By means of the exponential function $\exp(x) = e^x$ we define hyperbolic functions hyperbolic sine, etc. as follows

$$\sinh x \quad := \frac{e^x - e^{-x}}{2}, \quad \cosh x := \frac{e^x + e^{-x}}{2},$$

$$\tanh x \quad := \frac{e^x - e^{-x}}{e^x + e^{-x}} = \frac{e^{2x} - 1}{e^{2x} + 1} \text{ for } x \in \mathbb{R}.$$

The mapping tanh is obviously a bijection from $\mathbb{R}$ onto I and it satisfies

$$\tanh(x + y) = (\tanh x) * (\tanh y) \tag{4}$$

for all $x, y \in \mathbb{R}$. Equation (4) shows that the additive group $\mathbb{R}^+ = (\mathbb{R}, +)$ of $\mathbb{R}$ is isomorphic to $(I, *)$ under the isomorphism

$$g : \mathbb{R}^+ \to I \text{ with } g(x) := \tanh x.$$

Thus

$$\begin{cases} fg : \mathbb{R}^+ & \to H^+ \\ \mathbb{R} \ni x & \to \varphi_{\tanh x} \end{cases}.$$

is an isomorphism of $\mathbb{R}^+$ onto H^+.

The elements of I are called the *points* of the one–dimensional hyperbolic geometry and

$$H := H^+ \cup H^-$$

with

$$H^- := \varepsilon \cdot H^+, \ \varepsilon(x) := -x \text{ for } x \in I,$$

is said to be the *hyperbolic group* of I. (In remark 2 of section 1.4 we restricted ourselves on H^+ only. The geometry (I, H^+) is sometimes called proper 1–dimensional hyperbolic geometry.) The elements φ_p of H^+ are orientation–preserving mappings of I. In fact,

$$\forall_{a,b \in I} \ a \leq b \Rightarrow \varphi_p(a) \leq \varphi_p(b) :$$

Because of $a \leq b$ we get $a \cdot (1 - p^2) \leq b \cdot (1 - p^2)$ and hence

$$(a + p)(pb + 1) \leq (b + p)(pa + 1),$$

i.e. $\varphi_p(a) \leq \varphi_p(b)$. Obviously,

$$\forall_{a,b \in I} \ a \leq b \Rightarrow \psi_p(a) \geq \psi_p(b)$$

for all $\psi_p := \varepsilon \varphi_p$, $p \in I$. The elements of H^- are thus orientation–reversing mappings.

The question we would like to pose now is, whether there are mappings $\gamma \notin H$,

$$\gamma(x) = \frac{ax + b}{cx + d}, \tag{5}$$

with $a, b, c, d \in \mathbb{R}$ and $cx + d \neq 0$ for all $x \in I$ such that $\gamma : I \rightarrow I$ is a bijection. $c \cdot 0 + d \neq 0$ implies $d \neq 0$, so without loss of generality, we put $d = 1$ in (5). Assume that $c = 1$. Then a must be unequal to b because otherwise $\gamma(x) = a$ for $x \in I$. But $a \neq b$ implies $|\gamma(x)| > 1$ for $x \in I$ and sufficiently small $x + 1$. In the case $c = -1$ observe $a \neq -b$ and hence $|\gamma(x)| > 1$ for $x \in I$ and sufficiently small $-x + 1$. The mapping γ of (5) is thus defined and continuous in $[-1, +1]$. Together with the fact that $\gamma : I \rightarrow I$ is a bijection we hence get

$$\gamma(1), \gamma(-1) \in \{1, -1\}. \tag{6}$$

$\gamma(1) = \gamma(-1)$ is not possible, since γ is injective in I. Hence $\gamma(1) = -\gamma(-1)$. So we have proven

PROPOSITION 2. *Suppose that*

$$\gamma(x) = \frac{ax + b}{cx + d}$$

with $a, b, c, d \in \mathbb{R}$ and $cx + d \neq 0$ for all $x \in I$ is a bijection of I. Then $\gamma \in H$.

2.2 Transitivity properties and 2–point invariants

Let x_0, y_0 be elements of I. How many elements $\gamma \in H$ exist such that $\gamma(x_0) = y_0$? Assume $\gamma = \varphi_p$. Then

$$y_0 = \varphi_p(x_0) = \varphi_{x_0}(p)$$

leads to $p = \varphi_{-x_0}(y_0)$. On the other hand, $p := \varphi_{-x_0}(y_0)$ implies

$$\varphi_p(x_0) = \varphi_{x_0}(p) = \varphi_{x_0}\left[\varphi_{-x_0}(y_0)\right] = y_0.$$

We have thus obtained

PROPOSITION 3. *The group H^+ operates sharply transitively on I: For $x_0, y_0 \in I$ there exists exactly one $\varphi_p \in H^+$ such that $\varphi_p(x_0) = y_0$. Then $p = \varphi_{-x_0}(y_0) = \varphi_{y_0}(-x_0)$.*

There is also exactly one element $\psi_p = \varepsilon\varphi_p$ with $\psi_p(x_0) = y_0$, namely that belonging to $p = \varphi_{-x_0}(-y_0)$.

Let W be a set and n a positive integer. Define I_n to be the cartesian product $I \times \ldots \times I$ with n factors I. A mapping (compare section 1.1)

$$f : I_n \to W$$

is called an n–point–invariant of H if and only if

$$f(x_1, \ldots, x_n) = f\big(\gamma(x_1), \ldots, \gamma(x_n)\big)$$

holds true for all $\gamma \in H$ and all $(x_1, \ldots, x_n) \in I_n$. It is in principal not difficult to determine all n–point–invariants. In the case $n = 1$ we start with a set $W \neq \emptyset$ and a $w \in W$. We then put $f(x) := w$ for all $x \in I$. The reason for this construction is that H operates transitively on I. In the case $n > 1$ put

$$L(x_1, \ldots, x_n) := \Big\{\big(\gamma(x_1), \ldots, \gamma(x_n)\big) \,\big|\, \gamma \in H\Big\}$$

for $(x_1, \ldots, x_n) \in I_n$. Observe that two such sets are either identical or disjoint. Now take an arbitrary set $W \neq \emptyset$ and define

$$\mathbb{L} := \Big\{L(x_1, \ldots, x_n) \,\big|\, (x_1, \ldots, x_n) \in I_n\Big\}.$$

Let $g : \mathbb{L} \to W$ be a mapping and put

$$f(x_1, \ldots, x_n) := g\big(L(x_1, \ldots, x_n)\big).$$

Then this is an n–point invariant and all such invariants can be constructed this way.

We now would like to introduce the notion of hyperbolic distance $f(x, y)$ of two points x, y of I. We shall do this axiomatically and so first of all, we shall collect assumptions which should be satisfied by an abstract notion of distance. In our understanding, such a notion must be a 2–point–invariant of the group H and it must be symmetric: $f(x, y) = f(y, x)$. It is actually sufficient to ask for a 2–point–invariant with respect to H^+: This will then also be an invariant for H, as it turns out. Distances should be non–negative real numbers and they should satisfy the property of additivity: $x, y, z \in I$ and $x \le y \le z$ imply

$$f(x, y) + f(y, z) = f(x, z).$$

How far we shall come with these properties will be answered in the following theorem.

THEOREM 4. *Suppose that f is a mapping from $I \times I$ into the set of non–negative real numbers such that*

(i) $\forall_{x,y,p \in I} \; f(x, y) = f\left(\dfrac{x+p}{xp+1}, \dfrac{y+p}{yp+1}\right),$

(ii) $\forall_{x,y \in I} \; f(x, y) = f(y, x),$

(iii) $-1 < x \le y \le z < 1$ *implies that* $f(x, y) + f(y, z) = f(x, z)$

hold true. Then there exists a real number $k \ge 0$ with

$$f(x, y) = \frac{k}{2} \cdot \left| \ln \frac{(1-x)(1+y)}{(1+x)(1-y)} \right| \tag{7}$$

for all $x, y \in I$.

Proof.   Put $g(x) := f(0, x)$ for $0 \le x < 1$ and let p, q be elements of I with $0 \le p \le q$. Hence by (iii),

$$f(0, p) + f(p, q) \;=\; f(0, q), \text{ i.e.}$$

$$g(p) + g\left(\frac{q-p}{-qp+1}\right) \;=\; g(q), \tag{8}$$

from (i). Suppose that p, a are elements of I, both ≥ 0. Put $q := \varphi_p(a)$. Because of $0 \le a$ we get

$$0 \le p = \varphi_p(0) \le \varphi_p(a) = q < 1.$$

Equation (8) implies

$$g(p) + g(a) = g\left(\frac{p+a}{pa+1}\right) \tag{9}$$

for all $a, p \ge 0$ in I by observing that $a = \varphi_{-p}(q)$ is a consequence of $q = \varphi_p(a)$. In section 2.3, Theorem 6, we shall show that all functions

$$g : [0, 1[\rightarrow \mathbb{R}_{\ge 0}$$

satisfying (9) are given by

$$g(x) = \frac{k}{2} \, ln\frac{1+x}{1-x} \tag{10}$$

with a constant $k \geq 0$. Here $[0,1[$, $\mathbb{R}_{\geq 0}$ denote $\{x \in \mathbb{R} \,|\, 0 \leq x < 1\}$, $\{x \in \mathbb{R} \,|\, 0 \leq x\}$ respectively. If $x, y \in I$ satisfy $x \leq y$, we get

$$0 = \varphi_{-x}(x) \leq \varphi_{-x}(y)$$

and hence

$$f(x,y) \;\; = \;\; f(0, \varphi_{-x}(y)) = g\left(\frac{y-x}{-xy+1}\right), \text{ i.e.}$$

$$f(x,y) \;\; = \;\; \frac{k}{2} \, ln\frac{(1-x)(1+y)}{(1+x)(1-y)} \geq 0 \tag{11}$$

by applying (10). Assuming $y \leq x$ we obtain

$$f(x,y) = f(y,x) = \frac{k}{2} \, ln\frac{(1-y)(1+x)}{(1+y)(1-x)} \geq 0$$

and thus generally

$$f(x,y) = \frac{k}{2} \left| ln\frac{(1-x)(1+y)}{(1+x)(1-y)} \right|$$

for $x, y \in I$. $\square$

REMARK. A function (7) with $k \geq 0$ obviously satisfies (i), (ii), (iii). It also satisfies

$$f(x,y) = f(-x,-y)$$

for all $x, y \in I$, so that (i) can be extended to the whole group H. Putting $\xi := \min\{x,y\}$ and $\eta := \max\{x,y\}$ for $x, y \in I$ we trivially obtain

$$f(x,y) = \frac{k}{2} \, ln\frac{(1-\xi)(1+\eta)}{(1+\xi)(1-\eta)} \tag{12}$$

from (11).

The formula (12) does not really look nice since it distinguishes between min $\{x,y\}$ and max $\{x,y\}$. But there is another formula without this deficiency and we will now derive it. We shall assume $k > 0$ since $k = 0$ only leads to a trivial distance function. Then let x, y be elements of I with $x \leq y$. Hence (12) implies

$$e^{\frac{2f}{k}} = \frac{(1-x)(1+y)}{(1+x)(1-y)}, \text{ i.e.}$$

$$\cosh \frac{2f}{k} = \frac{(x-y)^2 + (1-xy)^2}{(1-x^2)(1-y^2)}. \tag{13}$$

For $t \in \mathbb{R}$ we get

$$1 + \cosh 2t = 2 \cosh^2 t$$

from

$$1 + \frac{e^{2t} + e^{-2t}}{2} = 2 \left(\frac{e^t + e^{-t}}{2} \right)^2.$$

Thus (13) leads to

$$\cosh \frac{f}{k} = \frac{1 - xy}{\sqrt{1-x^2}\sqrt{1-y^2}}.$$

($\sqrt{a}$ is the real number $b \geq 0$ in the case $b^2 = a \geq 0$.)

Since this formula is symmetric in x, y we can drop the assumption $x \leq y$. The same formula suggests a choice of $k = 1$ in order to make it look as simple as possible. $k = 1$ is equivalent to

(iv) $f(0, \tanh 1) = 1$.

When (iv) holds true we prefer to write $h(x, y)$ instead of $f(x, y)$. So according to Theorem 4 we can say that there exists exactly one function

$$h : I \times I \to \mathbb{R}_{\geq 0}$$

satisfying (i), (ii), (iii), (iv), namely

$$\cosh h(x, y) = \frac{1 - xy}{\sqrt{1-x^2}\sqrt{1-y^2}} \tag{14}$$

where the solution $h(x, y) \geq 0$ has to be chosen.

2.3 Two functional equations

In section 2.2 we encountered the following functional equations problem

(I) *Determine all functions*

$$g : [0, 1[\to \mathbb{R}_{\geq 0}$$

such that

$$g\left(\frac{x + y}{xy + 1}\right) = g(x) + g(y) \tag{15}$$

holds true for all $x, y \in [0, 1[$.

We shall solve this problem by reducing it to the following functional equations problem (see J. Aczél [1]).

(II) *Determine all functions*

$$f : \mathbb{R}_{\geq 0} \to \mathbb{R}_{\geq 0}$$

such that

$$f(x + y) = f(x) + f(y) \tag{16}$$

holds true for all $x, y \in \mathbb{R}_{\geq 0}$.

We shall begin with problem (II). Putting $x = y = 0$ in (16) we get $f(0) = 0$. Define $k := f(1)$. Hence $k \geq 0$ since the image of f is in $\mathbb{R}_{\geq 0}$. Equation (16) can be extended to

$$f(x_1 + \ldots + x_n) = \sum_{i=1}^{n} f(x_i)$$

for every positive integer n by induction. Hence

$$k = f(1) = f\left(\frac{1}{n} + \ldots + \frac{1}{n}\right) = n \cdot f\left(\frac{1}{n}\right),$$

i.e. $f\left(\frac{1}{n}\right) = \frac{k}{n}$ for every positive integer n. Thus $f\left(\frac{m}{n}\right) = f\left(\frac{1}{n} + \ldots + \frac{1}{n}\right)$
$= m \cdot f\left(\frac{1}{n}\right) = \frac{m}{n}k$ for $m \in \{1, 2, 3, \ldots\}$. This leads to $f(r) = kr$ for every non-negative rational number r. Suppose that $0 \leq x \leq y$. Then $y - x \geq 0$ and hence $f(y - x) \geq 0$. This implies $f(x) \leq f(y)$ because

$$f(x) + f(y - x) = f(y).$$

Now let $z > 0$ be a real number and let $\{r_i\}_{i=1,2,\ldots}, \{s_i\}_{i=1,2,\ldots}$ be sequences of rational and non-negative numbers satisfying

$$\lim_{i \to \infty} r_i = z = \lim_{i \to \infty} s_i$$

and

$$r_i \le z \le s_i$$

for all $i = 1, 2, \ldots$. Hence

$$kr_i = f(r_i) \le f(z) \le f(s_i) = ks_i$$

and thus $f(z) = \lim_{i \to \infty} kr_i = kz$. The result we have obtained is the following

THEOREM 5. *All solutions of* (II) *are given by* $f(x) = kx$, *where* k *is a constant* ≥ 0.

Adopting the notation of section 2.1, equation (15) can be written as

$$g(x * y) = g(x) + g(y) \tag{17}$$

for all $x, y \in [0, 1[$. We already know from section 2.1 that tanh is a bijection from $\mathbb{R}$ onto I. As a matter of fact, it is a bijection from $\mathbb{R}_{\ge}$ onto $[0, 1[$ as well. Employing equation (4) we hence get from (17)

$$g(\tanh[\xi + \eta]) = g(\tanh \xi) + g(\tanh \eta)$$

for all $\xi, \eta \in \mathbb{R}_{\ge 0}$. Define

$$f(\xi) := g(\tanh \xi)$$

for $\xi \ge 0$. Employing Theorem 5, we obtain

$$f(x) = kx$$

with a constant $k \ge 0$. Thus

$$g(\tanh x) = kx \tag{18}$$

for all $x \ge 0$. Put $y := \tanh x \in [0, 1[$ for $x \ge 0$. This implies that

$$y = \frac{e^{2x} - 1}{e^{2x} + 1}$$

and hence

$$e^{2x} = \frac{1+y}{1-y},$$

i.e. $x = \dfrac{1}{2} \ln \dfrac{1+y}{1-y}$. This together with (17) yields

$$g(y) = \frac{k}{2} \ln \frac{1+y}{1-y}$$

for all $y \in [0, 1[$. We have thus proved

THEOREM 6. *All solutions of* (I) *are given by*

$$g(x) = \frac{k}{2} \, ln\frac{1+x}{1-x}$$

for all $x \in [0, 1[$ *with a constant* $k \geq 0$.

2.4   Weierstrass coordinates

Let x be an element of I. The ordered pair

$$(x_1, x_2) := \left(\frac{x}{\sqrt{1-x^2}}, \frac{1}{\sqrt{1-x^2}} \right)$$

is called the pair of *Weierstrass coordinates* of x. Observe that $x_1^2 - x_2^2 = -1$. Since x_2 is always greater than 0 we obtain that

$$\omega(x) := (x_1, x_2)$$

is a bijection from I onto the upper branch (i.e. $x_2 > 0$) of the hyperbola of equation $x_1^2 - x_2^2 = -1$: This bijection

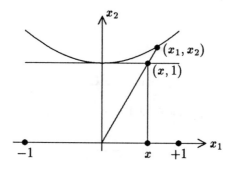

can be written, by employing a real parameter t, in the form

$$\omega(\tanh t) = (\sinh t, \cosh t)$$

with $t \in \mathbb{R}$. In Weierstrass coordinates the elements of H^+ or H^- can be expressed as follows. Instead of

$$y = \frac{x+p}{xp+1}$$

we get the matrix equation

$$\left(\frac{y}{\sqrt{1-y^2}} \quad \frac{1}{\sqrt{1-y^2}} \right) = \left(\frac{x}{\sqrt{1-x^2}} \quad \frac{1}{\sqrt{1-x^2}} \right) \left(\begin{array}{cc} \dfrac{1}{\sqrt{1-p^2}} & \dfrac{p}{\sqrt{1-p^2}} \\ \dfrac{p}{\sqrt{1-p^2}} & \dfrac{1}{\sqrt{1-p^2}} \end{array} \right)$$

and instead of

$$y = \frac{-x - p}{xp + 1}$$

we obtain

$$(y_1 \ y_2) = (x_1 \ x_2) \left(\begin{array}{cc} -\dfrac{1}{\sqrt{1-p^2}} & \dfrac{p}{\sqrt{1-p^2}} \\ -\dfrac{p}{\sqrt{1-p^2}} & \dfrac{1}{\sqrt{1-p^2}} \end{array} \right).$$

The matrices

$$\frac{1}{\sqrt{1-p^2}} \cdot \left(\begin{array}{cc} 1 & p \\ p & 1 \end{array} \right) \text{ and } \frac{1}{\sqrt{1-p^2}} \cdot \left(\begin{array}{cc} -1 & p \\ -p & 1 \end{array} \right)$$

are called Lorentz matrices,

$$L = \left(\begin{array}{cc} l_{11} & l_{12} \\ l_{21} & l_{22} \end{array} \right),$$

since they satisfy

$$l_{i1} l_{j1} - l_{i2} l_{j2} = \left\{ \begin{array}{ll} 0 & i \neq j \\ 1 & \text{for} \quad i = j < 2, \\ -1 & i = j = 2 \end{array} \right.$$

and furthermore, they are called orthochronous since $l_{22} \geq 1$ holds true. For many informations about Lorentz matrices and transformations, we refer to our book GT, chapter 6.

All Lorentz matrices

$$\left(\begin{array}{cc} l_{11} & l_{12} \\ l_{21} & l_{22} \end{array} \right), l_{ij} \in \mathbb{R},$$

are given, as it is trivial to prove, by

a) $\left(\begin{array}{cc} \cosh \alpha & \sinh \alpha \\ \sinh \alpha & \cosh \alpha \end{array} \right)$, b) $\left(\begin{array}{cc} -\cosh \alpha & \sinh \alpha \\ -\sinh \alpha & \cosh \alpha \end{array} \right)$,

c) $\left(\begin{array}{cc} -\cosh \alpha & \sinh \alpha \\ \sinh \alpha & -\cosh \alpha \end{array} \right)$, d) $\left(\begin{array}{cc} \cosh \alpha & \sinh \alpha \\ -\sinh \alpha & -\cosh \alpha \end{array} \right)$

with $\alpha \in \mathbb{R}$. Types a) and b) consist only of orthochronous matrices, types c) and d) do not. Types a) and c) consist only of matrices of determinant 1, types b) and d) only of those of determinant -1.

The types a) and b) occured in our considerations before: we have

$$\frac{1}{\sqrt{1-p^2}} \cdot \begin{pmatrix} 1 & p \\ p & 1 \end{pmatrix} = \begin{pmatrix} \cosh\alpha & \sinh\alpha \\ \sinh\alpha & \cosh\alpha \end{pmatrix}$$

for $p \in I$ or $\alpha \in \mathbb{R}$ by putting

$$\tanh\alpha = p$$

(define $\alpha \in \mathbb{R}$ by this equation if $p \in I$ is given and vice versa p for given α); similarly we have

$$\frac{1}{\sqrt{1-p^2}} \cdot \begin{pmatrix} -1 & p \\ -p & 1 \end{pmatrix} = \begin{pmatrix} -\cosh\alpha & \sinh\alpha \\ -\sinh\alpha & \cosh\alpha \end{pmatrix}$$

by also putting

$$\tanh\alpha = p.$$

We would like to emphasize that non–orthochronous Lorentz matrices did not occur as representatives of elements of H.

Formula (14) has in Weierstrass coordinates the form

$$-\cosh\ h\big((x_1, x_2), (y_1, y_2)\big) = x_1 y_1 - x_2 y_2.$$

2.5   A functional equation of distance preservance

In section 2.2 the problem was to find 2–point–invariants satisfying certain properties. We now would like to start with a 2–point–invariant of H and to determine all mappings preserving the invariant in question:

Find all functions

$$f : I \to I$$

such that

$$\frac{1 - f(x)f(y)}{\sqrt{1 - [f(x)]^2}\sqrt{1 - [f(y)]^2}} = \frac{1 - xy}{\sqrt{1 - x^2}\sqrt{1 - y^2}} \tag{19}$$

holds true for all $x, y \in I$.

Notice that f is not assumed to be injective or even bijective.

PROPOSITION 7. *The elements f of H and only these are the solutions of the functional equation* (19).

Proof.   It is not difficult to verify that $f \in H$ solves (19): since

$$h(x, y) = h\big(f(x), f(y)\big)$$

we also have (19) by means of (14). Suppose now that $f : I \to I$ is a solution of (19). According to Proposition 3 there exists a $g \in H^+$ such that

$$g[f(0)] = 0.$$

Hence $F(0) = 0$ for

$$F(x) := g[f(x)]$$

for $x \in I$. The function $F : I \to I$ also satisfies (19) and thus

$$\frac{1 - F(x)F(y)}{\sqrt{1 - [F(x)]^2}\sqrt{1 - [F(y)]^2}} = \frac{1 - xy}{\sqrt{1 - x^2}\sqrt{1 - y^2}} \tag{20}$$

for all $x, y \in I$. Putting $y = 0$ yields

$$\frac{1}{\sqrt{1 - [F(x)]^2}} = \frac{1}{\sqrt{1 - x^2}}$$

and hence $[F(x)]^2 = x^2$ for all $x \in I$. This together with (20) leads to

$$F(x)F(y) = xy \tag{21}$$

for all $x, y \in I$. Putting $x = y = \frac{1}{2}$ here, we get $F\left(\frac{1}{2}\right) \neq 0$ from (21) and thus

$$F(x) = \frac{1}{2F\left(\frac{1}{2}\right)} \cdot x =: kx \tag{22}$$

for all $x \in I$ and a constant $k \neq 0$. (21), (22) thus yield $k^2 = 1$. Suppose that $g =: \varphi_p$ with $p \in I$. Since

$$f = g^{-1} \cdot F$$

we get

$$f(x) = \begin{cases} \varphi_{-p}(x) \in H^+ & k = 1 \\ & \text{for} \\ -\varphi_p(x) \in H^- & k = -1 \end{cases}. \qquad \square$$

2.6 Hyperbolic spaces

Let $n \in \mathbb{N} := \{1, 2, 3, \ldots\}$ be a positive integer and define I^n to be the set

$$I^n := \left\{ (x_1, \ldots, x_n) \in \mathbb{R}^n \mid x_1^2 + \ldots + x_n^2 < 1 \right\}.$$

Our former interval I is now the space I^1. The next step will be the definition of the hyperbolic groups $\overset{(n)}{H^+}$ and $\overset{(n)}{H}$ which should be generalizations of H^+ and H to the case $n > 1$. Let $\mathbb{L}_{\text{orth}}^{n+1}$ be the set of all Lorentz matrices

$$L = \begin{pmatrix} l_{11} & \cdots & l_{1,n+1} \\ \vdots & & \vdots \\ l_{n+1,1} & \cdots & l_{n+1,n+1} \end{pmatrix}$$

over $\mathbb{R}$ which are orthochronous, i.e. which satisfy

$$LML^T = M := \begin{pmatrix} 1 & & & & \\ & 1 & & & 0 \\ & & \ddots & & \\ & 0 & & 1 & \\ & & & & -1 \end{pmatrix} \tag{23}$$

and $l_{n+1,n+1} \geq 1$. Put

$$\overset{(n)}{H^+} := \left\{ L \in \mathbb{L}_{\text{orth}}^{n+1} \mid \det L = 1 \right\},$$

$$\overset{(n)}{H^-} := \left\{ L \in \mathbb{L}_{\text{orth}}^{n+1} \mid \det L = -1 \right\}$$

and

$$\overset{(n)}{H} := \overset{(n)}{H^+} \cup \overset{(n)}{H^-} = \mathbb{L}_{\text{orth}}^{n+1}.$$

Instead of (23) we also can write

$$l_{i1}l_{j1} + \ldots + l_{in}l_{jn} - l_{i,n+1}l_{j,n+1} = \begin{cases} 0 & i \neq j \\ 1 & for & i = j < n+1 \\ -1 & i = j = n+1 \end{cases} \tag{24}$$

as can easily be verified. A consequence of (23) is

$$(\det L)^2 = 1$$

and hence that L^{-1} exists. Thus

$$L^{-1} = ML^T M = \begin{pmatrix} l_{11} & l_{21} & \cdots & l_{n1} & -l_{n+1,1} \\ \vdots & & \vdots & & \\ l_{1n} & l_{2n} & \cdots & l_{nn} & -l_{n+1,n} \\ -l_{1,n+1} & -l_{2,n+1} & \cdots & -l_{n,n+1} & +l_{n+1,n+1} \end{pmatrix}$$

holds true. Observe that (23) also implies $L^T = ML^{-1}M$, i.e.

$$L^T ML = ML^{-1}M \cdot M \cdot L = M,$$

so that L^T must be an orthochronous Lorentz matrix in the case that L is such a matrix. Notice furthermore

$$L^{-1}M(L^{-1})^T = ML^T M \cdot M \cdot MLM = M.$$

This implies that L^{-1} is an orthochronous Lorentz matrix provided that L is such a matrix.

In the case $i = j = n + 1$ we get

$$l_{n+1,1}^2 + \ldots + l_{n+1,n}^2 - l_{n+1,n+1}^2 = -1$$

from (24), i.e. $|l_{n+1,n+1}| \geq 1$. A matrix L satisfying (23) is called a Lorentz matrix. A Lorentz matrix L which is not in $\overset{(n)}{H}$ thus satisfies $l_{n+1,n+1} \leq -1$. If L is a Lorentz matrix, then $-L$ as well. Obviously, the Lorentz matrix L is not in $\overset{(n)}{H}$ if and only if, $-L$ belongs to $\overset{(n)}{H}$.

That the product of two matrices

$$\begin{pmatrix} & & & \\ & & & \\ a_1 & \cdots & a_n & a_{n+1} \end{pmatrix} , \begin{pmatrix} & & & b_1 \\ & & & \vdots \\ & & & b_n \\ \cdots & \cdots & \cdots & b_{n+1} \end{pmatrix}$$

of $\overset{(n)}{H}$ is also orthochronous is a consequence of the following inequality:

$$(a_1 b_1 + \ldots + a_n b_n)^2 \leq (a_1^2 + \ldots + a_n^2) \cdot (b_1^2 + \ldots + b_n^2) < a_{n+1}^2 b_{n+1}^2 :$$

notice that the transpose of the second Lorentz matrix is also a Lorentz matrix which hence satisfies

$$b_1^2 + \ldots + b_n^2 - b_{n+1}^2 = -1$$

according to (24). This inequality namely implies

$$a_1 b_1 + \ldots + a_n b_n + a_{n+1} b_{n+1} > 0.$$

In I^n we would like to work mainly with Weierstrass coordinates,

$$I^n \ni (\xi_1, \ldots, \xi_n) \to (x_1, \ldots, x_n, x_{n+1}) \tag{25}$$

with

$$x_i := \begin{cases} \dfrac{\xi_i}{\sqrt{1-\xi^2}} & i \in \{1, \ldots, n\} \\[4mm] \dfrac{1}{\sqrt{1-\xi^2}} & i = n+1 \end{cases} \quad \text{for} \quad .$$

In this formula, we applied the euclidean scalar product

$$\xi \cdot \eta := (\xi_1, \ldots, \xi_n) \cdot (\eta_1, \ldots, \eta_n) := \sum_{i=1}^{n} \xi_i \eta_i$$

in the case $\eta = \xi$. Mapping (25) is a bijection from I^n onto the sheet $x_{n+1} > 0$ of the surface of equation

$$x_1^2 + \ldots + x_n^2 - x_{n+1}^2 = -1. \tag{26}$$

By F we denote the set of points of this sheet. From the geometrical point of view, $(x_1, \ldots, x_{n+1})$ can be constructed as follows. Join the origin of $\mathbb{R}^{n+1}$ with $(\xi_1, \ldots, \xi_n, 1)$. This line then intersects F in $(x_1, \ldots, x_{n+1})$.

Theorem 8. *The mappings*

$$(y_1 \ldots y_{n+1}) = (x_1 \ldots x_{n+1})L \tag{27}$$

with $L \in \overset{(n)}{H}$ are bijections of I^n. If on the other hand L is a real $(n+1, n+1)-$ matrix such that (27) maps I^n into I^n, then $L \in \overset{(n)}{H}$.

Proof.   We do not distinguish between the points of I^n and those of F. However, attention must be paid to the coordinates with which we are working in a specific situation. Assume $x \in F$. Then

$$yMy^T = xLML^Tx^T = xMx^T = -1.$$

Observe that

$$y_{n+1} = x_1\, l_{1,n+1} + \ldots + x_{n+1}\, l_{n+1,n+1} > 0$$

holds true. This follows again from the inequality

$$(x_1 l_{1,n+1} + \ldots + x_n l_{n,n+1})^2 \le (x_1^2 + \ldots + x_n^2) \cdot (l_{1,n+1}^2 + \ldots + l_{n,n+1}^2) < x_{n+1}^2 l_{n+1,n+1}^2.$$

The mapping (27) is of course injective since det $L \neq 0$, and it is surjective because $yL^{-1} \in F$ for $y \in F$. — Suppose now that L is an $(n+1, n+1)$–matrix such that (27) maps I^n into I^n. Then

$$xLML^T x^T = -1 \tag{28}$$

for all $x \in F$, i.e. for all $x \in \mathbb{R}^{n+1}$ with $xMx^T = -1$. Putting $LML^T =: A$ (observe that A satisfies $A = A^T$) and

$$x_i := t, \ x_{n+1} := \sqrt{1+t^2}$$

for a fixed $i \in \{1, \ldots, n\}$ and $x_j = 0$ otherwise, we get

$$a_{ii} = 1, \ a_{n+1,n+1} = -1, \ a_{i,n+1} = 0.$$

Nothing more is needed in the case $n = 1$ in order to be sure that $A = M$. In the case $n > 1$ put

$$x_i := 1, \ x_j := 1, \ x_{n+1} := \sqrt{3}$$

for fixed and distinct $i, j \in \{1, \ldots, n\}$ and $x_k = 0$ otherwise. Then $a_{ij} = 0$ and hence finally

$$LML^T = M.$$

L is thus a Lorentz matrix. Assume that L is not orthochronous. Then $l_{n+1,n+1} \leq -1$ and hence

$$x := (l_{1,n+1}, \ldots, l_{n,n+1}, -l_{n+1,n+1}) \in F.$$

As a consequence of $y := xL \in F$ we get

$$0 < y_{n+1} = l_{1,n+1}^2 + \ldots + l_{n,n+1}^2 - l_{n+1,n+1}^2 = -1.$$

Our assumption that L is not orthochronous, was thus not correct. $\square$

The geometry $\left(I^n, \overset{(n)}{H}\right)$ is called *n–dimensional hyperbolic geometry*. $\left(I^n, \overset{(n)}{H^+}\right)$ is called *proper n–dimensional hyperbolic geometry*.

The same question we had in the case $n = 1$ concerning the notion of hyperbolic distance now arises for the higher dimensions $n \geq 2$:

THEOREM 9. *Let* $f : I^n \times I^n \to \mathbb{R}_{\geq 0}$ *be a mapping satisfying*

(i) $\forall_{x,y \in I^n} \ f(x,y) = f(xL, yL)$ *for every* $(n+1, n+1)$*–Lorentz-matrix* L, *provided that it is orthochronous,*

(ii) if we have points (this time written in cartesian coordinates)

$$x, \; z, \; y = \lambda x + (1 - \lambda)z \; \text{with} \; 0 \le \lambda \le 1$$

of I^n, then

$$f(x, z) = f(x, y) + f(y, z),$$

(iii) $\exists_{a,b \in I^n} \; f(a, b) > 0$.

Then there exists a positive real constant k such that

$$\cosh \frac{f(x, y)}{k} = \frac{1 - \sum_{i=1}^n x_i y_i}{\sqrt{1 - \sum_{i=1}^n x_i^2} \sqrt{1 - \sum_{i=1}^n y_i^2}}$$

holds true in cartesian coordinates and

$$-\cosh \frac{f(x, y)}{k} = x_1 y_1 + \ldots + x_n y_n - x_{n+1} \, y_{n+1}$$

in Weierstrass coordinates for all $x, y \in I^n$.

Proof.   a) Suppose that for

$$a := (a_1, \ldots, a_{n+1}) \in \mathbb{R}^{n+1},$$

$a_{n+1} > 0$ and $a_1^2 + \ldots + a_n^2 - a_{n+1}^2 = -1$ hold true. The following special matrix B is a Lorentz matrix which in addition is orthochronous. It is called a Lorentz boost (see GT, 251 ff).

Define

$$B := \begin{pmatrix} & & & a_1 \\ & C & & \vdots \\ & & & a_n \\ \hline a_1 & \cdots & a_n & a_{n+1} \end{pmatrix} \tag{29}$$

with $C := (c_{ij})$ and

$$c_{ij} := \frac{a_i a_j}{1 + a_{n+1}} + \delta_{ij} \tag{30}$$

for $i, j \in \{1, \ldots, n\}$, where

$$\delta_{ij} := \begin{cases} 0 & i \ne j \\ & \text{for} \\ 1 & i = j. \end{cases}$$

Hence

$$(a_1 \ldots a_{n+1}) = (0 \ldots 0\ 1)B$$

and $\overset{(n)}{H}$ operates transitively on I^n: from

$$x = (0 \ldots 0\ 1)B_1 \text{ and } y = (0 \ldots 0\ 1)B_2$$

we get $y = x \cdot (B_1^{-1}B_2)$.

b) Let $(z_1, \ldots, z_n)$ be an element of $\mathbb{R}^n$ which is supposed to be $\neq 0$ and let l be the real number $\sqrt{z_1^2 + \ldots + z_n^2}$. Then extend

$$\left(\frac{1}{l}z_1, \ldots, \frac{1}{l}z_n\right)$$

to an orthonormal basis

$$(v_{21}, \ldots, v_{2n}), \ldots, (v_{n1}, \ldots, v_{nn})$$

of $\mathbb{R}^n$ and define

$$A = \begin{pmatrix} v_{11} & \cdots & v_{1n} \\ \vdots & & \\ v_{n1} & \cdots & v_{nn} \end{pmatrix}$$

with $v_{1i} := \frac{1}{l}z_i$. Then

$$(z_1 \ldots z_n) = (l\ 0\ \ldots\ 0)A \tag{31}$$

and A is an orthogonal matrix of $\mathbb{R}^n$. Assuming now that $(z_1, \ldots, z_n)$ are the cartesian coordinates of a point $z \in I^n$, we go over to the corresponding Weierstrass coordinates, and (31) thus yields

$$\left(\frac{z_1}{\sqrt{1-l^2}} \cdots \frac{1}{\sqrt{1-l^2}}\right) = \left(\frac{l}{\sqrt{1-l^2}}\ 0 \ldots 0\ \frac{1}{\sqrt{1-l^2}}\right) \cdot D$$

with

$$D := \begin{pmatrix} & & & 0 \\ & A & & \vdots \\ & & & 0 \\ \hline 0 & \cdots & 0 & 1 \end{pmatrix} \overset{(n)}{\in H}.$$

c) Suppose that x, y are distinct points of I^n. Applying a) leads to the existence of $L_1 \overset{(n)}{\in H}$ with

$$(0 \ldots 0\ 1) = xL_1.$$

Observe $x \neq y$ and hence $yL_1 \neq xL_1 = (0 \ \ldots \ 0 \ 1)$. From b) we can find a $D \in \overset{(n)}{H}$ with last row $(0 \ \ldots \ 0 \ 1)$ satisfying

$$yL_1 = \left(\frac{l}{\sqrt{1-l^2}} \ 0 \ldots 0 \ \frac{1}{\sqrt{1-l^2}} \right) D$$

and

$$xL_1 = (0 \ \ldots \ 0 \ 1)D.$$

Put $L_1 D^{-1} =: L$. Hence

$$xL = (0 \ \ldots \ 0 \ 1)$$

and

$$yL = \left(\frac{l}{\sqrt{1-l^2}} \ 0 \ldots 0 \ \frac{1}{\sqrt{1-l^2}} \right).$$

This implies — notice $(x-y)M(x-y)^T = (x-y)LML^T(x-y)^T$ — that

$$(x_1 - y_1)^2 + \ldots + (x_n - y_n)^2 - (x_{n+1} - y_{n+1})^2 = 2\left(\frac{1}{\sqrt{1-l^2}} - 1 \right)$$

and thus

$$x_1 y_1 + \ldots + x_n y_n - x_{n+1}y_{n+1} = -\frac{1}{\sqrt{1-l^2}} < -1.$$

d) We are interested now in those mappings $y = xL$ of $\overset{(n)}{H}$ which are of the special form

$$
\begin{aligned}
y_1 &= l_{11}x_1 + l_{n+1,1} \, x_{n+1} \\
y_i &= x_i \text{ for } i = 2, \ldots, n \\
y_{n+1} &= l_{1,n+1} \, x_1 + l_{n+1,n+1} \, x_{n+1}
\end{aligned}
\tag{32}
$$

and, of course, we get exactly the matrices of $H = \overset{(1)}{H}$ as long as we restrict ourselves to the positions

$$\left(\begin{array}{cc} 11 & 1, n+1 \\ n+1, 1 & n+1, n+1 \end{array} \right).\tag{33}$$

Those mappings keep invariant the set

$$J := \left\{ \left(\frac{r}{\sqrt{1-r^2}}, 0, \ldots, 0, \frac{1}{\sqrt{1-r^2}} \right) \ \Big| \ -1 < r < 1 \right\}.$$

Our problem of determining certain functions $f(x, y)$ is now reduced to the space I^1, where we already solved it (Theorem 4). However, we must mention that in our present situation, $f(x, y) = f(y, x)$ can be proved for $x, y \in I^1$ since there exists a mapping (32) which just interchanges

$$x = \left(\frac{\xi}{\sqrt{1 - \xi^2}}, 0, \ldots, 0, \frac{1}{\sqrt{1 - \xi^2}} \right)$$

and

$$y = \left(\frac{\eta}{\sqrt{1 - \eta^2}}, 0, \ldots, 0, \frac{1}{\sqrt{1 - \eta^2}} \right),$$

namely (we are adopting the shortened form (33))

$$\frac{1}{\sqrt{1 - p^2}} \cdot \begin{pmatrix} -1 & p \\ -p & 1 \end{pmatrix}$$

with $-(\xi + \eta) =: p \cdot (\xi\eta + 1)$.

Sections 2.2 and 2.4 thus lead to a constant $k > 0$ (observe the existence of $a, b \in I^n$ with $f(a, b) > 0$ which can be carried over to two points of J) such that

$$-\cosh \frac{f(x, y)}{k} = x_1 y_1 - x_{n+1} \, y_{n+1} \tag{34}$$

holds true for all $x, y \in J$. — Suppose now that x, y are points of I^n. According to c) there exists an $L \in \overset{(n)}{H}$ such that

$$xL \quad = \quad (0 \ldots 0\ 1),$$

$$yL \quad = \quad \left(\frac{l}{\sqrt{1 - l^2}}\ 0 \ldots 0\ \frac{1}{\sqrt{1 - l^2}} \right),$$

$$-\frac{1}{\sqrt{1 - l^2}} \quad = \quad x_1 y_1 + \ldots + x_n y_n - x_{n+1} y_{n+1}.$$

Formula (34) hence yields

$$-\cosh \frac{f(xL, yL)}{k} = -\frac{1}{\sqrt{1 - l^2}}.$$

Applying assumption (i) we thus get

$$-\cosh \frac{f(x, y)}{k} = x_1 y_1 + \ldots + x_n y_n - x_{n+1} \, y_{n+1}.$$

In cartesian coordinates

$$\xi_i = \frac{x_i}{x_{n+1}}, \quad i = 1, \ldots, n,$$

3*

so this becomes

$$\cosh \frac{f(x,y)}{k} = x_{n+1}\, y_{n+1} \left(1 - \sum_{i=1}^{n} \xi_i \eta_i\right)$$

with

$$1 - \sum_{i=1}^{n} \xi_i^2 = \frac{x_{n+1}^2 - \sum_{i=1}^{n} x_i^2}{x_{n+1}^2} = \frac{1}{x_{n+1}^2},$$

i.e.

$$x_{n+1} = \frac{1}{\sqrt{1 - \sum_{i=1}^{n} \xi_i^2}}$$

and similarly

$$y_{n+1} = \frac{1}{\sqrt{1 - \sum_{i=1}^{n} \eta_i^2}}. \qquad \square$$

REMARK. It is easy to verify that the functions $f(x,y)$ determined in Theorem 9 satisfy properties (i), (ii), (iii). (In the case $k = 1$ we shall write $h(x,y)$ instead of $f(x,y)$ and we shall call $h(x,y)$ the *hyperbolic distance* of x,y.) As a matter of fact, (i) follows immediately from

$$-\cosh \frac{f(x,y)}{k} = \langle x,y\rangle := x_1\, y_1 + \ldots + x_n\, y_n - x_{n+1}\, y_{n+1} \qquad (35)$$

since

$$-\cosh \frac{f(xL, yL)}{k} = \langle xL, yL\rangle = \langle x,y\rangle.$$

For the two points $r = 0$, $\tanh 1$ of J (call them a, b), equation (35) yields

$$-\cosh \frac{f(a,b)}{k} = -\cosh 1,$$

i.e. $f(a,b) = k > 0$. In order to establish (ii) we first notice the following fact. Three points of I^n

$$x,\ z,\ y = \lambda x + (1-\lambda)z \quad (0 \le \lambda \le 1) \qquad (36)$$

(given in cartesian coordinates) go over into

$$x',\ z',\ y' = \mu x' + (1-\mu)z' \quad (0 \le \mu \le 1)$$

under a mapping

$$(\xi_1' \ldots \xi_{n+1}') = (\xi_1 \ldots \xi_{n+1})L \qquad (37)$$

(written in Weierstrass coordinates) of $\overset{(n)}{H}$. Taking

$$x_i = \frac{\xi_i}{\xi_{n+1}} \quad (i = 1, \ldots, n)$$

into account, (37) reads as

$$x'_i = \frac{\left(\sum_{\nu=1}^{n} x_\nu l_{\nu i}\right) + l_{n+1,i}}{\left(\sum_{\nu=1}^{n} x_\nu l_{\nu,n+1}\right) + l_{n+1,n+1}}, \quad i = 1, \ldots, n. \tag{38}$$

The denominator $D(x)$ of the right hand side of this formula is equal to

$$\frac{\xi'_{n+1}}{\xi_{n+1}}$$

and is thus positive. From (36) and (38) we get

$$y'_i = \frac{\lambda D(x) x'_i + (1 - \lambda) D(z) z'_i}{\lambda D(x) + (1 - \lambda) D(z)},$$

$i = 1, \ldots, n$. Obviously, $0 \le \mu \le 1$ for

$$\mu := \frac{\lambda D(x)}{\lambda D(x) + (1 - \lambda) D(z)}.$$

Hence $y' = \mu x' + (1 - \mu) z'$ with $0 \le \mu \le 1$. From this consideration, (ii) now needs to be verified only in the case

$$x = 0, \quad z = (z_1, 0, \ldots, 0),$$
$$y = (\varrho z_1, 0, \ldots, 0) \ (0 \le \varrho \le 1)$$

(these are cartesian coordinates), since the general case leads to this special one from step c) of the proof of Theorem 9. We get (in cartesian coordinates)

$$\cosh \frac{f(x, y)}{k} = \frac{1}{\sqrt{1 - (\varrho z_1)^2}}, \qquad \cosh \frac{f(x, z)}{k} = \frac{1}{\sqrt{1 - z_1^2}},$$

$$\cosh \frac{f(y, z)}{k} = \frac{1 - \varrho z_1^2}{\sqrt{1 - (\varrho z_1)^2} \sqrt{1 - z_1^2}}$$

and hence

$$\cosh \frac{f(x, y) + f(y, z)}{k} = \cosh \frac{f(x, z)}{k}$$

since

$$\cosh(u + v) = \cosh u \cdot \cosh v + \sinh u \cdot \sinh v.$$

□

REMARK. The following problem arises: Find all mappings

$$g : I^n \to I^n$$

such that

$$f\big(g(x), g(y)\big) = f(x, y) \tag{39}$$

holds true for all $x, y \in I^n$. This is again a functional equation (compare it with equation (19)), the solutions of which are the elements of $\overset{(n)}{H}$: put $g(0) =: s$ for a mapping $g : I^n \to I^n$ and take a $\gamma \in \overset{(n)}{H}$ with $\gamma(s) = 0$ as in step a) of the proof of Theorem 9. If g is distance preserving, then so is γg. In Weierstrass coordinates we have

$$\langle x, y \rangle = \langle x', y' \rangle \tag{40}$$

for $x' := \gamma g(x)$ etc. from (35). If $x = (0, \ldots, 0, 1)$ we hence get $y_{n+1} = y'_{n+1}$ for all y and thus

$$x_1\, y_1 + \ldots + x_n\, y_n = x'_1\, y'_1 + \ldots + x'_n\, y'_n.$$

Together with $x_{n+1} = x'_{n+1}$ and $y_{n+1} = y'_{n+1}$, this implies that γg is an orthogonal transformation on I^n. We thus get in cartesian coordinates

$$(\xi'_1 \ldots \xi'_n) = (\xi_1 \ldots \xi_n) \cdot A \tag{41}$$

where A is an orthogonal matrix. Observe that 0 remains invariant so that there is no non–trivial translation involved. (41) reads in Weierstrass coordinates

$$(x'_1 \ldots x'_{n+1}) = (x_1 \ldots x_{n+1}) \left(\begin{array}{c|c} A & \begin{matrix} 0 \\ \vdots \\ 0 \end{matrix} \\ \hline \begin{matrix} 0 \ \ldots \ 0 \end{matrix} & 1 \end{array}\right)$$

after observing that $x_{n+1} = x'_{n+1}$. One finally obtains $g(x) = xL$ for a Lorentz matrix L.   □

REMARK. In step a) of the proof of Theorem 9 we were able to construct a Lorentz matrix which transforms $0 \in I^n$ into a given point of I^n. This was accomplished by a Lorentz boost. The general Lorentz boost is defined by

$$\begin{pmatrix} \alpha p_1^2 + 1 & \alpha p_1\, p_2 & \cdots & \alpha p_1\, p_{n-1} & k p_1 \\ \vdots & \vdots & & \vdots & \vdots \\ \alpha p_{n-1}\, p_1 & \alpha p_{n-1}\, p_2 & \cdots & \alpha p_{n-1}^2 + 1 & k p_{n-1} \\ k p_1 & k p_2 & \cdots & k p_{n-1} & k \end{pmatrix}$$

where $\alpha, p_1, \ldots, p_{n-1}$ are real numbers and where k is a positive real number such that

$$k^2 \cdot (1 - p_1^2 - \ldots - p_{n-1}^2) = 1, \quad \alpha \cdot (k+1) = k^2$$

holds true. — Another type of Lorentz matrix which is also easy to construct is given by

$$\begin{pmatrix} 1 & 0 & \ldots & 0 & a_1 & a_1 \\ \vdots & \vdots & & \vdots & \vdots & \vdots \\ 0 & 0 & \ldots & 1 & a_{n-1} & a_{n-1} \\ -\dfrac{a_1}{k} & -\dfrac{a_2}{k} & \ldots & -\dfrac{a_{n-1}}{k} & \dfrac{k^2 - a^2 + 1}{2k} & \dfrac{k^2 - a^2 - 1}{2k} \\ \dfrac{a_1}{k} & \dfrac{a_2}{k} & \ldots & \dfrac{a_{n-1}}{k} & \dfrac{k^2 + a^2 - 1}{2k} & \dfrac{k^2 + a^2 + 1}{2k} \end{pmatrix}$$

where $k, a_1, \ldots, a_{n-1}$ are real numbers with $k > 0$ and where we put

$$a^2 := a_1^2 + \ldots + a_{n-1}^2.$$

The set of these Lorentz matrices is a group which acts sharply transitively on I^n. Thus with such a matrix we also can transform $0 \in I^n$ into a given point of I^n (see exercises 4., 5. at the end of this chapter).

REMARK. A *hyperplane* of $(I^n, \overset{(n)}{H})$ is defined as intersection of I^n with a hyperplane E of $\mathbb{R}^n$, provided that this intersection is not empty. Let E be the hyperplane of $\mathbb{R}^n$ of equation

$$b_1 \xi_1 + \ldots + b_n \xi_n + b_{n+1} = 0$$

with $b_i \in \mathbb{R}$, $0 \neq (b_1, \ldots, b_n)$. Observe that

$$I^n \cap E \neq \emptyset$$

holds true if and only if,

$$\frac{|b_{n+1}|}{\sqrt{b_1^2 + \ldots + b_n^2}} < 1.$$

Let ϱ be a real number with $\varrho b_{n+1} \geq 0$ and

$$\varrho^2 \cdot (b_1^2 + \ldots + b_n^2 - b_{n+1}^2) = 1.$$

Put $a_i = \varrho b_i$ for $i = 1, \ldots, n+1$. The equation of E is hence

$$a_1 \xi_1 + \ldots + a_n \xi_n + a_{n+1} = 0 \tag{42}$$

with

$$a_1^2 + \ldots + a_n^2 - a_{n+1}^2 = 1 \text{ and } a_{n+1} \geq 0. \tag{43}$$

If we replace the cartesian coordinates $(\xi_1, \ldots, \xi_n)$ by Weierstrass coordinates $(x_1, \ldots, x_n, x_{n+1})$, we get

$$a_1 x_1 + \ldots + a_n x_n + a_{n+1} x_{n+1} = 0 \tag{44}$$

instead of (42). Equation (44) is thus as simple as the equation of E in cartesian coordinates. However, there is a nice characterization of (44): let

$$p_1 x_1 + \ldots + p_n x_n + p_{n+1} x_{n+1} = 0 \tag{45}$$

be the equation of an arbitrary hyperplane $E' \ni 0$ of $\mathbb{R}^{n+1}$ with

$$E' \cap F \neq \emptyset \tag{46}$$

where F denotes again the sheet $x_{n+1} > 0$ of the surface of equation (26). Then and only then, (45) may be written in form (44) such that (43) holds true. In order to prove this statement, consider at first the case $p_{n+1} = 0$. In this situation (46) holds true and

$$\frac{1}{N} := p_1^2 + \ldots + p_n^2 > 0$$

is also satisfied. Now multiply (45) with $\sqrt{N}$ in order to get (43). Assume then that $p_{n+1} \neq 0$, and without loss of generality, that $p_{n+1} > 0$. Since (46) holds true, there must exist

$$(x_1, \ldots, x_{n+1}) \in \mathbb{R}^{n+1}$$

with (45) and $x_1^2 + \ldots + x_n^2 - x_{n+1}^2 = -1$. Hence

$$
\begin{aligned}
p_{n+1}^2 (x_1^2 + \ldots + x_n^2 + 1) &= (p_{n+1} x_{n+1})^2 \\
&= (p_1 x_1 + \ldots + p_n x_n)^2 \\
&\leq \sum_{i=1}^{n} p_i^2 \cdot \sum_{i=1}^{n} x_i^2,
\end{aligned}
$$

i.e.

$$\frac{1}{N} := p_1^2 + \ldots + p_n^2 - p_{n+1}^2 > 0.$$

Now multiply (45) with $\sqrt{N}$. —

This result may be expressed in other words as follows: the hyperplanes of $\left(I^n, \overset{(n)}{H} \right)$ (in Weierstrass coordinates) are exactly the intersections $E' \cap F$ where

$E' \ni 0$ is a hyperplane of $\mathbb{R}^{n+1}$ with $E' \cap F \neq \emptyset$. Obviously, this statement can be generalized: let $A \ni 0$ be an affine subspace of dimension m of $\mathbb{R}^{n+1}$ with

$$A \cap F \neq \emptyset$$

and $1 \leq m \leq n+1$. Then $A \cap F$ is a subspace of $\left(I^n, \overset{(n)}{H}\right)$ (in Weierstrass coordinates) of dimension $m - 1$. All subspaces $\neq \emptyset$ of $\left(I^n, \overset{(n)}{H}\right)$ may be obtained this way.

EXERCISES

1. Let (S, G) be a geometry and let $\sigma : S \rightarrow S'$ be a bijection from S onto a set S'. Assign to $g \in G$ the mapping $\tau(g) : S' \rightarrow S'$ with

$$\forall_{s' \in S'} \quad \tau(g)[s'] := \sigma\big(g[\sigma^{-1}(s')]\big). \tag{47}$$

   Show that $\tau(g)$ is a bijection with $\tau(g_1 g_2) = \tau(g_1)\tau(g_2)$ for all $g_1, g_2 \in G$, and that $G' := \{\tau(g) \mid g \in G\}$ is a subgroup of Perm S'. Show finally that the geometries (S, G) and (S', G') are isomorphic.

2. Let (I, H^+) be the geometry as defined in section 2.1 and put $S'_f := \{(t, f(t)) \in \mathbb{R}^2 \mid t \in \mathbb{R}\}$ with a bijection $f : \mathbb{R} \rightarrow \mathbb{R}$. Define

$$\sigma(\tanh t) := (t, f(t)) \text{ for all } t \in \mathbb{R}.$$

   Show that
$$\tau(\varphi_p)(t, f(t)) = (t + P, f(t + P))$$
   holds true with $P := \frac{1}{2} \ln \frac{1+p}{1-p}$, where $\tau(\varphi_p)$ is defined by (47).

3. Show that the multiplicative group of Lorentz matrices

$$\left\{ \begin{pmatrix} \cosh \alpha & \sinh \alpha \\ \sinh \alpha & \cosh \alpha \end{pmatrix} \,\middle|\, \alpha \in \mathbb{R} \right\}$$

   is isomorphic to the additive group $\mathbb{R}^+$ of real numbers.

4. Show that the determinant of a Lorentz boost (as defined in the third Remark of section 2.6) is $+1$.

5. Denote the second matrix of the third Remark of section 2.6 by

$$L(k, a_1, \ldots, a_{n-1}).$$

Show

$$L^{-1}(k, a_1, \ldots, a_{n-1}) = L\left(\frac{1}{k}, -\frac{a_1}{k}, \ldots, -\frac{a_{n-1}}{k}\right) \tag{48}$$

and

$$L(k, a_1, \ldots, a_{n-1}) \cdot L(l, b_1, \ldots, b_{n-1}) = L(kl, c_1, \ldots, c_{n-1}) \tag{49}$$

with $c_i = la_i + b_i$ for $i = 1, \ldots, n-1$.

6. Let $(\xi_1, \ldots, \xi_n)$ be the Weierstrass coordinates of a point x of I^n. Show that there exists exactly one L, namely

$$L\left(\frac{\sqrt{1-\xi^2}}{1-\xi_n}, \frac{\xi_1}{1-\xi_n}, \ldots, \frac{\xi_{n-1}}{1-\xi_n}\right), \tag{50}$$

which maps $0 \in I^n$ into x. With this information show that the group of all $L's$ acts sharply transitively on I^n: to $y, z \in I^n$ there exists exactly one L which transforms y into z.

Chapter 3

EINSTEIN'S CYLINDER UNIVERSE

3.1 Points and motions

Let $n \geq 2$ be a positive integer. The set C^n of *points* of *n–dimensional Einstein's cylinder universe* is then defined by

$$C^n := \left\{ x \in \mathbb{R}^{n+1} \,\middle|\, x_1^2 + \ldots + x_n^2 = 1 \right\}. \tag{1}$$

Suppose that $f : \mathbb{R}^{n+1} \to \mathbb{R}^{n+1}$ is a so–called Lorentz transformation

$$f(x) = xL + a \tag{2}$$

such that $f(C^n) \subseteq C^n$: here L and a denote real matrices

$$
L \;=\; \begin{pmatrix} l_{11} & \cdots & l_{1n} & l_{1,n+1} \\ \vdots & & & \\ l_{n+1,1} & \cdots & l_{n+1,n} & l_{n+1,n+1} \end{pmatrix},
$$

$$
a \;=\; (a_1 \;\ldots\; a_n \; a_{n+1})
$$

such that L is a Lorentz matrix. The restriction $f \,|\, C^n$ of f on C^n is then called a *motion* of Einstein's cylinder universe. Obviously,

$$e_i := (\delta_{i1}, \ldots, \delta_{in}, 0) \in C^n$$

for $i = 1, \ldots, n$ and hence $f(e_i) \in C^n$. Also $-e_i$ and $f(-e_i)$ are in C^n. This implies

$$\sum_{\nu=1}^{n} (\eta \, l_{i\nu} + a_\nu)^2 = 1$$

for $\eta \in \{1, -1\}$ and thus

$$\sum_{\nu=1}^{n} l_{i\nu}^2 + \sum_{\nu=1}^{n} a_\nu^2 = 1$$

for $i = 1, \ldots, n$. Since L is a Lorentz matrix, we also have

$$\sum_{\nu=1}^{n} l_{i\nu}^2 - l_{i,n+1}^2 = 1,$$

i.e. $\displaystyle\sum_{\nu=1}^{n} a_\nu^2 = -l_{i,n+1}^2$ and hence

$$
\begin{aligned}
a_1 \quad &= \quad \ldots \quad = \quad a_n \quad &= \quad 0, \\
l_{1,n+1} \quad &= \quad \ldots \quad = \quad l_{n,n+1} \quad &= \quad 0.
\end{aligned}
$$

The two equations

$$
\begin{aligned}
l_{1,n+1}^2 + \ldots + l_{n,n+1}^2 - l_{n+1,n+1}^2 &= -1, \\
l_{n+1,1}^2 + \ldots + l_{n+1,n}^2 - l_{n+1,n+1}^2 &= -1
\end{aligned}
$$

then imply $l_{n+1,n+1}^2 = 1$ and

$$l_{n+1,1} = \ldots = l_{n+1,n} = 0.$$

The Lorentz transformation (2) thus reads

$$f(x) = x \left(\begin{array}{ccc|c} & & & 0 \\ & A & & \vdots \\ & & & 0 \\ \hline 0 & \ldots & 0 & \varepsilon \end{array} \right) + (0 \ldots 0 \, a) \qquad (3)$$

where we put $\varepsilon := l_{n+1,n+1}$, $a := a_{n+1}$ and where

$$A := \left(\begin{array}{ccc} l_{11} & \ldots & l_{1n} \\ \vdots & & \\ l_{n1} & \ldots & l_{nn} \end{array} \right)$$

is orthogonal. Observe that $\varepsilon^2 = 1$. The result we have obtained is

THEOREM 1. *The group $M^n = M(C^n)$ of motions of Einstein's cylinder universe consists exactly of all mappings $f \mid C^n$, where $f : \mathbb{R}^{n+1} \to \mathbb{R}^{n+1}$ is of the form* (3).

Every motion is of course a bijection of C^n. It is also easy to show that M^n operates transitively on C^n. In fact, suppose that $(x_1, \ldots, x_{n+1})$ is a point of C^n. Observe that $x_1^2 + \ldots + x_n^2 = 1$ and extend

$$(x_1, \ldots, x_n) \tag{4}$$

to an orthonormal basis of $\mathbb{R}^n$ thus getting an orthogonal matrix A, the first row of which is (4). Now put $\varepsilon := 1$ and $a := x_{n+1}$ in (3) and f maps

$$(1, 0, \ldots, 0) \text{ into } (x_1, \ldots, x_{n+1}).$$

The group M^n does not operate transitively on the set of ordered pairs (a, b) of points $a \neq b$. There is for instance no $\gamma \in M^n$ with

$$\gamma (1, 0, \ldots, 0) = (1, 0, \ldots, 0),$$
$$\gamma (-1, 0, \ldots, 0) = (1, 0, \ldots, 0, 1).$$

The first equation namely implies that $a = 0$ in (3) for f, and the second, that $a = 1$. But as we know, the situation in euclidean geometry is not different from the present situation. Even there we don't find a motion which transforms two points of distance 1 into two points of distance 2.

PROPOSITION 2. *Suppose that a, b, c, d are points of C^n. Then there exists a mapping $f \in M^n$ with*

$$f(a) = c \text{ and } f(b) = d$$

if, and only if,

$$ab = cd \text{ and } (a_{n+1} - b_{n+1})^2 = (c_{n+1} - d_{n+1})^2$$

hold true, where xy is defined to be

$$xy := x_1 y_1 + \ldots + x_n y_n$$

for $x = (x_1, \ldots, x_n, x_{n+1})$ and $y = (y_1, \ldots, y_n, y_{n+1})$.

Proof.   If such a mapping f exists, then

$$c - d = (a - b) \cdot \begin{pmatrix} & & & 0 \\ & A & & \vdots \\ & & & 0 \\ 0 & \cdots & 0 & \varepsilon \end{pmatrix}$$

and hence

$$(c_1 - d_1 \ldots c_n - d_n) \;=\; (a_1 - b_1 \ldots a_n - b_n) \cdot A,$$

$$c_{n+1} - d_{n+1} \;=\; \varepsilon \cdot (a_{n+1} - b_{n+1}). \tag{5}$$

This implies that

$$(c_{n+1} - d_{n+1})^2 = (a_{n+1} - b_{n+1})^2$$

and that

$$(c - d)^2 = (a - b)^2, \tag{6}$$

i.e. $cd = ab$ since $c^2 = d^2 = a^2 = b^2 = 1$.

If, on the other hand,

$$ab = cd \text{ and } (a_{n+1} - b_{n+1})^2 = (c_{n+1} - d_{n+1})^2$$

hold true, then also (6) and (5) hold, with a suitable $\varepsilon \in \{+1, -1\}$. Since the triangles (see section 5.1.4, Lemma 6)

$$0, \quad (a_1, \ldots, a_n), \quad (b_1, \ldots, b_n)$$
$$0, \quad (c_1, \ldots, c_n), \quad (d_1, \ldots, d_n)$$

are congruent in the euclidean sense, there exists an orthogonal A such that

$$(c_1 \ldots c_n) \;=\; (a_1 \ldots a_n)A,$$
$$(d_1 \ldots d_n) \;=\; (b_1 \ldots b_n)A$$

holds true. Thus $c = f(a)$ and $d = f(b)$ are satisfied for

$$f(x) := x \left(\begin{array}{c|c} A & \begin{array}{c} 0 \\ \vdots \\ 0 \end{array} \\ \hline 0 \ \ldots\ 0 & \varepsilon \end{array} \right) + (0\ \ldots\ 0\ p)$$

with $p := c_{n+1} - \varepsilon a_{n+1} = d_{n+1} - \varepsilon b_{n+1}$. $\qquad\qquad\qquad\square$

REMARK. (C^n, M^n) is a substructure (see section 1.3) of $(\mathbb{R}^{n+1}, G)$ where G denotes the group of Lorentz transformations (2) of $\mathbb{R}^{n+1}$. Notice that it was possible in the present case $S_0 = C^n$ to replace $g(S_0) = S_0$ in

$$G_0 = \{g \in G \mid g(S_0) = S_0\}$$

by the condition $g(S_0) \subseteq S_0$.

3.2 The functional equation of 2–point–invariants

We are now interested in the 2–point–invariants of the structure consisting of C^n and the group M^n:

Let $W \neq \emptyset$ be a set. Determine then all functions

$$f : C^n \times C^n \to W$$

such that

$$f(x, y) = f(\gamma(x), \gamma(y)) \tag{7}$$

holds true for all $x, y \in C^n$ and all $\gamma \in M^n$.

In order to solve the functional equation (7) we define the cartesian product

$$W_0 := [-1, +1] \times \mathbb{R}_{\geq 0}.$$

THEOREM 3. *Suppose that g is a mapping from W_0 into W. Then*

$$f(x, y) := g(xy, |x_{n+1} - y_{n+1}|) \tag{8}$$

is a solution of the functional equation (7). If, on the other hand,

$$f : C^n \times C^n \to W$$

is a solution of (7), then there exists a $g : W_0 \to W$ such that (8) holds true.

Proof.   Let γ be an element of M^n and define

$$\gamma(z_1, \ldots, z_{n+1}) =: (z'_1, \ldots, z'_{n+1})$$

for $z \in C^n$. Then the f of (8) satisfies

$$f(x', y') = g(x'y', |x'_{n+1}, -y'_{n+1}|) = g(xy, |x_{n+1} - y_{n+1}|) = f(x, y)$$

for $x, y \in C^n$ from Proposition 2. — Assume now that f satisfies (7). For

$$(p, q) \in W_0$$

define $g(p, q)$ as follows: take elements x, y of C^n such that $xy = p$ and $|x_{n+1} - y_{n+1}| = q$. Then put $g(p, q) := f(x, y)$. Such elements x, y exist: for instance (observe $n \geq 2$)

$$x = (1, 0, \ldots, 0), \ y = (p, \sqrt{1 - p^2}, 0, \ldots, 0, q).$$

Moreover, g is well-defined: if u, v are also points of C^n such that $uv = p$ and $|u_{n+1} - v_{n+1}| = q$, then, according to Proposition 2, there exists $\gamma \in M^n$ with

$$u = \gamma(x), \quad v = \gamma(y).$$

Hence $f(x, y) = f(\gamma(x), \gamma(y)) = f(u, v)$. Now, bearing in mind the definition of g, we get

$$f(x, y) = g(p, q) = g(xy, |x_{n+1} - y_{n+1}|). \qquad \square$$

It is easy to find simple examples of 2–point–invariants. The following are examples.

a) $f(x, y) = 0$ for $x, y \in C^n$,

b) $f(x, y) = (x_1 - y_1)^2 + \ldots + (x_n - y_n)^2 - (x_{n+1} - y_{n+1})^2$,

c) $f(x, y) = (x_1 - y_1)^2 + \ldots + (x_n - y_n)^2 + (x_{n+1} - y_{n+1})^2$,

d) $f(x, y) = x_1 y_1 + \ldots + x_n y_n$,

e) $f(x, y) = (x_{n+1} - y_{n+1})^2$,

f) $f(x, y) = (\arccos xy)^2 - (x_{n+1} - y_{n+1})^2$
   with $\quad \arccos xy \in [0, \pi]$,

g) $f(x, y) = (s(x, y), |x_{n+1} - y_{n+1}|)$
   with $\quad s(x, y) \in [0, \pi]$ and $\cos s(x, y) = xy$,

h) $f(x, y) = (xy, |x_{n+1} - y_{n+1}|)$.

3.3   Strong, definite 2–point–invariants

A 2–point–invariant $f(x, y)$ is said to be *strong* whenever every mapping $\varphi : C^n \to C^n$ which satisfies

$$\forall_{x, y \in C^n} \; f(x, y) = f(\varphi(x), \varphi(y)),$$

is an element of M^n. (If we ask this condition only for bijections φ, we would speak of a defining 2–point–invariant of (C^n, M^n), see section 1.2.) Otherwise it is called *weak*.

A 2–point–invariant $f(x, y)$ is said to be *definite* whenever

$$f(a, b) = f(c, d)$$

holds true for elements $a, b, c, d \in C^n$ if and only if there exists $\gamma \in M^n$ such that $\gamma(a) = c$ and $\gamma(b) = d$. Otherwise it is called *indefinite*.

The invariant a) of course is weak. Example h) is definite according to Proposition 2. We would like to show that example f) is indefinite. In fact, put

$$x = (1, 0, \ldots, 0), \ y = (1, 0, \ldots, 0, 1)$$
$$\text{and } z = \left(0, 1, 0, \ldots, 0, \sqrt{1 + \tfrac{\pi^2}{4}}\right).$$

According to Proposition 2 there is no $\gamma \in M^n$ with

$$\gamma(x) = x \text{ and } \gamma(y) = z.$$

But nevertheless

$$(\arccos\ xy)^2 - (x_{n+1} - y_{n+1})^2 = (\arccos\ xz)^2 - (x_{n+1} - z_{n+1})^2$$

holds true. However, example f) is strong, despite the fact that it is not definite. We find ourselves again confronted with a functional equations problem:

Put

$$f(x, y) := (\arccos\ xy)^2 - (x_{n+1} - y_{n+1})^2 \ with\ \arccos\ xy \in [0, \pi]$$

for $x, y \in C^n$ and determine all mappings

$$\varphi : C^n \to C^n$$

such that

$$f(x, y) = f\big(\varphi(x), \varphi(y)\big) \tag{9}$$

holds true for all $x, y \in C^n$.

THEOREM 4. *The solutions of the functional equation (9) are precisely the elements of M^n.*

Proof. a) Let φ be a solution of (9). Without loss of generality we may assume that
$$e_1 := (1, 0, \ldots, 0)$$
remains invariant under φ. We now prove: If $\varphi(x_1, \ldots, x_{n+1}) = (y_1, \ldots, y_{n+1})$, then
$$\varphi(-x_1, \ldots, -x_n, x_{n+1}) = (-y_1, \ldots, -y_n, y_{n+1}).$$
In fact, we have $f(x, \bar{x}) = \pi^2$ by putting

$$\bar{x} := (-x_1, \ldots, -x_n, x_{n+1})$$

for $x = (x_1, \ldots, x_{n+1})$. Hence

$$\pi^2 = f(x, \bar{x}) = f(\varphi(x), \varphi(\bar{x})) =: f(y, z),$$

i.e.

$$\pi^2 = (\arccos yz)^2 - (y_{n+1} - z_{n+1})^2. \qquad (10)$$

This leads to

$$(\arccos yz)^2 = \pi^2 \text{ and } (y_{n+1} - z_{n+1})^2 = 0$$

because otherwise the right hand side of equation (10) becomes smaller since arc cos $yz \in [0, \pi]$. Hence $z = \bar{y}$.

b) By applying a), we get

$$\varphi(-1, 0, \ldots, 0) = (-1, 0, \ldots, 0).$$

Define $e_i := (\delta_{i1}, \ldots, \delta_{in}, 0)$ for $i = 1, \ldots, n$ and put $\varphi(e_2) =: x$. Then

$$\frac{\pi^2}{4} = f(\ e_1, e_2) = f(\ e_1, x),$$
$$\frac{\pi^2}{4} = f(-e_1, e_2) = f(-e_1, x)$$

and thus

$$x_1 = \cos \sqrt{\frac{\pi^2}{4} + x_{n+1}^2} = -x_1,$$

i.e. $x_1 = 0$ and $x_{n+1} = 0$, i.e.

$$x = (0, x_2, \ldots, x_n, 0)$$

where of course $x_2^2 + \ldots + x_n^2 = 1$. Without loss of generality we may assume $x = e_2$ because otherwise we can apply a mapping (3),

$$g(y) = y \begin{pmatrix} 1 & 0 & \cdots & 0 & 0 \\ 0 & & & & 0 \\ \vdots & & B & & \vdots \\ 0 & & & & 0 \\ 0 & 0 & \cdots & 0 & \varepsilon \end{pmatrix} \qquad (11)$$

with $g(e_2) = x$ and then proceed with $g^{-1}\varphi$ instead of φ. That g exists, follows from the fact that

$$\begin{matrix} (1 & 0 & \cdots & 0) \\ (0 & x_2 & \cdots & x_n) \end{matrix}$$

can be extended to an orthonormal basis of $\mathbb{R}^n$. In this connection we must notice that the special form of (11) guarantees that our assumption that e_1 remains unaltered under $g^{-1}\varphi$ continues to hold.

c) From a) and b) we get $\varphi(-e_2) = -e_2$. Now put $\varphi(e_3) =: x$. The equations

$$\frac{\pi^2}{4} = f(\ e_1, e_3)\ = f(\ e_1, x)$$

$$\frac{\pi^2}{4} = f(-e_1, e_3)\ = f(-e_1, x)$$

$$\frac{\pi^2}{4} = f(\ e_2, e_3)\ = f(\ e_2, x)$$

$$\frac{\pi^2}{4} = f(-e_2, e_3)\ = f(-e_2, x)$$

lead to

$$x_1 = \cos\sqrt{\frac{\pi^2}{4} + x_{n+1}^2} = -x_1,$$

$$x_2 = \cos\sqrt{\frac{\pi^2}{4} + x_{n+1}^2} = -x_2$$

and hence to $x_1 = x_2 = x_{n+1} = 0$. Similarly, for b) we may assume that $\varphi(e_3) = e_3$ by arranging a suitable B in (11),

$$B = \begin{pmatrix} 1 & 0 & \cdots & 0 \\ 0 & x_3 & \cdots & x_n \\ \vdots & & & \\ 0 & & & \end{pmatrix}.$$

Repeating this procedure, we may assume (without loss of generality) that

$$\varphi(e_i) = e_i \text{ and } \varphi(-e_i) = -e_i$$

for all $i = 1, \ldots, n$.

d) Define $v := (0, \ldots, 0, 1)$. Then we get

$$\varphi(e_i + v) \in \{e_i + v, e_i - v\} \text{ for } i = 1, \ldots, n$$

by observing that

$$f(\pm e_j, e_i + v) = f(\pm e_j, \varphi(e_i + v))$$

for $j = 1, \ldots, n$. Without loss of generality we may assume that

$$\varphi(e_1 + v) = e_1 + v$$

because otherwise we can apply, as before, a mapping (3) where $\varepsilon = -1$, where $A = (\delta_{ij})$ and $a = 0$. We now can prove that

$$\varphi(e_i + v) = e_i + v$$

for $i = 2, \ldots, n$ because of

$$f(e_1 + v, e_i + v) \neq f(e_1 + v, e_i - v)$$

for $i = 2, \ldots, n$.

e) We finally prove $\varphi(x) = x$ for $x \in C^n$. Put $\varphi(x) =: y$. Then

$$f(e_i, x) \quad = f(e_i, y),$$
$$f(e_i + v, x) \quad = f(e_i + v, y)$$

leads to

$$(\arccos x_i)^2 - x_{n+1}^2 \quad = (\arccos y_i)^2 - y_{n+1}^2,$$
$$(\arccos x_i)^2 - (x_{n+1} - 1)^2 \quad = (\arccos y_i)^2 - (y_{n+1} - 1)^2$$

and hence to $x_{n+1} = y_{n+1}$ and to

$$\arccos x_i = \arccos y_i$$

since those values are always in $[0, \pi]$. Thus $x_i = y_i$, i.e. $x = y$. Since we were using only mappings of the group M^n in order to reduce the original mapping φ to the identity, this original φ must be itself an element of M^n. □

REMARK. *A 2–point–invariant $f(x,y)$ which is definite, must also be strong.*

Proof.   It is a consequence of Proposition 2 that $f(a, b) = f(c, d)$ holds true for $a, b, c, d \in C^n$ if, and only if, $s(a, b) = s(c, d)$ is satisfied, where $s(x, y)$ denotes the 2–point–invariant h). Suppose that $\varphi : C^n \to C^n$ is a mapping with

$$\forall_{x,y \in C^n} \; f(x, y) = f\big(\varphi(x), \varphi(y)\big).$$

Then

$$\forall_{x,y \in C^n} \; s(x, y) = s\big(\varphi(x), \varphi(y)\big).$$

Obviously, s can also be replaced here by the invariant f). Theorem 4 then implies that φ is an element of M^n. □

3.4 Lines in Einstein's cylinder universe

Let p, q be distinct points of C^2 with

$$p = (\cos \alpha, \sin \alpha, p_3), \quad q = (\cos \beta, \sin \beta, q_3),$$

$\alpha, \beta, p_3, q_3 \in \mathbb{R}$, such that $0 \leq \beta - \alpha < \pi$ holds true. We would like to determine the set

$$S(p, q) := \left\{ x = (\cos \xi, \sin \xi, x_3) \in C^2 \,\middle|\, |\xi - \alpha|, |\xi - \beta| \leq \pi \text{ and } f(p, x) = f(x, q) \right\}$$

where f again denotes the 2–point–invariant

$$f(y, z) = (\arccos yz)^2 - (y_{n+1} - z_{n+1})^2$$

with $\arccos yz \in [0, \pi]$. Since

$$px = \cos \alpha \cdot \cos \xi + \sin \alpha \cdot \sin \xi = \cos(\xi - \alpha)$$

and since $|\xi - \alpha| \leq \pi$ we get

$$\arccos px = |\xi - \alpha|.$$

Hence $f(p, x) = f(x, q)$ implies

$$(\xi - \alpha)^2 - (p_3 - x_3)^2 = (\xi - \beta)^2 - (x_3 - q_3)^2, \tag{12}$$

i.e.

$$(\beta - \alpha)\xi + \frac{1}{2}(\alpha^2 - \beta^2) = (q_3 - p_3)x_3 + \frac{1}{2}(p_3^2 - q_3^2). \tag{13}$$

Three cases are important:

Case 1: If $\alpha = \beta$, then $p_3 \neq q_3$ since $p \neq q$. Hence (13) implies $x_3 = \frac{1}{2}(p_3 + q_3)$. Thus

$$S(p, q) = \left\{ \left(\cos \xi, \sin \xi, \frac{p_3 + q_3}{2} \right) \,\middle|\, |\xi - \alpha| \leq \pi \right\}.$$

This is the circle on C^2 which is also in the plane of $\mathbb{R}^3$ with equation $x_3 = \frac{1}{2}(p_3 + q_3)$.

Case 2: If $p_3 = q_3$, then $\alpha \neq \beta$ since $p \neq q$. Hence (13) implies $\xi = \frac{1}{2}(\alpha + \beta)$. Here

$$S(p, q) = \left\{ \left(\cos \frac{\alpha + \beta}{2}, \sin \frac{\alpha + \beta}{2}, x_3 \right) \,\middle|\, x_3 \in \mathbb{R} \right\}$$

is the line through $\left(\cos\dfrac{\alpha+\beta}{2}, \sin\dfrac{\alpha+\beta}{2}, p_3\right)$, parallel to the axis of the circular cylinder C^2.

Case 3: Suppose finally that $\alpha \neq \beta$ and $p_3 \neq q_3$. Then (13) implies

$$x_3 = r\xi + s_0$$

with real constants r, s_0 such that $r \neq 0$. Set $\eta := \xi - \alpha$ and $s := r\alpha + s_0$. Furthermore, put

$$a := (\cos\alpha, \sin\alpha), \quad b := (-\sin\alpha, \cos\alpha).$$

Hence

$$x = (\cos\xi, \sin\xi, r\xi + s_0) =: (x_1, x_2, x_3)$$

with

$$(x_1, x_2) = a\cos\eta + b\sin\eta \quad \text{and} \quad x_3 = r\eta + s.$$

$S(p, q)$ is the set of these points x with $\beta - \alpha - \pi \leq \eta \leq \pi$. (For a geometrical construction of $S(p, q)$ see section 3.6.)

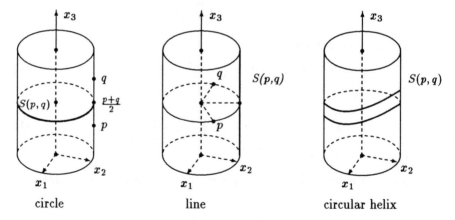

circle   line   circular helix

We are now in the position to define the notion of a *line* of C^2. *Lines* are the circles on C^2, the euclidean lines on C^2, and every circular helix

$$\left\{(\cos t, \sin t, kt + \lambda) \,\middle|\, t \in \mathbb{R}\right\}$$

with real numbers $k \neq 0$ and λ. The *lines* of every circular cylinder $Z \subseteq C^n$ of radius 1 are then called the *lines* of $C^n, n \geq 2$. They can be described as follows (see section 3.6).

Suppose that

$$a = (a_1, \ldots, a_n) \quad \text{and} \quad b = (b_1, \ldots, b_n)$$

are elements of $\mathbb{R}^n$ with

$$ab = a_1b_1 + \ldots + a_nb_n = 0,$$
$$a_1^2 + \ldots + a_n^2 = 1 \text{ and } b_1^2 + \ldots + b_n^2 = 1.$$

Let k, l, m be fixed real numbers with $k^2 + m^2 \neq 0$. Then

$$\left\{ \left(x_1(t), \ldots, x_n(t), \ kt + \lambda\right) \,\middle|\, t \in \mathbb{R} \right\}$$

with

$$\left(x_1(t), \ldots, x_n(t)\right) = a\cos(mt) + b\sin(mt)$$

is a line of C^n. In the case $k = 0$ we get a circle; in the case $m = 0$, a euclidean line. Finally, the case $km \neq 0$ leads to a circular helix.

3.5   The notion of distance

In this section we would like *to determine functions*

$$d : C^2 \times C^2 \to \mathbb{R}_{\geq 0}$$

which satisfy the following properties

(i) d is a 2–point–invariant of M^2,

(ii) if x, y, z are on a line l of C^2, then

$$d(x, z) = d(x, y) + d(y, z),$$

provided that (x, y, z) is admissible on l.

We say that the ordered triple (x, y, z) is *admissible on a line l* of C^2, if the following holds true: x, y, z are points on l. Moreover: $x_3 \leq y_3 \leq z_3$ in case that l is also an euclidean line; otherwise there exists a representation of l,

$$l = \left\{ (\cos t, \sin t, kt + \lambda) \,\middle|\, t \in \mathbb{R} \right\},$$

with $t_z - t_x < \pi$ and $t_x \leq t_y \leq t_z$ by putting $x = (\cos t_x, \sin t_x, kt_x + \lambda)$ etc.

The question we posed at the beginning of this section is of course again a functional equations problem. Because of (i) and Theorem 3 there exists a function

$$g : [-1, +1] \times \mathbb{R}_{\geq 0} \to \mathbb{R}_{\geq 0}$$

with $d(x, y) = g(xy, |x_3 - y_3|)$. It is worthwhile to look again at 3 cases.

Case 1: $(x_1, x_2) = (y_1, y_2)$.
Here we get $d(x, y) = g(1, |x_3 - y_3|)$. Put $h(t) := g(1, t)$ for $t \geq 0$. Suppose that t_1, t_2 are non–negative real numbers. Define points

$$a := (a_1, a_2, 0), \quad b := (a_1, a_2, t_1), \quad c := (a_1, a_2, t_1 + t_2)$$

with $a_1^2 + a_2^2 = 1$. Then (ii) implies

$$d(a, c) = d(a, b) + d(b, c),$$

i.e.

$$g(1, t_1 + t_2) = g(1, t_1) + g(1, t_2).$$

By Theorem 5, chapter 2, we thus get $h(t) = kt$, where $k \geq 0$ is a constant.

Case 2: Suppose that a, b, c are points on the line

$$\left\{ (\cos t, \sin t, \lambda) \,\big|\, t \in \mathbb{R} \right\}$$

with $\alpha \leq \beta \leq \gamma$, $\gamma - \alpha < \pi$ and

$$a = (\cos \alpha, \sin \alpha, \lambda) \text{ etc.}$$

Here (ii) implies

$$d(a, c) = d(a, b) + d(b, c)$$

and hence

$$g\big(\cos(\gamma - \alpha), 0 \big) = g\big(\cos(\beta - \alpha), 0 \big) + g\big(\cos(\gamma - \beta), 0 \big).$$

Putting $s(t) := g(\cos t, 0)$ for $0 \leq t < \pi$ we then get

$$s(t_1 + t_2) = s(t_1) + s(t_2) \tag{14}$$

for all $t_1, t_2 \geq 0$ with $t_1 + t_2 < \pi$. Equation (14) is also valid for n summands $t_1, \ldots, t_n$ provided that $t_1 + \ldots + t_n < \pi$ and that all t_i are ≥ 0. For $t_1 = t_2 = 0$ (14) yields $s(0) = 0$. Put $s(1) =: r$. With $t_1 = \ldots = t_n = \dfrac{1}{n}$ we get $r = n \cdot s\left(\dfrac{1}{n}\right)$ and we also get $s\left(\dfrac{m}{n}\right) = ms\left(\dfrac{1}{n}\right) = \dfrac{m}{n}r$ provided that m is a positive integer with $\dfrac{m}{n} < \pi$. Hence $s(\varrho) = \varrho \cdot r$ for all rational numbers $\varrho \in [0, \pi[$. Proceeding now as in the proof of Theorem 5, chapter 1, we finally arrive at $s(t) = rt$ for all $t \in [0, \pi[$ with a constant $r \geq 0$.

The results we have obtained are the following:

(1): $d(x, y) = k \cdot |x_3 - y_3|$ for $(x_1, x_2) = (y_1, y_2)$,

(2): $d(x, y) = r \cdot \arccos(xy)$ for
$x = (\cos \alpha, \sin \alpha, \lambda)$, $y = (\cos \beta, \sin \beta, \lambda)$ with $|\beta - \alpha| < \pi$.

k and r are non–negative constants, not depending on x, y, in view of (i). For result 2 we agree again that $\arccos z \in [0, \pi]$.

Case 3: Suppose that a, b, c are points on the line

$$\big\{(\cos t, \sin t, \mu t + \lambda) \mid t \in \mathbb{R}\big\}, \ \mu \neq 0,$$

with $\alpha \leq \beta \leq \gamma$, $\gamma - \alpha < \pi$ and

$$a = (\cos \alpha, \sin \alpha, \mu \alpha + \lambda) \text{ etc.}$$

Here (ii) implies

$$g\big(\cos(\gamma-\alpha), |\mu|\cdot|\gamma-\alpha|\big) = g\big(\cos(\beta-\alpha), |\mu|\,|\beta-\alpha|\big) + g\big(\cos(\gamma-\beta), |\mu|\cdot|\gamma-\beta|\big).$$

Carrying through, mutatis mutandis, the discussion in case 2, we get the result

(3): $d(x, y) = w(|\mu|) \cdot \arccos(xy)$ for
$x = (\cos \alpha, \sin \alpha, \mu \alpha + \lambda)$, $y = (\cos \beta, \sin \beta, \mu \beta + \lambda)$ with $|\beta - \alpha| < \pi$ such that $w(|\mu|) \geq 0$ depends only on $|\mu|$.

It seems reasonable to ask for $k = 1$. This is a consequence of

(iii) $d\big((1,0,0), (1,0,1)\big) = 1$.

Another property will play a role in our discussion, namely

(iv) $\displaystyle \lim_{\tau \to 0} \frac{d\big((1,0,0), (\cos \tau, \sin \tau, \mu \tau)\big)}{|\tau|} = |1 - \mu^2|^{\frac{1}{2}}$ *for every* $\mu \in \mathbb{R}$.

The philosophy behind property (iv) is the assumption in general relativity theory that $d(x, y)$ should be close to $|\Delta(x, y)|^{\frac{1}{2}}$ in the case that x and y are close together where

$$\Delta(x, y) := (x_1 - y_1)^2 + (x_2 - y_2)^2 - (x_3 - y_3)^2$$

is the so–called Lorentz–Minkowski–distance of x, y. If we apply this idea to the points

$$a = (1, 0, 0) \text{ and } b(\tau) = (\cos \tau, \sin \tau, \mu \tau)$$

for small τ, we get that $d(a,b)$ should be approximately equal to the square root of

$$\left|(\cos\tau - 1)^2 + \sin^2\tau - \mu^2\tau^2\right| = \left|4\sin^2\frac{\tau}{2} - \mu^2\tau^2\right|,$$

i.e. to $|\tau| \cdot \sqrt{|1 - \mu^2|}$. This consideration motivates our assumption (iv).

THEOREM 5. *Suppose that* $d : C^2 \times C^2 \to \mathbb{R}_{\geq 0}$ *satisfies properties* (i), (ii), (iii), (iv) *of this section 3.5. Then*

$$d^2(x,y) = \left|(\arccos xy)^2 - (x_3 - y_3)^2\right| \tag{15}$$

for all

$$x = (\cos\alpha, \sin\alpha, x_3), \quad y = (\cos\beta, \sin\beta, y_3)$$

with $|\beta - \alpha| < \pi$, *where* arccos xy *is chosen in* $[0, \pi]$.

It remains to show that $d(x,y)$ can be written in the form (15) in cases (1), (2), (3). Now (iv) and (2), (3) imply (put $w(0) := r$)

$$w(|\mu|) = \frac{d(a,b)}{|\tau|} \to \sqrt{|1 - \mu^2|},$$

i.e.

$$w(|\mu|) = \sqrt{|1 - \mu^2|}.$$

Hence

$$\begin{aligned} d^2(x,y) &= w^2(|\mu|)(\arccos xy)^2 \\ &= \left|(1 - \mu^2)(\arccos xy)^2\right| \\ &= \left|(\arccos xy)^2 - (x_3 - y_3)^2\right| \end{aligned}$$

in cases (2), (3). In case (1) we get

$$\left|(\arccos xy)^2 - (x_3 - y_3)^2\right| = \left|x_3 - y_3\right|^2 = d^2(x,y).$$

This finally proves Theorem 5.

REMARK. The same ideas lead, mutatis mutandis, to a version of Theorem 5 in the general case of $n \geq 2$ dimensions.

A function d which satisfies (i), (ii), (iii), (iv) is called a *distance* of C^2. Obviously, the solution $d \geq 0$ of (15) is a distance of C^2.

3.6   The affine structure

If we cut open the circular cylinder C^2 along a euclidean line, we get a somewhat better view of the situation when we then put, without distortion, the surface into a plane. Let (ξ, x_3) be the cartesian coordinates of the point

$$(\cos \xi, \sin \xi, x_3) \in C^2$$

in this plane. The image of C^2 is then given by all $(\xi, x_3) \in \mathbb{R}^2$ with

$$0 \le \xi < 2\pi.$$

Our lines on C^2 are now easily represented: we get segments, euclidean lines and for every circular helix

$$\left\{ (\cos t, \sin t, \mu t + \lambda) \,\middle|\, t \in \mathbb{R} \right\}$$

with $\mu \ne 0$ an infinite set of suitable segments. Sometimes it might be useful to describe $(\cos \xi, \sin \xi, x_3)$ by all points

$$(\xi + 2k\pi, x_3) \text{ with } k \in \mathbb{Z}.$$

In this case, $x_3 = \mu t + \lambda$ represents exactly a line in $\mathbb{R}^2$. If we again look to $S(p, q)$ of section 3.4, we may easily construct the line (in $\mathbb{R}^2$) containing $S(p, q)$ by observing (see (12))

$$(\xi - \alpha)^2 + (x_3 - q_3)^2 = (\xi - \beta)^2 + (x_3 - p_3)^2 :$$

go over from $p(\alpha, p_3)$, $q(\beta, q_3)$ to $\overline{p}(\alpha, q_3)$, $\overline{q}(\beta, p_3)$ and take then all (ξ, x_3) in $\mathbb{R}^2$ of the same euclidean distance from $\overline{p}$ and $\overline{q}$.

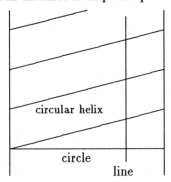

circular helix

circle

line

Let $x = (x_1, x_2, x_3)$ and $y = (y_1, y_2, y_3)$ be distinct points on C^2. When $x_3 = y_3$, there is exactly one C^2–line joining them, namely a circle. When

$x_3 \neq y_3$, there are infinitely many C^2–lines joining x, y. In order to prove this statement, it is sufficient to look at the case $x = (1, 0, 0)$ only. If $y = (1, 0, r)$, $r \neq 0$, then x, y are both on every circular helix

$$h\left(\frac{r}{2\pi k}\right) := \left\{\left(\cos t, \sin t, \frac{r}{2\pi k}t\right) \,\Big|\, t \in \mathbb{R}\right\}$$

with $k = 1, 2, 3, \ldots$. If

$$y = (\cos \alpha, \sin \alpha, r)$$

with $\alpha \in \,]0, 2\pi[$ and $r \neq 0$, then x, y are both on all $h\left(\dfrac{r}{\alpha + 2k\pi}\right)$, $k = 1, 2, 3, \ldots$.

The *euclidean parallel axiom*, however, is valid. The C^2–lines l_1, l_2 are said to be *parallel* in cases $l_1 = l_2$ or $l_1 \cap l_2 = \emptyset$. The axiom in question is the following statement.

If l is a C^2–line and x a point, then there is exactly one C^2–line l' through x which is parallel to l.

There is nothing to prove when l is a circle or an euclidean line. If

$$l = \left\{(\cos t, \sin t, \mu t + \nu) \,\big|\, t \in \mathbb{R}\right\}$$

and $x = (\cos \alpha, \sin \alpha, r)$, then

$$l' = \left\{(\cos t, \sin t, \mu t + r - \mu\alpha) \,\big|\, t \in \mathbb{R}\right\}.$$

Returning to the general case of $n \geq 2$ dimensions, things are not really much different. A circular cylinder $Z \subseteq C^n$ of radius 1 replaces C^2. If an euclidean line of the $\mathbb{R}^{n+1}$,

$$\left\{p + \lambda v \,\big|\, \lambda \in \mathbb{R}\right\}, \; v \neq 0,$$

is completely in C^n,

$$(p + \lambda v)^2 = 1$$

must be valid for all $\lambda \in \mathbb{R}$. (We are still working here with the scalar product $(x_1, \ldots, x_{n+1}) \cdot (y_1, \ldots, y_{n+1}) = x_1 y_1 + \ldots + x_n y_n$.) This implies that

$$v = (0, \ldots, 0, v_{n+1}), \; v_{n+1} \neq 0.$$

The axis of Z must hence be parallel (in the usual sense) to the x_{n+1}–axis. As a matter of fact, the axis g of Z is the x_{n+1}–axis: suppose that

$$c = (c_1, \ldots, c_n, 0)$$

is on the axis of Z and that the points $a + c$ and $b + c$ are on Z such that

$$a, b, (0, \ldots, 0, 1)$$

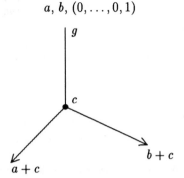

are pairwise perpendicular (in the euclidean sense), then $a_{n+1} = 0 = b_{n+1}$ and

$$(c + a \cos \eta + b \sin \eta)^2 = 1$$

for all $\eta \in \mathbb{R}$. This together with the fact that the radius of Z is 1, i.e. $a^2 = b^2 = 1$, leads to $c^2 = 0$, i.e. to $c = 0$, by taking $c_{n+1} = 0$ into account.

The situation with Z is now very convenient, since its axis is just the x_{n+1}-axis and its points are given by

$$(x_1, \ldots, x_n, x_{n+1}) \tag{16}$$

with

$$(x_1, \ldots, x_n) = a \cdot \cos \eta + b \cdot \sin \eta$$

where $a = (a_1, \ldots, a_n)$ $b = (b_1, \ldots, b_n)$ satisfy

$$a_1^2 + \ldots + a_n^2 = 1 = b_1^2 + \ldots + b_n^2 \tag{17}$$

and

$$a_1 b_1 + \ldots + a_n b_n = 0. \tag{18}$$

Instead of (16), we prefer to write

$$x = (a \cos \eta + b \sin \beta, x_{n+1}). \tag{19}$$

The situation with Z is now indeed as it was with C^2. The three types of C^n-lines are actually given by

$$l(a, b; \mu, \nu) := \left\{ (a \cos t + b \sin t, \mu t + \nu) \,\middle|\, t \in \mathbb{R} \right\}$$

and

$$l(a, b; t_0) := \left\{ (a \cos t_0 + b \sin t_0, x_{n+1}) \,\middle|\, x_{n+1} \in \mathbb{R} \right\}.$$

Observe that $l(a,b;0,\nu)$ are the circles. μ is called the *slope* of $l(a,b;\mu,\nu)$. Slope 0 thus leads to the circles. A C^n–line $l(a,b;\mu,\nu)$ determines the circular cylinder Z of which it is part uniquely. This is not true for $l(a,b;t_0)$ in the case $n > 2$: The intersection of

$$Z_1 : \;=\; \Big\{ (e_1 \cos \eta + e_2 \sin \eta, x_4) \,\big|\, \eta, x_4 \in \mathbb{R} \Big\},$$
$$Z_2 : \;=\; \Big\{ (e_1 \cos \zeta + e_3 \sin \zeta, x_4) \,\big|\, \zeta, x_4 \in \mathbb{R} \Big\},$$

where $e_1 = (1,0,0)$, $e_2 = (0,1,0)$, $e_3 = (0,0,1)$, consists of exactly two lines.

M^n operates transitively on the set of C^n–lines $l(a,b;t_0)$. Moreover:

PROPOSITION 6. *Suppose that $l(a,b;\mu,\nu)$ and $l(c,d;\mu_1,\nu_1)$ are C^n–lines. There exists a $\gamma \in M^n$ which transforms the first line onto the second if and only if $|\mu| = |\mu_1|$.*

Proof.   Assume $|\mu| = |\mu_1|$ and take an orthogonal matrix A of $\mathbb{R}^n$ such that

$$c = aA \text{ and } d = bA.$$

Put $\varepsilon := \operatorname{sgn}(\mu_1 \mu^{-1})$ for $\mu \neq 0$ and $\varepsilon := 1$ otherwise. Then

$$\gamma(x) := x \left(\begin{array}{ccc|c} & & & 0 \\ & A & & \vdots \\ & & & 0 \\ \hline 0 & \cdots & 0 & \varepsilon \end{array} \right) + (0 \ldots 0 \; \nu_1 - \nu\varepsilon)$$

transforms $l(a,b;\mu,\nu)$ onto $l(c,d;\mu_1,\nu_1)$. — The other direction of the proof is obvious. $\square$

3.7 Null–lines

The C^n–lines of slope $\mu \in \{+1, -1\}$ are called *null–lines*.

PROPOSITION 7. *There exists a null–line through the distinct points $x, y \in C^n$, if, and only if*

$$g(x,y) := xy - \cos(x_{n+1} - y_{n+1}) = 0$$

holds true.

Proof.   If x, y are on $l(a, b; \mu, \nu)$ with $\mu^2 = 1$, and

$$x = (a\cos\alpha + b\sin\alpha, \ \mu\alpha + \nu),$$
$$y = (a\cos\beta + b\cos\beta, \ \mu\beta + \nu),$$

then $xy = \cos(\beta - \alpha) = \cos(x_{n+1} - y_{n+1})$. If, on the other hand, $g(x, y) = 0$ holds true for $x \neq y$, we consider two cases, namely $(xy)^2 = 1$, $(xy)^2 < 1$. In the first case put

$$a := (x_1, \ldots, x_n), \ t := y_{n+1} - x_{n+1}.$$

Then

$$x = (a\cos 0 + b\sin 0, \ 1 \cdot 0 + x_{n+1}),$$
$$y = (a\cos t + b\sin t, \ 1 \cdot t + x_{n+1})$$

for some b satisfying (17), (18). Hence x and y are on $l(a, b; 1, x_{n+1})$. Assume now that $(xy)^2 < 1$. Put

$$a := (x_1, \ldots, x_n) \text{ and } b \cdot \sqrt{1 - (xy)^2} := -(xy)a + (y_1, \ldots, y_n).$$

The elements a, b hence satisfy (17), (18). Put $t := y_{n+1} - x_{n+1}$ and

$$b' := b \cdot \operatorname{sgn}\left[\sin(y_{n+1} - x_{n+1})\right].$$

Observe that $\sin^2(y_{n+1} - x_{n+1}) = 1 - (xy)^2 \neq 0$ and

$$a\cos t + b'\sin t = a(xy) + b \cdot \sqrt{1 - (xy)^2} = (y_1, \ldots, y_n).$$

Hence $x, y \in l(a, b'; 1, x_{n+1})$.   □

For a point $x = (x_1, \ldots, x_{n+1})$ of C^n define

$$x_0 := (x_1, \ldots, x_n, 0). \tag{20}$$

The points $x, y \in C^n$ are said to be *separated* whenever $x_0 \neq y_0 \neq -x_0$ holds true.

PROPOSITION 8. *Through the separated points x, y there exists exactly one circular cylinder $Z \subseteq C^n$ of radius 1.*

Proof.   This is clear since the circle with center 0, i.e. the origin, and points x_0, y_0 on it must be on such a cylinder Z, and thus determine it uniquely, because its axis must be the x_{n+1}–axis.   □

THEOREM 9. *There is exactly one null–line through* $x, y \in C^n$ *if, and only if,* x, y *are separated and* $g(x, y) = 0$.

Proof.   There is a null–line through the separated points x, y whenever $g(x, y) = 0$, in view of Proposition 7. Let l be an arbitrary null–line through x, y. Since there exists exactly one circular cylinder $Z \subseteq C^n$ of radius 1 through x, y because of Proposition 8, the C^n–line l must be on Z. Without loss of generality we thus may assume that $Z = C^2$ and $x = (1, 0, 0)$. Since the motions of C^n are linear and orthogonal mappings with respect to the first n coordinates, the condition $x_0 \neq y_0 \neq -x_0$ remains unchanged. Also $g(x, y) = 0$ remains true. Therefore

$$y = (\cos y_3, y_2, y_3)$$

with $(\cos y_3, y_2) \notin \{(1, 0), (-1, 0)\}$, i.e. $\cos^2 y_3 \neq 1$. Hence

$$y = (\cos y_3, \sin y_3, y_3) \tag{21}$$

or

$$y = (\cos y_3, -\sin y_3, y_3) \tag{22}$$

with $\cos^2 y_3 \neq 1$. There are exactly two null–lines on C^2 through x. We shall show that the null–line of slope -1 does not contain y in the case (21). Otherwise

$$
\begin{aligned}
(1, 0, 0) &= (\cos t_0, \sin t_0, -t_0 + \nu), \\
(\cos y_3, \sin y_3, y_3) &= (\cos t_1, \sin t_1, -t_1 + \nu)
\end{aligned}
$$

holds true for suitable $t_0, t_1, \nu \in \mathbb{R}$. Hence $t_0 = 2k\pi$ with $k \in \mathbb{Z}$ and furthermore

$$t_1 = \nu - y_3 = 2k\pi - y_3.$$

This contradicts

$$\sin y_3 = \sin t_1 = -\sin y_3$$

since $\cos^2 y_3 \neq 1$. — In the case (22), the null–line through x, y must have slope -1. — Assume now that

$$x, y \text{ are separated and } g(x, y) = 0$$

does not hold true. If $g(x, y) \neq 0$ there is no null–line at all through x, y because of Proposition 7. If

$$g(x, y) = 0 \text{ and } (x_0 = y_0 \text{ or } x_0 = -y_0)$$

there are two such lines containing x, y.   □

PROPOSITION 10. *Let $x \in C^n$ be a point and let $\lambda \ni x$ be the euclidean line parallel to the x_{n+1}-axis. Then there exist exactly $\aleph_0$ points $y \in \lambda$ with $g(x, y) = 0$.*

Proof.   Without loss of generality assume that $x = (1, 0, \ldots, 0)$. Then $g(x, y) = 0$ for
$$y = (1, 0, \ldots, 0, y_{n+1})$$
if and only if $y_{n+1} = 2k\pi, k \in \mathbb{Z}$.   □

3.8 Null–line preserving mappings

We define
$$x \equiv y$$
for $x, y \in C^n$ to mean that
$$\forall_{z \in C^n} \quad g(x, z) = 0 \Leftrightarrow g(y, z) = 0. \tag{23}$$

LEMMA 11 (J. Lester [1]). *The relation $\equiv$ is an equivalence relation and the equivalence class $[x]$ containing $x \in C^n$ is given by*
$$[x] = \Big\{ \big((-1)^\nu x_0, x_{n+1} + \nu\pi\big) \,\big|\, \nu \in \mathbb{Z} \Big\}.$$

Here (y_0, y_{n+1}) stands for y.

Proof.   Suppose that for $x \in C^n$ points
$$p = \big((-1)^\nu x_0, x_{n+1} + \nu\pi\big), \quad q = \big((-1)^\mu x_0, x_{n+1} + \mu\pi\big)$$
of $[x]$ are given. Then a point $z \in C^n$ with $g(p, z) = 0$ must satisfy
$$(-1)^\nu x_0 z_0 = \cos(x_{n+1} + \nu\pi - z_{n+1}) = (-1)^\nu \cos(x_{n+1} - z_{n+1})$$
and hence $g(q, z) = 0$. We thus get $p \equiv q$. — Assume that $y \equiv x$ for $y \in C^n$. Then $x_0 y_0 = \cos t$ holds true for a suitable $t \in \mathbb{R}$. Put
$$z := (y_0, x_{n+1} + t) \text{ and } \zeta := (y_0, x_{n+1} - t).$$
From $g(x, z) = 0 = g(x, \zeta)$ and (23) we get
$$\begin{aligned} 0 &= g(y, z) &= y_0^2 - \cos(y_{n+1} - x_{n+1} - t), \\ 0 &= g(y, \zeta) &= y_0^2 - \cos(y_{n+1} - x_{n+1} + t), \end{aligned}$$

4 Benz

i.e.

$$y_{n+1} - x_{n+1} - t = 2k\pi,$$

$$y_{n+1} - x_{n+1} + t = 2l\pi$$

for suitable $k, l \in \mathbb{Z}$. Hence

$$y_{n+1} = x_{n+1} + (k+l)\pi,$$

$$t = (k+l)\pi - 2k\pi.$$

Thus $x_0 y_0 = \cos t = (-1)^{k+l}$, i.e. $y \in [x]$.   □

The following mapping σ was introduced by J. Lester, loc. cit.: associate to $x = (x_0, x_{n+1})$ of $C^n, n \geq 2$, the point

$$\sigma(x) := \mathbb{R}(\cos x_{n+1}, x_1, \ldots, x_n, \sin x_{n+1})$$

of the $(n+1)$–dimensional projective space $\Pi^{n+1}(\mathbb{R})$ over $\mathbb{R}$ (see sections 5.6.1, 5.6.2). Then $\sigma(x)$ is a point of the Lie quadric L^{n-1} (see GT, 190f) of all projective points $\mathbb{R}(\xi_0, \xi_1, \ldots, \xi_{n+1})$ satisfying

$$-\xi_0^2 + \xi_1^2 + \ldots + \xi_n^2 - \xi_{n+1}^2 = 0.$$

We say that $\xi, \eta \in L^{n-1}$ $(n-1 \geq 2)$ are in *contact with each other* iff

$$-\xi_0 \eta_0 + \xi_1 \eta_1 + \ldots + \xi_n \eta_n - \xi_{n+1}\eta_{n+1} = 0$$

holds true. If ξ, η are in contact with each other we shall write $\xi - \eta$. A bijection λ of L^{n-1} is called a *Lie transformation* iff

$$\xi - \eta \text{ and } \lambda(\xi) - \lambda(\eta)$$

are equivalent for all $\xi, \eta \in L^{n-1}$. All Lie transformations are determined in GT, section 4.9. Sophus Lie defined his geometry via *oriented hyperspheres* and *oriented hyperplanes* (see GT, chapter 4). For another possible definition see section 6.3.2 and GT, section 4.10.

PROPOSITION 12 (J. Lester [1]). $\sigma : C^n \rightarrow L^{n-1}$ *is surjective, and* $\sigma(x) = \sigma(y)$ *holds true for* $x, y \in C^n$ *iff* $x \equiv y$.

Proof. Let $P = \mathbb{R}(\xi_0, \ldots)$ be a point of L^{n-1}. Then $\xi_0^2 + \xi_{n+1}^2$ must be unequal to 0 and we thus may assume $\xi_0^2 + \xi_{n+1}^2 = 1$ without loss of generality. In order to find all $x \in C^n$ with $\sigma(x) = P$ we put

$$\xi_0 = \cos t \text{ and } \xi_{n+1} = \sin t.$$

The pre–images of P are then given by

$$x_0 = (\xi_1, \ldots, \xi_n), \; x_{n+1} = t + 2k\pi$$

and

$$y_0 = -x_0, \; y_{n+1} = (t + \pi) + 2k\pi$$

with $k \in \mathbb{Z}$. We thus have

$$\sigma^{-1}(P) = \left[(\xi_1, \ldots, \xi_n, t)\right].$$

□

Again we encounter a functional equations problem:

THEOREM 13 (J. Lester [1]). *All bijections*

$$f : C^n \to C^n (n \geq 3)$$

such that $g(x, y) = 0$ holds true iff $g\big(f(x), f(y)\big) = 0$ is satisfied, are given precisely as follows: let $\lambda : L^{n-1} \to L^{n-1}$ be an arbitrary Lie transformation of L^{n-1} and let f then be an arbitrary bijection of C^n which maps the class $[x]$ onto the class $\sigma^{-1}\big(\lambda\sigma(x)\big)$ for all $x \in C^n$.

Proof. a) Let f be a bijection of C^n such that $g(x, y) = 0$ holds true iff $g\big(f(x), f(y)\big) = 0$ is valid. Then $x \equiv y$ iff $f(x) \equiv f(y)$, because of the definition of the relation $\equiv$.

b) Because of a) we can define

$$\varphi([x]) := [f(x)]$$

for $x \in C^n$. The function φ must be a bijection of the set S of equivalence classes of the relation $\equiv$. We put

$$[x] \sim [y]$$

if and only if $g(x, y) = 0$. This definition does not depend on the representatives of $[x], [y]$ as can easily be checked: assume $g(x, y) = 0$ and define

$$x' := \big((-1)^\nu x_0, x_{n+1} + \nu\pi\big), \; y' := \big((-1)^\mu y_0, y_{n+1} + \mu\pi\big)$$

with $\nu, \mu \in \mathbb{Z}$. Now

$$g(x', y') = (-1)^{\nu+\mu} \cdot g(x, y) = 0.$$

c) Obviously, $[x] \sim [y]$ iff $\varphi([x]) \sim \varphi([y])$. Observe moreover that $[x] \sim [y]$ holds true for $x, y \in C^n$ if and only if $\sigma(x)$ is in contact with $\sigma(y)$ (GT, 191f), i.e. $\sigma(x) - \sigma(y)$: this is a consequence of the fact that $g(x, y) = 0$ holds true iff

$$- \cos x_{n+1} \cdot \cos y_{n+1} + x_0 y_0 - \sin x_{n+1} \cdot \sin y_{n+1} = 0$$

4*

is satisfied, i.e. iff

$$-\xi_0\eta_0 + \xi_1\eta_1 + \ldots + \xi_n\eta_n - \xi_{n+1}\eta_{n+1} = 0$$

is valid for $\sigma(x) =: \mathbb{R}(\xi_0, \ldots), \sigma(y) =: \mathbb{R}(\eta_0, \ldots)$.

d) $\lambda := \sigma\varphi\sigma^{-1}$ must be hence a Lie transformation of L^{n-1} and f has the form as described in the Theorem. On the other hand it can immediately be seen that, starting with a mapping f as described, $g(x,y) = 0$ holds true for $x, y \in C^n$ iff $g\big(f(x), f(y)\big) = 0$. $\square$

REMARK. June Lester [1] pointed out that Theorem 13 cannot be improved in such a way that a mapping f there is doing the same as a suitable mapping of M^n on the set of equivalence classes: Obviously,

$$\mathbb{R}(\xi_0, \ldots, \xi_{n+1}) \to \mathbb{R}(\sqrt{3}\,\xi_n + 2\xi_0, \xi_1, \ldots, \xi_{n-1}, 2\xi_n + \sqrt{3}\,\xi_0, \xi_{n+1})$$

is a Lie transformation λ of L^{n-1}. We now would like to show that there is no $\gamma \in M^n$ with

$$\big[\gamma(x)\big] = \sigma^{-1}\big[\lambda\sigma(x)\big] \tag{24}$$

for all $x \in C^n$. Take the points

$$p := (1, 0, 0, \ldots, 0),$$

$$q := (0, 1, 0, \ldots, 0)$$

of C^n. Then for $n > 2$

$$\sigma^{-1}\big(\lambda\sigma(p)\big) = \sigma^{-1}\left(\mathbb{R}\left(1, \frac{1}{2}, 0, \ldots, 0, \frac{\sqrt{3}}{2}, 0\right)\right)$$

$$= \left[\left(\frac{1}{2}, 0, 0, \ldots, 0, \frac{\sqrt{3}}{2}, 0\right)\right],$$

$$\sigma^{-1}\big(\lambda\sigma(q)\big) = \left[\left(0, \frac{1}{2}, 0, \ldots, 0, \frac{\sqrt{3}}{2}, 0\right)\right].$$

Let γ be of the form

$$\gamma(x) = x \cdot \left(\begin{array}{ccc|c} & & & 0 \\ & A & & \vdots \\ & & & 0 \\ \hline 0 & \cdots & 0 & \varepsilon \end{array}\right) + (0 \ldots 0a),$$

where $A = (a_{ij})$ is orthogonal. Applying (24) for the points p, q we thus get

$$[(a_{11}, \ldots, a_{1n}, a)] = \left[\left(\frac{1}{2}, 0, 0, \ldots, 0, \frac{\sqrt{3}}{2}, 0 \right) \right],$$

$$[(a_{21}, \ldots, a_{2n}, a)] = \left[\left(0, \frac{1}{2}, 0, \ldots, 0, \frac{\sqrt{3}}{2}, 0 \right) \right].$$

Now

$$0 = \sum_{\nu=1}^{n} a_{1\nu} a_{2\nu} = \pm \left(\frac{1}{2} \cdot 0 + 0 \cdot \frac{1}{2} + \frac{3}{4} \right)$$

is a contradiction.

LEMMA 14. *Let* $f : C^n \to C^n, n \geq 2$, *be a bijection such that l is a null–line iff $f(l)$ is a null–line. Then* $g(x, y) = 0$ *iff* $g(f(x), f(y)) = 0$ *for all* $x, y \in C^n$.

Proof. Assume that $g(x, y) = 0$ for distinct points $x, y \in C^n$. In view of Proposition 7, there exists a null–line l through x, y. Since $f(x), f(y)$ are distinct points on the null–line $f(l)$, we get $g(f(x), f(y)) = 0$ because of Proposition 7. Conversely, assume that $g(f(x), f(y)) = 0$ for $f(x) \neq f(y)$. Then there is a null–line l' through $f(x), f(y)$. Put $f^{-1}(l') =: l$. Since $l' = f(l)$ is a null–line, so is l itself. Since $x, y \in l$ we thus get $g(x, y) = 0$. $\square$

THEOREM 15: *All bijections*

$$f : C^n \to C^n (n \geq 3)$$

such that l is a null–line iff $f(l)$ is a null–line, are given precisely as follows: Let $\lambda : L^{n-1} \to L^{n-1}$ *be an arbitrary Lie transformation of L^{n-1} and let f then be an arbitrary bijection of C^n which maps the class $[x]$ onto the class* $\sigma^{-1}(\lambda\sigma(x))$ *for all* $x \in C^n$.

Proof. a) *Let x be a point on a null–line l. Then* $[x] \subset l$: suppose that $l := l(a, b; \mu, \nu)$ with $|\mu| = 1$ and that

$$x = (a \cos t_0 + b \sin t_0, \mu t_0 + \nu).$$

Then

$$((-1)^\varepsilon x_0, x_{n+1} + \varepsilon \pi) = (a \cos t_1 + b \sin t_1, \mu t_1 + \nu) \in l$$

for $\varepsilon \in \mathbb{Z}$ and $t_1 = t_0 + \varepsilon\mu\pi$.

b) *Let x, y be separated points such that $g(x, y) = 0$. The uniquely determined null–line l through x, y is then given by*

$$l = \{z \in C^n \mid g(x, z) = 0 = g(y, z)\}.$$

This needs to be proved only in case

$$x = (1, 0, \ldots, 0)$$

and

$$y = (\cos \alpha, \sin \alpha, 0, \ldots, 0, \mu \alpha)$$

with $\mu^2 = 1$ and $\alpha \notin \pi \cdot \mathbb{Z}$. For $z \in l$ we have of course $g(x, z) = 0$ since x, z are on a common null–line. Let now $z \in C^n$ be a point such that $g(x, z) = 0 = g(y, z)$. This implies $z_1 = \cos z_{n+1}$ and

$$z_1 \cos \alpha + z_2 \sin \alpha = \cos(z_{n+1} - \mu\alpha)$$

and thus $z_2 = \mu \sin z_{n+1}$ since $\sin \alpha \neq 0$. From $z_0^2 = 1$ and $z_1^2 + z_2^2 = 1$ we then have

$$z = (\cos \mu z_{n+1}, \sin \mu z_{n+1}, 0, \ldots, 0, \mu \cdot \mu z_{n+1}) \in l.$$

c) *Let* $f : C^n \to C^n, n \geq 2$, *be a bijection such that* $g(x, y) = 0$ *iff* $g(f(x), f(y)) = 0$ *for all* $x, y \in C^n$. *Then* l *is a null–line iff* $f(l)$ *is a null–line.* Let l be the null–line

$$l = l(a, b; \mu, \nu) \text{ with } \mu^2 = 1.$$

Define $l_1 \subset l$ as follows

$$l_1 = \{(a \cos t + b \sin t, \mu t + \nu) \,|\, t \in [0, \pi [\}.$$

Any two distinct points of l_1 are then separated. Take $x \in l_1$ and put $x' := f(x)$. Since l_1 has cardinality $\aleph$, so does $f(l_1)$. For all $y \in l_1, g(x, y) = 0$ holds true and thus also $g(f(x), f(y)) = 0$. Because of Proposition 10 there then exists a $y \neq x$ in l_1 such that $f(x), f(y)$ are separated. Denote the null–line through $f(x), f(y)$ by L. We would like to show that $L = f(l)$. But according to b) we have

$$l = \{z \in C^n \,|\, g(x, z) = 0 = g(y, z)\}$$

and

$$\begin{aligned} L &= \{v \in C^n \,|\, g(f(x), v) = 0 = g(f(y), v)\} \\ &= \{f(z) \in C^n \,|\, g(f(x), f(z)) = 0 = g(f(y), f(z))\} \\ &= f(l). \end{aligned}$$

Working with f^{-1} instead of f, we get the proof of the other direction of statement c).

d) In view of Lemma 14 and Theorem 13, we finally get Theorem 15 from a). $\square$

3.9 Distance–0–preserving mappings

In this section we would like to study 0–preserving bijections of C^n, i.e. bijections $f : C^n \to C^n, n \geq 3$, with $d(x, y) = 0$ iff $d\big(f(x), f(y)\big) = 0$ for all $x, y \in C^n$, where $d : C^n \times C^n \to \mathbb{R}$ denotes the distance function

$$d(x, y) = (\arccos xy)^2 - (x_{n+1} - y_{n+1})^2$$
$$\text{with } \arccos xy \in [0, \pi].$$

For distinct points $p, q \in C^n$ such that $d(p, q) = 0$, define the *segment*

$$I(p, q) := \{z \in C^n \,|\, d(p, z) = 0 = d(q, z)\}.$$

If f is a 0–preserving bijection then obviously

$$f\big(I(p, q)\big) = I\big(f(p), f(q)\big) \tag{25}$$

holds true.

The segment $I(p, q)$ is called *separated* whenever p, q are separated.

LEMMA 16. *If $I(p, q)$ is separated then so is $I\big(f(p), f(q)\big)$ for every 0–preserving bijection f of C^n.*

Proof. Observe that $d(x, y) = 0$ is equivalent to $g(x, y) = 0$ and $\big| x_{n+1} - y_{n+1} \big| \leq \pi$. Put $x' := f(x)$ for $x \in C^n$ and let $I(p, q)$ be a separated segment. Assume that $q_0' = -p_0'$. By l denote the uniquely determined null–line through p, q; then $I(p, q) \subset l$. Suppose that Z is a circular cylinder of radius 1 through p', q'. Denote by l_1, l_2 the two null–lines through p', q' on Z and denote by $\pi(l_i)$ the piece of l_i, $i = 1, 2$, between p', q'. Then

$$\pi(l_1) \cup \pi(l_2) \subseteq I(p', q').$$

The set
$$P := \{z \in I(p, q) \,|\, \forall_{x \in I(p,q)} \, d(z, x) = 0\}$$
contains infinitely many elements, thus so does

$$f(P) = \{z' \in I(p', q') \,|\, \forall_{x' \in I(p',q')} \, d(z', x') = 0\}.$$

But the set
$$\{r \in C^n \,|\, \forall_{s \in \pi(l_1) \cup (l_2)} \, d(r, s) = 0\}$$
which must contain $f(P)$ as a subset, consists of only two elements, namely of p' and q'.— In the case $q_0' = p_0'$, observe that $\#I(p', q') \leq 1$. $\square$

LEMMA 17. *Let $I(a,b)$ and $I(c,d)$ be separated segments with $\#I(a,b)\cap I(c,d)\geq 3$. Then there exists a uniquely determined null–line l with*

$$I(a,b)\cup I(c,d)\subset l.$$

Proof.   Since a,b are separated, there is exactly one null–line l_1 through a,b in view of Theorem 9. Similarly, let l_2 be the uniquely determined null–line containing $I(c,d)$. We have to show $l_1=l_2$. Suppose that x,y,z are distinct points on $I(a,b)\cap I(c,d)$. At least one of the pairs xy,xz must be separated, say x,y. Since there is exactly one null–line through x,y, in view of Theorem 9, we get $l_1=l_2$.   □

THEOREM 18. *Let f be a 0–preserving bijection of C^n. Then l is a null–line if and only if $f(l)$ is a null–line.*

Proof.   Take separated segments $I(A_\nu,A_{\nu+1}),\nu\in\mathbb{Z}$, such that

$$l=\bigcup_{\nu\in\mathbb{Z}}I(A_\nu,A_{\nu+1})$$

holds true for the given null–line l. Then

$$f(l)\subseteq\bigcup_{\nu\in\mathbb{Z}}I(A'_\nu,A'_{\nu+1})$$

must be a subset of a null–line L because of Lemmas 16 and 17: observe that $I(A'_\nu,A'_{\nu+1}),I(A'_{\nu+1},A'_{\nu+2})$ are on the same null–line from Lemma 17. Since f^{-1} is also 0–preserving, we get that $f^{-1}(L)$ is on a null–line l_0 as well. Hence

$$l\subseteq f^{-1}(L)\subseteq l_0,$$

i.e. $l=l_0$ and thus $f(l)=L$. For the converse, proceed with f^{-1} instead of f.   □.

REMARK. Lemma 14 and step c) of the proof of Theorem 15 show the equivalence of the following two properties for a bijection f of $C^n,n\geq 2$:

(i) $\forall_{x,y\in C^n}\, g(x,y)=0\Leftrightarrow g(f(x),f(y))=0$,

(ii) $\forall_{l\subset C^n}\, l$ is a null–line $\Leftrightarrow f(l)$ is a null–line.

Property

(iii) $\forall_{x,y \in C^n} \; d(x,y) = 0 \Leftrightarrow d(f(x), f(y)) = 0$

implies (ii) and hence (i) as well, in view of Lemma 18. But we would like to point out that (ii) does not imply (iii): Put $P_\nu := ((-1)^\nu, 0, \ldots, 0, \pi + \nu\pi)$ and

$$f(x) = \begin{cases} P_{-\nu} & \text{for } x = P_\nu \text{ and } \nu^2 = 1 \\ x & \text{otherwise} \end{cases}.$$

The mapping f leaves invariant every equivalence class and it permutes, in a trivial way, the points of a given class. It hence satisfies (ii), in view of Theorem 15. Observe moreover that

$$d(P_1, P_2) = 0 \neq d(P_{-1}, P_2) = d(f(P_1), f(P_2)).$$

REMARK. Let f be a bijection of $C^n, n \geq 3$, satisfying (iii) and let $P_\nu, \nu \in \mathbb{Z}$, be the points introduced in the previous Remark. We take a $\gamma \in M^n$ such that $\gamma(f(P_0)) = P_0$. We shall again write f instead of γf. To the mapping f, as operating on the set of equivalence classes, thus corresponds a Lie transformation, in view of Theorem 15 which fixes $\sigma(P_0) = \infty$ (GT, 190f) and which is thus a Laguerre transformation (GT, 194f). To the classes on null–lines through P_0 there correspond precisely the spears (GT, 194f) and to the other classes the Laguerre cycles. Spears and Laguerre cycles are permuted separately. The mapping f, in view of (iii), does not have the freedom on a single equivalence class as a mapping f that satisfies only (ii). Since P_0 remains fixed under f and since $d(P_0, P_\nu) = 0$ has only the solutions P_0, P_1, P_{-1}, we get $\{P_1, P_{-1}\} = \{f(P_1), f(P_{-1})\}$. In the case $f(P_1) = P_1$ we thus have $f(P_\nu) = P_\nu$ for all $\nu \in \mathbb{Z}$ and in the case $f(P_1) = P_{-1}$ obviously $f(P_\nu) = P_{-\nu}$ for all $\nu \in \mathbb{Z}$. A similar situation occurs for the other classes.

3.10 Einstein's cylinder universe over a ring

In section 1.2 we introduced the notion of a distance space (S, W, d). Let R be a ring as described in the Remark of section 1.3 and let $n \geq 2$ be an integer. The distance space

$$C_R^n = (S, W, d)$$

is defined as follows:

$$\begin{aligned} S &= \{(x_1, \ldots, x_{n+1}) \in R^{n+1} \mid x_1^2 + \ldots + x_n^2 = 1\}, \\ W &= R \times R, \\ d(x, y) &= (xy, (x_{n+1} - y_{n+1})^2) \end{aligned}$$

where the scalar product

$$x \cdot = (x_1, \ldots, x_{n+1}) \cdot (y_1, \ldots, y_{n+1})$$

is again given by

$$xy = x_1 y_1 + \ldots + x_n y_n.$$

We shall now prove the following result:

THEOREM 19. *Let $n \geq 2$ be an integer and let R be a ring as described previously such that $2 = 1+1$ is a unit element. Then every distance preserving mapping of C_R^n must be bijective and they are all given by the transformations*

$$f(x) = (x_1 \ldots x_{n+1}) \cdot \left(\begin{array}{c|c} A & \begin{array}{c} 0 \\ \vdots \\ 0 \end{array} \\ \hline 0 \ \ldots \ 0 & c \end{array} \right) + (0 \ \ldots \ 0 \ a)$$

where A is an $n \times n$-matrix over R with

$$AA^T = E := \left(\begin{array}{ccc} 1 & & 0 \\ & \ddots & \\ 0 & & 1 \end{array} \right)$$

and where c and a are elements of R with $c^2 = 1$.

Proof.   Let α be an isometry (i.e. distance preserving mapping) of C_R^n and put

$$\alpha(x_1, \ldots, x_{n+1}) \ =: \ (x_1', \ldots, x_{n+1}'),$$
$$x_{n+1}' \ =: \ f(x_1, \ldots, x_{n+1}).$$

Set

$$a := f(1, 0, \ldots, 0), \ b := f(1, 0, \ldots, 0, 1)$$

and observe that $b - a$ is a unit because of $(b - a)^2 = (1 - 0)^2$. Then

$$(x_{n+1}' - a)^2 = x_{n+1}^2, \ (x_{n+1}' - b)^2 = (x_{n+1} - 1)^2,$$

i.e. $x_{n+1}' = cx_{n+1} + a$ where c, a are fixed elements of R with $c^2 = 1$, since

$$(x_{n+1}' - y_{n+1}')^2 = (x_{n+1} - y_{n+1})^2.$$

Let p be a fixed element of R and define a mapping of the $(n-1)$–dimensional spherical geometry (see sections 1.3, 5.8, and GT, 78ff) by

$$\gamma_p((x_1, \ldots, x_n) := (x_1', \ldots, x_n')$$

with

$$\alpha(x_1, \ldots, x_n, p) =: (x_1', \ldots, x_n', cp + a).$$

Since $x \cdot y$ is invariant we get (GT, 81ff)

$$\gamma_p(x) = x A(p)$$

for an orthogonal $n \times n$–matrix $A(p)$. We would like to show that $A(p)$ does not really depend on p: suppose that $q \in R$ is unequal to p. For arbitrary elements

$$(x_1, \ldots, x_n, p), \ (y_1, \ldots, y_n, q) \in C_R^n$$

we then have

$$x_1 y_1 + \ldots + x_n y_n = x A(p) A(q)^T y =: \sum_{ij=1}^{n} a_{ij} x_i y_j.$$

Put $x_i = 1 = y_j$ for $i, j \in \{1, \ldots, n\}$ and $x_\mu = 0 = y_\nu$ otherwise. Then $a_{ij} = \delta_{ij}$ and hence $A(p)A(q)^T = E$, i.e. $A(p) = A(q) =: A$. $\qquad\square$

3.11   Laguerre model of Einstein's plane

Let $l := \{(x_1, x_2) \in \mathbb{R}^2 \mid a_0 + a_1 x_1 + a_2 x_2 = 0\}$ be a line of $\mathbb{R}^2$, where a_0, a_1, a_2 are real numbers with $a_1^2 + a_2^2 \neq 0$. We will call the ordered pair

$$\big(l, (v_1, v_2)\big) \tag{26}$$

an *oriented line* or a *spear* whenever

(i) $v_1, v_2 \in \mathbb{R}$ with $v_1^2 + v_2^2 \neq 0$,

(ii) $a_1 v_1 + a_2 v_2 = 0$

hold true. We define
$$\big(l, (v_1, v_2)\big) = \big(m, (w_1, w_2)\big)$$
iff $l = m$ and $(v_1, v_2) = \lambda(w_1, w_2)$ with a real number $\lambda > 0$. So a spear can be considered simply as a line l traversed in the sense given by the vector (v_1, v_2).

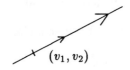

(v_1, v_2)

A line l of equation

$$a_0 + a_1 x_1 + a_2 x_2 = 0 \tag{27}$$

belongs to precisely two distinct spears, namely to

$$\big(l, (-a_2, a_1)\big) \text{ and } \big(l, (a_2, -a_1)\big).$$

We call

$$(a_0, a_1, a_2, a_3)$$

the *spear coordinates* of $\big(l, (v_1, v_2)\big)$ iff (27) is the equation of l and

$$a_3 = \sqrt{a_1^2 + a_2^2} \cdot \operatorname{sgn} \begin{vmatrix} a_1 & a_2 \\ v_1 & v_2 \end{vmatrix} \tag{28}$$

holds true. Spear coordinates are determined up to a real factor $\varrho \neq 0$. In fact, if we start with equation

$$(ka_0) + (ka_1)\, x_1 + (ka_2)\, x_2 = 0,$$

$k \neq 0$, for l instead of (27) and with

$$\big(l, \lambda \cdot (v_1, v_2)\big), \ \lambda > 0,$$

we get the new coordinates

$$(ka_0, ka_1, ka_2, ka_3)$$

since

$$\sqrt{(ka_1)^2 + (ka_2)^2} \cdot \operatorname{sgn} \begin{vmatrix} ka_1 & ka_2 \\ \lambda v_1 & \lambda v_2 \end{vmatrix} =$$

$$|k| \cdot \sqrt{a_1^2 + a_2^2} \cdot \operatorname{sgn} k \cdot \operatorname{sgn} \begin{vmatrix} a_1 & a_2 \\ v_1 & v_2 \end{vmatrix} = ka_3 .$$

REMARK. Observe that $(a_0, a_1, a_2, a_3) \in \mathbb{R}^4$ determines one and only one spear provided

$$a_1^2 + a_2^2 = a_3^2 \neq 0.$$

In fact, the equation (27) determines l. Then

$$\big(l, (-\varepsilon a_2, \varepsilon a_1)\big) \tag{29}$$

with $\varepsilon := \operatorname{sgn} a_3$ must be the underlying spear.

Fundamental for our model of Einstein's plane will be the mapping

$$\mu : (x_1, x_2, x_3) \to (-x_3, x_1, x_2, 1) \tag{30}$$

which is a bijection from C^2 onto the set Σ^2 of all spears of $\mathbb{R}^2$.

Two spears
$$S = \big(l, (v_1, v_2)\big), \ T = \big(m, (w_1, w_2)\big)$$
are called *parallel*, written $S \parallel T$, iff

$$l \parallel m \text{ and } (v_1, v_2) = \lambda (w_1, w_2) \text{ with } \lambda > 0$$

hold true. Let a, b be the coordinates of S, T, respectively, then $S \parallel T$ is satisfied precisely whenever

$$\left(\frac{a_1}{a_3}, \frac{a_2}{a_3} \right) = \left(\frac{b_1}{b_3}, \frac{b_2}{b_3} \right). \tag{31}$$

The relation $\parallel$ is an equivalence relation on Σ^2. The equivalence classes are called parallel classes.

We now would like to study the mapping μ. Let $s = (s_1, s_2, s_3)$ be a point of C^2 and let S be the spear $\mu(s)$. Then

$$S = \big(l, (-s_2, s_1)\big)$$

with

$$l : -s_3 + s_1 x_1 + s_2 x_2 = 0. \tag{32}$$

Observe that $s \in C^2$ implies that $s_1^2 + s_2^2 = 1$.

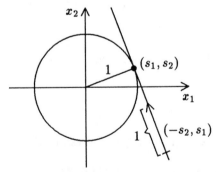

If $s_3 = 1$ then l is the tangent in (s_1, s_2) of the unit circle with center $(0, 0)$. Keeping s_1, s_2 fixed and changing the values of s_3 of $(s_1, s_2, s_3) \in C^2$, we get spears parallel to the one with $s_3 = 1$ considered before.

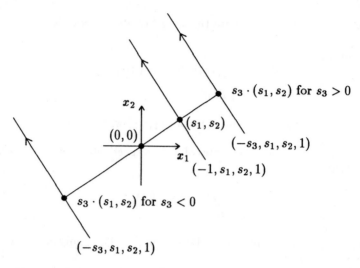

Lines $\{(s_1, s_2, \lambda) \mid \lambda \in \mathbb{R}\}$ on C^2 are thus mapped onto parallel classes of Σ^2. What are the images of the other lines

$$\{(\cos t, \sin t, kt + \lambda) \mid t \in \mathbb{R}\}$$

of C^2? Define $S(t)$ to be the spear with coordinates

$$(-kt - \lambda, \cos t, \sin t, 1).$$

Then

$$S(t) = \big(l(t), (-\sin t, \cos t)\big) \tag{33}$$

with

$$l(t) : x_1 \cos t + x_2 \sin t = kt + \lambda. \tag{34}$$

Case 1: $k = 0$ and $\lambda > 0$:

Take the circle C with center $(0, 0)$ and radius $|\lambda|$. Then

$$L = \{S(t) \mid t \in \mathbb{R}\}$$

consists of all spears $S(t)$ such that $l(t)$

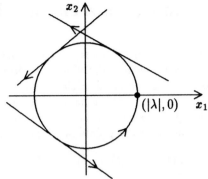

is tangent of C and such that

$$(-\sin t, \cos t)$$

prescribes the orientation of $S(t)$.

Case 2: $k = 0$ and $\lambda < 0$:

Here we take the same circle C and the tangents of C as before, but instead of (33) we choose

$$S^*(t) := \big(l(t), (\sin t, -\cos t)\big).$$

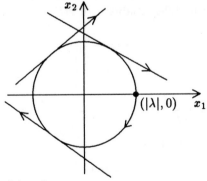

Case 3: $k = 0$ and $\lambda = 0$:

L consists of all spears S such that the underlying line of S contains the origin.

REMARK. As usual in Laguerre geometry (see section 6.2.2 and GT, 157ff) we may identify the sets L of spears in the different cases with oriented circles (as already indicated by arrows in two of our pictures) or with the point $(0, 0)$.

3.12 Laguerre image of a circular helix

It was easy to find the images of C^2-lines in our model for the case $k = 0$. There was the set of all spears with underlying lines through $(0, 0)$, and there were sets of spears touching an oriented circle in the right orientation in the points of contact. Exactly the same thing happens in case of the images of the remaining lines with $k \neq 0$: They will touch special oriented curves and this even in the correct orientation in the points of contact. Let C be the curve

$$x(t) = \big(x_1(t), x_2(t)\big), \; t \in \mathbb{R},$$

with

$$x(t) = (t\;1) \begin{pmatrix} k & 0 \\ \lambda & k \end{pmatrix} \begin{pmatrix} \cos t & \sin t \\ -\sin t & \cos t \end{pmatrix}. \tag{35}$$

This curve is easy to construct in terms of the simple mappings

$$(t, 1) \to k(t, 1) = (kt, k) \to (kt, k) + (\lambda, 0) =$$

$$(kt + \lambda, k) \to (kt + \lambda, k) \begin{pmatrix} \cos t & \sin t \\ -\sin t & \cos t \end{pmatrix}$$

which turn out to be a dilatation, a translation, a rotation, respectively. The curve (35) is everywhere differentiable with $\dot{x}(t) \neq 0$ with the exception of

$$t = \alpha := -\frac{\lambda}{k}. \tag{36}$$

In fact, we have

$$\dot{x} := \frac{dx(t)}{dt} = (kt + \lambda) \cdot (-\sin t, \cos t). \tag{37}$$

The point $x(\alpha)$ of C is a cusp: Put

$$t = \alpha + \varepsilon$$

for small ε. Then neglecting powers of ε from the 4th power on, we get

$$\cos t = \cos \alpha \cdot \left(1 - \frac{1}{2}\varepsilon^2\right) \; -\sin \alpha \cdot \left(\varepsilon - \frac{1}{6}\varepsilon^3\right),$$

$$\sin t = \sin \alpha \cdot \left(1 - \frac{1}{2}\varepsilon^2\right) \; +\cos \alpha \cdot \left(\varepsilon - \frac{1}{6}\varepsilon^3\right)$$

and hence

$$x(\alpha + \varepsilon) = x(\alpha) + \xi \cdot (\cos \alpha, \sin \alpha) + \eta \cdot (-\sin \alpha, \cos \alpha)$$

with $3\,\xi := -k\varepsilon^3$ and $2\eta := k\varepsilon^2$. Thus

$$\eta^3 = \frac{9k}{8}\,\xi^2.$$

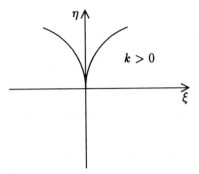

$k > 0$

The point $(\cos t, \sin t, kt + \lambda)$ has as image the spear $S(t)$ of (33), taking (34) into account. The line $l(t)$ of (34) is the tangent of $x(t)$ for $t \neq \alpha$. Even in case $t = \alpha$, the line $l(t)$ is the tangent of both curves

(a) $x(t)$, $t \geq \alpha$,

(b) $x(t)$, $t \leq \alpha$,

in the sense that it is the limit of the neighbour tangents. We now prescribe orientations of both curves (a) and (b) by simply extending continuously the initial orientation (see (33))

$$(-\sin \alpha, \cos \alpha)$$

of $S(\alpha)$ to both branches. Then the spears

$$S(t), \quad t \geq \alpha,$$
$$S(t), \quad t \leq \alpha,$$

touch (a), (b) respectively in the correct orientation. We will call $l(\alpha)$ the initial tangent. Denote by M the set

$$\{x \in \mathbb{R} \mid x \neq 0 \text{ and } \tan x = x\}.$$

We are now interested in all pairs $t \neq \tau$ of real numbers such that

$$x(t) = x(\tau)$$

holds true. Such a pair is said to be *admissible*.

PROPOSITION 20. *The pair* (t, τ) *is admissible if and only if*

$$t + \tau = 2\alpha \text{ and } t - \alpha \in M.$$

If (t, τ) *is admissible, then* $x(t)$ *is on* $l(\alpha)$.

Proof.   Let t, τ be admissible. Then

$$(t - \alpha)\cos t - \sin t = (\tau - \alpha)\cos \tau - \sin \tau \qquad (38)$$
$$(t - \alpha)\sin t + \cos t = (\tau - \alpha)\sin \tau + \cos \tau \qquad (39)$$

holds true. Multiplying the first equation with $-\sin \tau$, the second with $\cos \tau$, and adding leads to

$$(t - \alpha)\sin (t - \tau) + \cos (t - \tau) = 1.$$

Similarly,

$$(\tau - \alpha)\sin (\tau - t) + \cos (\tau - t) = 1.$$

Hence

$$(t + \tau - 2\alpha) \cdot \sin(t - \tau) = 0. \qquad (40)$$

Assume that $\sin(t - \tau) = 0$, i.e.

$$t - \tau = 2r\pi, \ r \in \mathbb{Z},$$

taking $\cos(t - \tau) = 1$ into account. This, together with (38) and (39), leads to

$$2r\pi \cdot \cos \tau = 0 = 2r\pi \cdot \sin \tau,$$

i.e. to $r = 0$, i.e. to $t = \tau$. Equation (40) hence implies

$$t + \tau = 2\alpha. \qquad (41)$$

Multiplying equation (38) with $\cos \alpha$, equation (39) with $\sin \alpha$, and adding yields

$$(t - \alpha)\cos (t - \alpha) - \sin (t - \alpha) = (\tau - \alpha)\cos (\tau - \alpha) - \sin (\tau - \alpha),$$

i.e.

$$(t - \alpha)\cos(t - \alpha) = \sin(t - \alpha),$$

taking (41) into consideration. Here $\cos (t - \alpha) \neq 0$, because otherwise $\sin (t - \alpha) = 0$, which is a contradiction. Hence

$$t - \alpha \in M. \qquad (42)$$

Assume now that (41), (42) hold true. Then $t \neq \tau$ because otherwise $t = \tau = \alpha$ and hence $0 \in M$. We now have to show that equations (38), (39) hold true. Put

$$t = \alpha - (\alpha - t),$$
$$\tau = \alpha + (\alpha - t).$$

Then with $r := \alpha - t$ we have

$$
\begin{aligned}
(t - \alpha)\cos t - \sin t &= -r[\cos\alpha\cos r + \sin\alpha\sin r] \\
&\quad -[\sin\alpha\cos r - \cos\alpha\sin r] \\
&= -\sin\alpha \cdot [r\sin r + \cos r]
\end{aligned}
$$

by observing $r \in M$. Similarly,

$$
\begin{aligned}
(\tau - \alpha)\cos\tau - \sin\tau &= r[\cos\alpha\cos r - \sin\alpha\sin r] \\
&\quad -[\sin\alpha\cos r + \cos\alpha\sin r] \\
&= -\sin\alpha \cdot [r\sin r + \cos r].
\end{aligned}
$$

Hence (38) holds true. Equation (39) also follows this way. We finally observe that

$$x_1(t)\cos\alpha + x_2(t)\sin\alpha = k \cdot \Big[(t-\alpha)\cos(t-\alpha) - \sin(t-\alpha)\Big].$$

The right hand side is 0 whenever (42) holds true. Hence $x(t)$ is on $l(\alpha)$. □

REMARK. The following statement is also easy to prove: Take $t \neq \alpha$ in $\mathbb{R}$ and put $\tau := 2\alpha - t$. Then

$$
\begin{aligned}
\frac{x(t) + x(\tau)}{2} &= k\big((t-\alpha)\sin(t-\alpha) + \cos(t-\alpha)\big)(-\sin\alpha, \cos\alpha), \\
x(t) - x(\tau) &= 2k\big((t-\alpha)\cos(t-\alpha) - \sin(t-\alpha)\big)(\cos\alpha, \sin\alpha)
\end{aligned}
$$

hold true. This means that the midpoint of $x(t), x(\tau)$ is on $l(\alpha)$ and that $x(t) - x(\tau)$ is orthogonal to $l(\alpha)$.

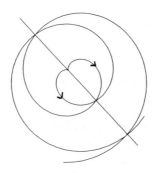

REMARK. If x is in M then so is $-x$. So it is sufficient to look only at the positive elements of M. The smallest is

$$\zeta_1 = 4,493\,409\,457\,909\,064\ldots.$$

For the other positive elements of $M, \zeta_1 < \zeta_2 < \zeta_3 < \ldots$, we have $\zeta_\nu \in]\nu\pi, \frac{\pi}{2} + \nu\pi[$, $\nu = 1, 2, \ldots$. All admissible pairs (t, τ) with $t > \alpha$ are given by $(\alpha + \zeta_\nu, \alpha - \zeta_\nu)$, $\nu = 1, 2, \ldots$, according to (42) and (41).

REMARK. The set of motions

$$\xi(x_1, x_2, x_3) \quad := \quad (x_1, x_2, -x_3),$$

$$\eta(x_1, x_2, x_3) \quad := \quad (x_1, -x_2, x_3),$$

$$\tau_a(x_1, x_2, x_3) \quad := \quad (x_1, x_2, x_3 + a), \ a \in \mathbb{R},$$

$$\theta_a(x_1, x_2, x_3) \quad := \quad (x_1 \cos a - x_2 \sin a, x_1 \sin a + x_2 \cos a, x_3), \ a \in \mathbb{R},$$

generates the group of motions of C^2. It is easy to figure out that all these mappings have simple representations in our model. These representations are Laguerre transformations (see GT, chapter 4).

REMARK. The expression $(\arccos xy)^2 - (x_3 - y_3)^2$ can also be easily represented in the model (note that $\omega := \arccos xy \in [0, \pi]$) as a picture shows.

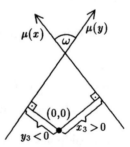

EXERCISES

1. Determine all mappings

$$f(x) = (x_1 \ldots x_{n+1}) Q + (a_1 \ldots a_{n+1})$$

of $\mathbb{R}^{n+1}$ into itself with $f(C^n) \subseteq C^n$ where Q is an orthogonal and real $(n + 1, n + 1)$–matrix and where $a_1, \ldots, a_{n+1}$ are real numbers.

2. Determine all 3–point–invariants of (C^2, M^2).

3. Determine all 2–line–invariants of (C^2, M^2).

4. Determine all bijections of C^2 such that images and pre–images of lines are lines.

5. Let l be a line of (C^n, M^n). Determine all $f \in M^n$ with $f(l) = l$ and determine all $g \in M^n$ with $g(p) = p$ for all points p of l.

6. Let V be an m–dimensional subspace of the vector space $\mathbb{R}^n$ with $m \geq 2$. Put

$$C(V) := \{(x_1, \ldots, x_{n+1}) \in \mathbb{R}^{n+1} \mid (x_1, \ldots, x_n) \in V \text{ and } x_1^2 + \ldots + x_n^2 = 1\}.$$

Then $C(V)$ is called an m–dimensional subspace of (C^n, M^n). Let V_1, V_2 be subspaces of the vector space $\mathbb{R}^n$. Show that there exists a motion $f \in M^n$ with $f(C(V_1)) = C(V_2)$ iff dim $V_1 = $ dim V_2.

Chapter 4

DE SITTER'S WORLD

4.1   De Sitter's world as a substructure

Let (S, G) be a geometry and let $S_0 \neq \emptyset$ be a subset of S such that $g \in G$ and $g(s) = s$ for all $s \in S_0$ imply $g = \text{id}$. Put

$$G_0 := \{g \in G \mid g(S_0) = S_0\}. \tag{1}$$

Then (S_0, G_0) is a *substructure* of (S, G) (see section 1.3). The $(n + 1)$–dimensional Lorentz–Minkowski geometry is defined to be the geometry of the structure $(\mathbb{R}^{n+1}, \mathcal{L}^{n+1})$, where $\mathcal{L}^{n+1}$ denotes the Lorentz group of $\mathbb{R}^{n+1}$, i.e. the group of all mappings (Lorentz transformations)

$$(x_1 \ldots x_{n+1}) \rightarrow xL + a \tag{2}$$

with real matrices $a = (a_1 \ldots a_{n+1})$,

$$L = \begin{pmatrix} l_{11} & \cdots & l_{1,n+1} \\ \vdots & & \\ l_{n+1,1} & \cdots & l_{n+1,n+1} \end{pmatrix}$$

such that

$$LML^T = M := \begin{pmatrix} 1 & & & 0 \\ & \ddots & & \\ & & 1 & \\ 0 & & & -1 \end{pmatrix}. \tag{3}$$

Einstein's cylinder universe was defined to be the substructure $\left(C^n, (\mathcal{L}^{n+1})_0\right)$ of $(\mathbb{R}^{n+1}, \mathcal{L}^{n+1})$. De Sitter's n–dimensional geometry is defined to be the sub-structure

$$\left(S^n, (\mathcal{L}^{n+1})_0\right) \tag{4}$$

of $\left(\mathbb{R}^{n+1}, (\mathcal{L}^{n+1})_0\right)$, where

$$S^n := \{x \in \mathbb{R}^{n+1} \mid x_1^2 + \ldots + x_n^2 - x_{n+1}^2 = 1\}.$$

The elements of the group $(\mathcal{L}^{n+1})_0$ in (4) will be called *motions* of de Sitter's geometry. Instead of de Sitter's geometry also the name *de Sitter's world* is in use. The set of all motions of S^n will be denoted by Δ^n. The elements of S^n are called the *points* of de Sitter's world.

4.2   The group of motions

Let

$$f(x) = xL + a \tag{5}$$

be an element of $\mathcal{L}^{n+1}$ such that

$$f(S^n) = S^n.$$

Observe that (3) implies

$$xMx^T = 1 \Leftrightarrow (xL)M(xL)^T = 1.$$

The mapping $g(x) = xL$ thus preserves S^n. Assume that the mapping $h(x) = x + a$ preserves S^n. This implies that

$$aMx^T = 0$$

for all $x \in \mathbb{R}^{n+1}$ and thus $aM = 0$, i.e. $a = 0$. Assume finally that

$$x \to xL + a$$

preserves S^n. Then

$$x \to (xL + a)L^{-1} = x + aL^{-1}$$

also leaves S^n invariant. This implies that $aL^{-1} = 0$, i.e. $a = 0$. In this connection observe that (3) yields that

$$\det L \in \{+1, -1\}, \tag{6}$$
$$L^{-1} = ML^T M, \tag{7}$$
$$L^T ML = M, \tag{8}$$
$$L^{-1}M(L^{-1})^T = M : \tag{9}$$

In fact, (3) implies

$$(\det L)^2 \cdot \det M = \det M$$

and hence implies (6). In view of (3), we also have

$$L^{-1} \cdot (LML^T) = L^{-1} \cdot M$$

and thus (7) holds. From equation (7) we get

$$M \cdot L^{-1} \cdot L = M \cdot ML^T M \cdot L,$$

i.e. (8). Equation (7) leads to $(L^{-1})^T = MLM$. Hence

$$L^{-1}M(L^{-1})^T = ML^T M \cdot M \cdot MLM = M$$

because of (8). Calling matrices L which satisfy (3) Lorentz matrices again (see section 2.6), L^T and L^{-1} must also be Lorentz matrices provided that L is such a matrix.

The group Δ^n is thus the group of all elements of $\mathcal{L}^{n+1}$ which preserve the origin 0, i.e. Δ^n is the group of all mappings (5) with $a = 0$, i.e. the group of all Lorentz matrices of $n + 1$ rows and $n + 1$ columns.

4.3 Lines

We first look to the 2–dimensional case S^2. Let Π be the set of all planes of $\mathbb{R}^3$ passing through the origin 0. Let $\pi \in \Pi$ be such a plane, say the plane with equation

$$a_1 x_1 + a_2 x_2 + a_3 x_3 = 0 \tag{10}$$

with $(a_1, a_2, a_3) \neq (0, 0, 0)$. We are interested in the intersection $\pi \cap S^2$. In the case $a_1 = a_2 = 0$, $a_3 = 1$ we get the euclidean circle

$$x_1^2 + x_2^2 = 1 \text{ and } x_3 = 0 \tag{11}$$

as this intersection. In the case $a_3 = 0$ in (10) we get hyperbolas for $\pi \cap S^2$. The remaining cases (10) can be written in the form

$$x_3 = a_1 x_1 + a_2 x_2 \tag{12}$$

with $(a_1, a_2) \neq (0,0)$. Take real numbers $r > 0$ and $\alpha \in [0, 2\pi[$ with

$$a_1 = r \cos \alpha, \ a_2 = r \sin \alpha$$

and let ϱ be the rotation

$$(x_1 x_2 x_3) = (y_1 y_2 y_3) \begin{pmatrix} \sin \alpha & -\cos \alpha & 0 \\ \cos \alpha & \sin \alpha & 0 \\ 0 & 0 & 1 \end{pmatrix}$$

with the x_3–axis as axis. Obviously, $\varrho(S^2) = S^2$, and equation (12) goes over into

$$y_3 = ry_2 \tag{13}$$

with $r > 0$ and $r^2 = a_1^2 + a_2^2$. The intersection $\pi \cap S^2$ is now given by

$$\{(y_1, y_2, ry_2) \in \mathbb{R}^3 \,|\, y_1^2 + (1 - r^2)y_2^2 = 1\}.$$

In the case $r = 1$ we get the two lines

$$(1, 0, 0) \quad + \quad \mathbb{R}(0, 1, 1),$$
$$(-1, 0, 0) \quad + \quad \mathbb{R}(0, 1, 1).$$

For $0 < r < 1$ we will represent $\pi \cap S^2$ in coordinates y_1, z_2, where

$$y_1(1, 0, 0) + z_2 \frac{1}{\sqrt{1 + r^2}} \cdot (0, 1, r) \tag{14}$$

are the points of π. We get the ellipse

$$y_1^2 + \frac{z_2^2}{b^2} = 1 \tag{15}$$

with $b > 0$ and $b^2 \cdot (1 - r^2) = 1 + r^2$. With the same coordinates, $\pi \cap S^2$ is the hyperbola

$$y_1^2 - \frac{z_2^2}{c^2} = 1 \tag{16}$$

such that $c > 0$ and $c^2 \cdot (r^2 - 1) = r^2 + 1$ if $r > 1$. We shall now define the *lines* of de Sitter's plane S^2. The ellipses (especially the circle) we obtained are *lines*, moreover every euclidean line on S^2 and finally every branch of a hyperbola $\pi \cap S^2$ are de Sitter lines.

The group Δ^2 of S^2 consists of linear mappings only. Therefore, the image of a plane π through 0 under a $\delta \in \Delta^2$ is again such a plane. As a consequence S^2–lines are mapped onto S^2–lines under transformations in Δ^2.

We now would like to consider the general case of a dimension $n \geq 2$. Let $a, b \in S^n$ be points with

$$a \neq b \neq -a \tag{17}$$

and let π be the set of points

$$\pi = \{\xi a + \eta b \,|\, \xi, \eta \in \mathbb{R}\}. \tag{18}$$

Then every ellipse, every euclidean line, every branch of a hyperbola in $\pi \cap S^n$ is called a *line of S^n* or a S^n–*line*.

Points $a, b \in S^n$ satisfying (17) are said to be *separated*. Such a pair must be linearly independent. Otherwise an equation

$$\alpha a = \beta b$$

holds true with $\alpha, \beta \in \mathbb{R}$ and $(\alpha, \beta) \neq (0, 0)$. But this implies that

$$\alpha^2 = (\alpha a)^2 = (\beta b)^2 = \beta^2, \tag{19}$$

i.e. $a = b$ or $a = -b$, contradicting (17). In (19) we made use of the scalar product

$$x \cdot y = x_1 y_1 + \ldots + x_n y_n - x_{n+1} y_{n+1} \tag{20}$$

for $x = (x_1, \ldots, x_{n+1})$, $y = (y_1, \ldots, y_{n+1})$. Let A be an orthogonal matrix of $\mathbb{R}^n$ with

$$(p_1 0\, 0 \ldots 0) := (a_1 \ldots a_n)A,$$
$$(q_1\, q_2\, 0 \ldots 0) := (b_1 \ldots b_n)A$$

for separated points $a, b \in S^n$. The points

$$a' := (p_1, 0, \ldots, 0, a_{n+1}), \ b' := (q_1, q_2, 0, \ldots, 0, b_{n+1})$$

are then on S^n and they are linearly independent because

$$a' = aB \text{ and } b' = bB$$

with

$$B := \left(\begin{array}{c|c} A & \begin{array}{c} 0 \\ \vdots \\ 0 \end{array} \\ \hline 0 \ \ldots \ 0 & 1 \end{array} \right). \tag{21}$$

B is orthogonal and also a Lorentz matrix. In order to classify intersections $\pi \cap S^n$ it is thus sufficient to assume that

$$a_2 = a_3 \;\; = \ldots = a_n = 0,$$
$$b_3 \;\; = \ldots = b_n = 0$$

in (18) for points $a, b \in S^n$ satisfying (17). We are thus looking for all points

$$(\xi a_1 + \eta b_1, \eta b_2, 0, \ldots, 0, \xi a_{n+1} + \eta b_{n+1})$$

which are in S^n, i.e. which satisfy

$$x_1^2 + x_2^2 - x_{n+1}^2 = 1. \tag{22}$$

But this is exactly the situation we already discussed at the beginning of this section. So we know that $\pi \cap S^n$ is an ellipse, a pair of euclidean lines or a hyperbola.

REMARK. Obviously, separated points a, b are transformed in separated points under mappings $\delta \in \Delta^n$.

4.4   Transitivity properties

Those lines of S^n which are also euclidean lines are called *null–lines*. We will say that the line l of S^n is *closed* if it is an ellipse. The remaining lines, namely branches of hyperbolas, are called the *open lines* of S^n. Suppose that δ is an element of Δ^n and that π is a plane (18) such that (17) holds true. Since δ is also a linear transformation of $\mathbb{R}^{n+1}$, $\delta(\pi)$ is again of the form (18) such that $\delta(a), \delta(b)$ are separated. Moreover,

$$\delta(\pi \cap S^n) = \delta(\pi) \cap S^n.$$

δ, as an affine mapping of $\mathbb{R}^{n+1}$, thus permutes the set L_0 of null–lines and it is also a permutation of the set L_c of closed lines. Assume that $\pi \cap S^n$ is a hyperbola. This is an unbounded point set. Hence $\delta(\pi \cap S^n)$ is also unbounded and is thus again a hyperbola. Since δ is continuous, branches of hyperbolas $\pi \cap S^n$ must be mapped onto branches.

THEOREM 1. *The elements of* Δ^n, $n \geq 2$, *map open lines onto open lines, null–lines onto null–lines, closed lines onto closed lines. Moreover* Δ^n *operates transitively on* L_0, *on* L_c, *and on the set* L_∞ *of open lines.*

Proof. If l is an S^n–line, then there exists a mapping δ of form (21) such that $\delta(l)$ is on the surface of equation (22). Observe again that mappings (21) are at the same time orthogonal and Lorentz transformations. In order to prove the transitivity statement of our present theorem, it is therefore sufficient to prove it only in case S^2. But there it is sufficient, in view of section 4.3, to look only at the curves

$$\{(x_1, x_2, rx_2) \in \mathbb{R}^3 \mid x_1^2 + (1 - r^2)x_2^2 = 1\} \tag{23}$$

with $r \geq 0$, and at the curves

$$\{(x_1, x_2, x_3) \in \mathbb{R}^3 \mid x_1^2 + x_2^2 - x_3^2 = 1 \text{ and } a_1x_1 + a_2x_2 = 0\} \tag{24}$$

with $(a_1, a_2) \neq (0,0)$. It remains to prove:

(A) Δ^2 is transitive on the set of curves (23) satisfying $0 \leq r < 1$,

(B) Δ^2 is transitive on the set of the two lines (23) with $r = 1$,

(C) Δ^2 is transitive on the set of all branches of hyperbolas of equation (24) or of equation (23) with $r > 1$.

The Lorentz transformation $(x_1, x_2, x_3) \to (-x_1, x_2, x_3)$ interchanges the two lines (23) with $r = 1$. This proves (B).

Suppose that $r \in [0, 1[$ and that δ_r is the Lorentz transformation

$$\delta_r : x \to x \cdot \begin{pmatrix} 1 & 0 & 0 \\ 0 & R & rR \\ 0 & rR & R \end{pmatrix}$$

with $R > 0$ and $R^2 \cdot (1 - r^2) = 1$. The image of the circle (11) under δ_r is then (23) with that given r. Let $C(r_1), C(r_2)$ be curves (23) with $0 \leq r_1, r_2 < 1$. Then obviously

$$C(r_2) = \delta_{r_2} \cdot \delta_{r_1}^{-1} C(r_1). \tag{25}$$

This proves (A).

Every branch of a hyperbola with equation (24) can be mapped onto any other branch of a hyperbola with equation (24) by means of a rotation with x_3–axis as axis. Since those rotations are Lorentz transformations, it is sufficient for the proof of (C) to replace all branches of hyperbolas (24) by only one branch, say by

$$\{(\cosh t, 0, \sinh t) \in \mathbb{R}^3 \mid t \in \mathbb{R}\}. \tag{26}$$

The two branches of the hyperbola (23), $r > 1$, can be interchanged by the Lorentz transformation

$$(x_1, x_2, x_3) \rightarrow (-x_1, x_2, x_3).$$

Now, putting $R > 0$ and $R^2 \cdot (r^2 - 1) = 1$ for $r > 1$, we define the Lorentz transformation

$$\sigma_r : x \rightarrow x \cdot \begin{pmatrix} 1 & 0 & 0 \\ 0 & rR & R \\ 0 & R & rR \end{pmatrix}.$$

The image of (26) under σ_r is then the branch

$$\{(\cosh t, R \sinh t, rR \sinh t) \in \mathbb{R}^3 \,|\, t \in \mathbb{R}\}$$

of (23). This together with a formula corresponding to (25) proves (C).   □

The pseudo–euclidean scalar product plays an important role in this chapter

$$xy := x \cdot y := x_1 \, y_1 + \ldots + x_n \, y_n - x_{n+1} \, y_{n+1} \qquad (27)$$

for elements

$$x = (x_1, \ldots, x_{n+1}) \text{ and } y = (y_1, \ldots, y_{n+1})$$

of $\mathbb{R}^{n+1}$. Identifying x also with the matrix $(x_1 \ldots x_{n+1})$, we get

$$x \cdot y = x M y^T$$

and hence

$$(xL) \cdot M \cdot (yL)^T = x M y^T = x \cdot y$$

in view of (3). The mapping

$$s : S^n \times S^n \rightarrow \mathbb{R}$$

with $s(x, y) := xy$ is thus a 2–point–invariant of (S^n, Δ^n).

PROPOSITION 2. *The group Δ^n operates transitively on S^n. — Let a, b and c, d be pairs of separated points. There exists an element $\delta \in \Delta^n$ such that*

$$\delta(a) = c \text{ and } \delta(b) = d$$

if and only if $a \cdot b = c \cdot d$.

Proof.   Let $a = (a_1, \ldots, a_{n+1})$ be a point of S^n. With a suitable Lorentz matrix (21), B, we get

$$(p_1 \, 0 \ldots 0 \, a_{n+1}) = aB.$$

Furthermore, multiplying this equation on the right with the Lorentz matrix $C = (c_{ij})$,

$$
\begin{aligned}
c_{11} &= c_{n+1,n+1} &:= p_1 \\
c_{1,n+1} &= c_{n+1,1} &:= -a_{n+1} \\
c_{ij} &= \delta_{ij} \text{ otherwise,}
\end{aligned}
$$

we get

$$(1\,0\ldots0) = aL$$

with $L := BC$. The group Δ^n hence operates transitively on S^n. Now let a, b and c, d be pairs of separated points. If $\delta \in \Delta^n$ exists with $\delta(a) = c$ and $\delta(b) = d$, then $ab = cd$ holds true since xy is a 2–point–invariant of Δ^n. Assume vice versa that $ab = cd$. We have to show that there exists a $\delta \in \Delta^n$ with $\delta(a) = c$ and $\delta(b) = d$. If we can prove this in the special case $a = (1, 0, \ldots, 0) = c$, then the general case is also established: In fact, put $N := (1, 0, \ldots, 0)$. Take $\delta_1, \delta_2 \in \Delta^n$ with $\delta_1(a) = N$ and $\delta_2(c) = N$. Then

$$\delta_1(a) \cdot \delta_1(b) = ab = cd = \delta_2(c) \cdot \delta_2(d).$$

If there now exists $\delta \in \Delta^n$ with

$$\delta\delta_1(a) = \delta(c) \text{ and } \delta\delta_1(b) = \delta_2(d),$$

then

$$\delta_2^{-1}\delta\delta_1(a) = c \text{ and } \delta_2^{-1}\delta\delta_1(b) = d.$$

In the special case $a = N = c$ our assumption $ab = cd$ is just $b_1 = d_1$. This implies

$$b_2^2 + \ldots + b_n^2 - b_{n+1}^2 = d_2^2 + \ldots + d_n^2 - d_{n+1}^2$$

since $b, d \in S^n$, i.e. $b^2 = 1 = d^2$. Hence there exists a Lorentz matrix L of $\mathbb{R}^n$ (notice $n \geq 2$) such that

$$(d_2 \ldots d_{n+1}) = (b_2 \ldots b_{n+1})L$$

in view of the following Lemma 3; b, N separated and $b^2 = 1$ imply that $(b_2, \ldots, b_{n+1}) \neq 0$. Similarly, $(d_2, \ldots, d_{n+1}) \neq 0$. Put

$$
\hat{L} := \begin{pmatrix} 1 & 0 & \cdots & 0 \\ 0 & & & \\ \vdots & & L & \\ 0 & & & \end{pmatrix}.
$$

Then $N\hat{L} = N$ and $d = b\hat{L}$. $\qquad\qquad\square$

LEMMA 3. *Let $p \neq 0$ and $q \neq 0$ be elements of $\mathbb{R}^n$, $n \geq 2$, such that*

$$P := p_1^2 + \ldots + p_{n-1}^2 - p_n^2 = q_1^2 + \ldots + q_{n-1}^2 - q_n^2 =: Q.$$

Then there exists a Lorentz matrix L of $\mathbb{R}^n$ with $q = pL$.

Proof.   Case $n = 2$: For $P \neq 0$ define

$$Pa := p_1 q_1 - p_2 q_2 \text{ and } Pb := p_1 q_2 - p_2 q_1.$$

Then $P^2 \cdot (a^2 - b^2) = P \cdot (q_1^2 - q_2^2)$, i.e. $a^2 - b^2 = 1$. Hence

$$L = \begin{pmatrix} a & b \\ b & a \end{pmatrix}$$

is a Lorentz matrix with $q = pL$. — For $P = 0$ we have

$$p = (p_1, \alpha p_1) \text{ and } q = (q_1, \beta q_1)$$

with $\alpha^2 = 1 = \beta^2$. Take $t \in \mathbb{R}$ such that

$$\gamma \cdot q_1 = p_1 \cdot (\cosh t + \alpha \sinh t)$$

with $\gamma := sgn \dfrac{p_1}{q_1}$. Then

$$q = p \cdot \begin{pmatrix} \gamma \cosh t & \alpha \beta \gamma \sinh t \\ \gamma \sinh t & \alpha \beta \gamma \cosh t \end{pmatrix}.$$

Case $n > 2$: Take orthogonal matrices A_1, A_2 of $\mathbb{R}^{n-1}$ such that

$$\begin{aligned}
(r_1 0 \dots 0) &= (p_1 \dots p_{n-1}) A_1, \\
(s_1 0 \dots 0) &= (q_1 \dots q_{n-1}) A_2.
\end{aligned}$$

Then

$$B_i := \left(\begin{array}{c|c} \begin{array}{c} A_i \end{array} & \begin{array}{c} 0 \\ \vdots \\ 0 \end{array} \\ \hline 0 \ \ \dots \ \ 0 & 1 \end{array} \right), \quad i = 1, 2,$$

are Lorentz matrices of $\mathbb{R}^n$ with

$$\begin{aligned}
(r_1 0 \dots 0\, p_n) &= p B_1, \\
(s_1 0 \dots 0\, q_n) &= q B_2
\end{aligned}$$

and

$$r_1^2 - p_n^2 = P = Q = s_1^2 - q_n^2.$$

In view of the discussion of case $n = 2$, then, there exists a Lorentz matrix L of $\mathbb{R}^n$ with

$$l_{ij} = \delta_{ij} \text{ for } ij \notin \{11, 1n, n1, nn\}$$

and

$$(s_1 \, 0 \ldots 0 \, q_n) = (r_1 \, 0 \ldots 0 \, p_n)L.$$

Thus

$$q = p \cdot B_1 L B_2^{-1}. \qquad \square$$

REMARK. There exist points $a \neq b$ and $c \neq d$ on S^n with $a \cdot b = c \cdot d$ and such that there is no $\delta \in \Delta^n$ with $\delta(a) = c$ and $\delta(b) = d$: Put $a = -b = c = (1, 0, \ldots, 0)$ and $d = (-1, 1, 0, \ldots, 0, 1)$. If there existed a Lorentz matrix L of $\mathbb{R}^{n+1}$ with

$$aL = c \text{ and } bL = d$$

we would get the contradiction

$$d = bL = -aL = -c.$$

The points c, d of our example are separated, but not the points a, b. Therefore Proposition 2 does not apply to this example.

4.5 Pairs of points on lines

PROPOSITION 4. *Let a, b be distinct points of S^n on a line l of S^n. If l is closed, then*

$$-1 \leq a \cdot b < 1.$$

In this case $a \cdot b = -1$ is equivalent to $b = -a$. If l is a null–line, then $a \cdot b = 1$. Finally, if l is open, then $a \cdot b > 1$.

Proof.   Since Δ^n operates transitively on each of the sets L_c, L_0, L_∞, and since Δ^n preserves the scalar product (27), and finally since $\delta(-a) = -\delta(a)$ holds true for all $\delta \in \Delta^n$, we may assume that l is one of the following lines

$$\{(\cos t, \sin t, 0, \ldots, 0) \in S^n \mid 0 \leq t < 2\pi\}, \tag{28}$$

$$\{(1, t, 0, \ldots, 0, t) \in S^n \mid t \in \mathbb{R}\}, \tag{29}$$

$$\{(\cosh t, 0, \ldots, 0, \sinh t) \in S^n \mid t \in \mathbb{R}\}. \tag{30}$$

If a, b belong to t and τ for the line (28), then

$$a \cdot b = \cos(t - \tau) \in [-1, 1[. \tag{31}$$

Obviously, $a \cdot b = \cos(t - \tau) = -1$ iff $b = -a$. For points a, b on (29) we get $a \cdot b = 1$. For the line (30) we finally have

$$a \cdot b = \cosh(t - \tau) > 1$$

since $t \neq \tau$.

As a consequence of Proposition 4 we mention that there is no line through $a, b \in S^n$ if $a \cdot b < -1$. An example of such points is given by

$$a = \left(\frac{5}{4}, 0, \ldots, 0, \frac{3}{4}\right) \text{ and } (1, 4, 0, \ldots, 0, 4).$$

REMARK. It follows from Proposition 4 that if $a \neq b$ are points on a line l with $ab = -1$ that then $b = -a$ holds true. In fact, l must be closed since otherwise $ab \geq 1$. If we drop the assumption that the points $a \neq b$ of S^n are on a line l, then $a \cdot b = -1$ does not necessarily imply $b = -a$. As an example, consider

$$a = (1, 0, \ldots, 0) \text{ and } b = (-1, 4, 0, \ldots, 0, 4).$$

The question we now would like to pose is the following: Suppose that $a \neq b$ are points of S^n. Is there a line joining a and b, and if so, how many? The answer is given by

THEOREM 5. *Let $a \neq b$ be points of S^n, $n \geq 2$. There is no line joining a, b when $a \cdot b < -1$. There is exactly one line through a, b if $a \cdot b > -1$ holds true. Assume finally that $a \cdot b = -1$. Then there is no line joining a, b if $b \neq -a$ and there are infinitely many lines through a, b if $b = -a$ holds true.*

Proof.   We already mentioned as a consequence of Proposition 4 that there is no line through a, b if $a \cdot b < -1$. Assume that $a \cdot b > -1$. The points a, b are then separated since $a \neq b$. If there exists a line $l \ni a, b$, say $l \subseteq \pi \cap S^n$, then $a, b \in \pi$ and π must have the form (18). Even if we do not know whether there is a line $l \ni a, b$ we may define π with the points a, b by (18). The conclusion is then that there is exactly one line through a, b, provided we can show that $\{a, b\}$ does not meet both euclidean lines or both branches of $\pi \cap S^n$ when $\pi \cap S^n$ is not a closed line. Without loss of generality we may assume that (29) or (30) are in $\pi \cap S^n$. Since the elements of (29) with $t = 0$ and $t = 1$ are linearly independent, π is uniquely determined. Hence, we may take

$$a = (1, t, 0, \ldots, 0, t) \text{ and } b = (-1, s, 0, \ldots, 0, s).$$

But here $a \cdot b = -1$ which contradicts $ab > -1$. Similarly,

$$a = (\cosh t, 0, \ldots, 0, \sinh t) \text{ and } b = (-\cosh s, 0, \ldots, 0, \sinh s).$$

Here also $a \cdot b = -\cosh(t + s) \leq -1$ is a contradiction, since $ab > -1$. We shall finally consider the case $ab = -1$. If there is a line through a, b, Proposition 4 implies that $b = -a$. In this case we assume without loss of generality that $a = (1, 0, \ldots, 0) = -b$. Then all the lines l_r with $0 \leq r < 1$ contain a and b, where we put

$$l_r := \{(x_1, x_2, 0, \ldots, 0, rx_2) \in \mathbb{R}^{n+1} \mid x_1^2 + (1 - r^2)x_2^2 = 1\}.$$

4.6   The functional equation of 2–point-invariants

We would like to solve the following functional equations problem:

Let $W \neq \emptyset$ be a set. Find all functions

$$f : S^n \times S^n \to W \tag{32}$$

such that

$$f(x,y) = f\big(\delta(x), \delta(y)\big) \tag{33}$$

holds true for all $x, y \in S^n$ and all $\delta \in \Delta^n$.

THEOREM 6. *Let $g : \mathbb{R} \to W$ be a function and let w_0, w_1 be fixed elements of W. Then*

$$f(x,y) = \begin{cases} g(x \cdot y) & x, y \text{ separated} \\ w_0 & \text{for} \quad x = y \\ w_1 & x = -y \end{cases} \tag{34}$$

is a solution of (33). If, on the other hand,

$$f : S^n \times S^n \to W$$

solves (33), then there exists a function $g : \mathbb{R} \to W$ and elements $w_0, w_1 \in W$ such that (34) holds true.

Proof.   Obviously, (34) solves (33). Asume now that (32) is a solution of (33). For $k \in \mathbb{R}$, define $g(k)$ as follows: take separated points $x, y \in S^n$ such that $x \cdot y = k$, for instance

$$x = (1, 0, \ldots, 0) \quad \text{and} \quad y = (k, 1, 0, \ldots, 0, k).$$

Then put $g(k) := f(x,y)$. The function g is well–defined. In fact, assume that

$$xy = k = x'y'$$

for points $x, y, x', y' \in S^n$ such that x, y are separated and x', y' are also separated. Then according to Proposition 2 there exists $\delta \in \Delta^n$ with $\delta(x) = x'$ and $\delta(y) = y'$. Hence

$$f(x,y) = f(x',y')$$

in view of (33). Thus

$$f(x,y) = g(k) = g(x \cdot y)$$

holds true for separated points x, y. Since Δ^n is transitive on S^n, (33) yields $f(x,x) = f(y,y)$ for all $x, y \in S^n$. Put $w_0 := f(x,x)$ for all $x \in S^n$. Since $a = -b$ implies $\delta(a) = -\delta(b)$ for all $\delta \in \Delta^n$, we get $f(x,-x) = f(y,-y)$ for all $x, y \in S^n$. Finally, put $w_1 := f(x,-x)$. This proves the theorem.   □

4.7 A functional equation in connection with rings

In section 3.10 we suggested that the notion of Einstein's cylinder universe can be defined over a suitable ring. A similar notion can be introduced in connection with de Sitter's world. What we would like to do in this section is to solve in a more general framework the following functional equations problem:

Determine all mappings $f : S^n \to S^n$ such that

$$x \cdot y = f(x) \cdot f(y)$$

holds true for all $x, y \in S^n$.

Let R be a commutative and associative ring with identity element 1 such that $1+1$ is not a zero–divisor in R. For the integer $n \geq 2$, define R^{n+1} as in the Remark of section 1.3. Put

$$x \cdot y := x_1 y_1 + \ldots + x_n y_n - x_{n+1} y_{n+1}$$

for elements $x = (x_1, \ldots)$, $y = (y_1, \ldots)$ of R^{n+1}. Then $S^n(R)$ is defined as follows:

$$S^n(R) := \{x \in R^{n+1} \,|\, x^2 = 1\}. \tag{35}$$

The functional equations problem we would like to solve is the following:

Find all mappings $f : S^n(R) \to S^n(R)$ such that

$$x \cdot y = f(x) \cdot f(y) \tag{36}$$

holds true for all $x, y \in S^n(R)$.

This problem in the case $R := \mathbb{R}$ is obviously the previously mentioned functional equations problem.

THEOREM 7. *A mapping $f : S^n(R) \to S^n(R)$ which solves (36) for all $x, y \in S^n(R)$ must be bijective, and moreover of the form*

$$f(x) = xL \tag{37}$$

for $x \in S^n(R)$ with

$$LML^T = M := \begin{pmatrix} 1 & & & 0 \\ & \ddots & & \\ & & 1 & \\ 0 & & & -1 \end{pmatrix} \tag{38}$$

for

$$L = \begin{pmatrix} l_{11} & \cdots & l_{1,n+1} \\ \vdots & & \\ l_{n+1,1} & \cdots & l_{n+1,n+1} \end{pmatrix}$$

with $l_{ij} \in R$. — On the other hand, (37) solves (36) if (38) holds true.

Proof.   Define $n+1$ elements of $S^n(R)$:

$$E_i := (\delta_{i1}, \ldots, \delta_{in}, 0), \qquad i = 1, \ldots, n,$$
$$E := (-1, -1, 0, \ldots, 0, 1) \quad.$$

Observe that $E_i E_j = \delta_{ij}$ and

$$E^2 = 1, EE_1 = -1 = EE_2, \ EE_i = 0 \text{ for } i = 3, \ldots, n.$$

Put $A := f(E)$ for a given solution of (36), and also $A_i := f(E_i)$. (36) yields

$$A_i A_j = \delta_{ij}, \ A^2 = 1, \ AA_1 = -1 = AA_2, \ AA_i = 0 \text{ for } i = 3, \ldots, n.$$

Let L be the matrix with successive rows $A_1, A_2, \ldots, A_n, A + A_1 + A_2$. Then

$$LML^T = M \tag{39}$$

holds true. The mapping $h(x) = xL$ is a bijection of R^{n+1} because of (39) and it solves (36) as far as points $x, y \in S^n(R)$ are concerned. Observe that $h(S^n) = S^n$. Let p be the restriction of h on S^n. Then $p^{-1}f$ also solves (36) and, moreover, it fixes all the points $E_1, \ldots, E_n, E$. Suppose that x is a point of $S^n(R)$ and that $y := p^{-1}f(x)$. Then

$$x_i = x E_i = p^{-1}f(x) \cdot p^{-1}f(E_i) = y_i$$

for $i = 1, \ldots, n$ and

$$-x_1 - x_2 + x_{n+1} = xE = yE = -y_1 - y_2 + y_{n+1},$$

i.e. $x_{n+1} = y_{n+1}$. Hence $x = y$ and thus $p^{-1}f = \mathrm{id}$, i.e. $f = p$. $\qquad\square$

4.8   The notion of distance

Let $a \neq b$ be elements of S^n such that $a \cdot b = 1$. Because of Theorem 5, there then exists exactly one line l through a, b. Because of Proposition 4, l must be a null–line. Put $v := b - a$ and observe that

$$v^2 = 0, \ v \neq 0, \ va = 0, \ a^2 = 1. \tag{40}$$

Obviously,

$$l = \{a + t \cdot v \,|\, t \in \mathbb{R}\}. \tag{41}$$

LEMMA 8. *Let a, v be elements of $\mathbb{R}^{n+1}$ satisfying (40). Then (41) is a null–line. Conversely, let l be a null–line of S^n. Then there exist $a, v \in \mathbb{R}^{n+1}$ such that (40) and (41) hold true.*

Proof.   If $a, v \in \mathbb{R}^{n+1}$ satisfy (40), then a and $b := a + v$ are distinct elements of S^n with $a \cdot b = 1$. Hence (41) is a null–line. Let now l be a null–line. Take distinct points $a \neq b$ of l. Because of Proposition 4, $a \cdot b$ must be equal to 1. Hence $v := b - a$ satisfies (40) and l may be represented in the form (41).   □

The group Δ^n operates transitively on L_c and also on L_∞ in view of Theorem 1. So multiplying (28) or (30) with an arbitrary Lorentz matrix L of $\mathbb{R}^{n+1}$, we get the general equation of a line of S^n which is not a null–line. Denote the first two rows of L by a and b, then

$$\{a \cos t + b \sin t \,|\, 0 \leq t < 2\pi\} \tag{42}$$

is the general form of a closed line. Since $a \neq b$ are rows of a Lorentz matrix, unequal to the last row, we have

$$a^2 = 1 = b^2 \text{ and } ab = 0. \tag{43}$$

Since $a, b \in \mathbb{R}^{n+1}$ satisfying (43) can be extended to a Lorentz matrix L (a and b being the first two rows of L), (42) with these a, b must be a closed line of S^n. The general form of an open line comes mutatis mutandis from (30). It is

$$\{a \cosh t + b \sinh t \,|\, t \in \mathbb{R}\} \tag{44}$$

with points $a, b \in \mathbb{R}^{n+1}$ such that

$$a^2 = 1 = -b^2 \text{ and } ab = 0. \tag{45}$$

We now would like *to determine all functions*

$$d : S^n \times S^n \to \mathbb{R}_{\geq 0} \tag{46}$$

which satisfy the following properties

(*i*) *d is a 2–point–invariant of Δ^n,*

(ii) if x, y, z are on a line l of S^n, then

$$d(x, z) = d(x, y) + d(y, z),$$

provided that (x, y, z) is admissible on l.

We say that (x, y, z) is *admissible on a line l of S^n* whenever there exists a representation (41) or (44) with

$$x = a + t_x v, \text{ etc.}$$

or

$$x = a \cosh t_x + b \sinh t_x, \text{ etc.},$$

where $t_x \leq t_y \leq t_z$. For a closed line l we ask for the existence of a representation

$$l = \{a \cos t + b \sin t \mid t \in \mathbb{R}\},$$

$a^2 = 1 = b^2$, $ab = 0$, with

$$t_z - t_x < \pi \text{ and } t_x \leq t_y \leq t_z$$

and $x = a \cos t_x + b \sin t_x$, etc.

PROPOSITION 9 *Suppose that d is a function (46) which satisfies (i) and (ii). Let l be a null-line and let a, b be points on l. Then $d(a, b) = 0$.*

Proof.   If $a = b$, put $x = y = z = a$ in (ii). Then $d(a, b) = 0$. Consider then the case $a \neq b$. Now l can be written in the form

$$l = \{a + t \cdot (b - a) \mid t \in \mathbb{R}\}.$$

Put $x = a$, $y = b$, $z = 2b - a$. Then

$$d(x, z) = d(x, y) + d(y, z) \tag{47}$$

because of (ii). The points x, z are separated and also the points y, z. Observe $y \neq -z$ because $(3b)^2 \neq a^2$. Since furthermore $x \cdot z = 1 = y \cdot z$, there exists $\delta \in \Delta^n$ with $\delta(x) = y$ and $\delta(z) = z$, in view of Proposition 2. Hence

$$d(x, z) = d(\delta(x), \delta(z)) = d(y, z) \tag{48}$$

because of (i). Thus (47), (48) imply

$$d(a, b) = d(x, y) = 0. \square$$

The same argument as we used it for null–lines also leads to $d(a,a) = 0$ for the other lines.

Let d be a solution of (i) and (ii). We are interested in values $d(x,y)$ in the case that x, y are separated. Then there exists a function

$$g : \mathbb{R} \to \mathbb{R}_{\geq 0}$$

with $d(x,y) = g(x \cdot y)$ from (i) and Theorem 6. We define $g(1) = 0$. This covers the case $x = y$ and also the case $x \neq y$ for $x, y \in S^n$ with $xy = 1$. —

Now take the line (44). Then

$$d(x,y) = g\big(\cosh (t_y - t_x)\big)$$

for $x = a \cosh t_x + b \sinh t_x$ etc. Let α, β be non–negative real numbers. Put

$$h(t) := g(\cosh t) \text{ for } t \geq 0.$$

Then

$$d(x,z) = d(x,y) + d(y,z)$$

for $t_x := 0$, $t_y := \alpha$, $t_z := \alpha + \beta$, and hence

$$h(\alpha + \beta) = h(\alpha) + h(\beta).$$

Thus Theorem 5 of chapter 2 implies that $h(t) = kt$ for all $t \geq 0$, where k is a constant ≥ 0. Let x, y be distinct points on the line (44). Two distinct points of (44) are automatically separated. Hence

$$d(x,y) = g(x \cdot y) = g(y \cdot x) = d(y,x).$$

Thus, without loss of generality, assume that

$$x = a \cosh t_x + b \sinh t_x,$$
$$y = a \cosh t_y + b \sinh t_y$$

with $t_x < t_y$. Then,

$$d(x,y) = g\big(\cosh(t_y - t_x)\big) = k \cdot (t_y - t_x),$$

and hence

$$d(x,y) = k \cdot \text{arg } \cosh(xy) \tag{49}$$

with arg $\cosh z \geq 0$ for $z \geq 1$.

One could think that the k in formula (49) depends on the line (44). But this is actually not true, since there exists $\delta \in \Delta^n$ which maps (44) onto any other given open line: let l, l' be the two lines, let $x \neq y$ be points on l, and $\delta(x), \delta(y)$ be points on l'. Then

$$d(x, y) = d\big(\delta(x), \delta(y)\big) = k(l') \text{ arg cosh } \big(\delta(x), \delta(y)\big)$$

and hence $k(l') = k(l)$ from (49).

We thus have obtained the following result:

PROPOSITION 10. *Suppose that d is a function (46) which satisfies (i) and (ii). Then there exists a non–negative real number k such that (49) holds true for all pairs x, y of points on open lines.*

We finally consider the case that x, y are separated points on (42). As in the case before, we also have $d(x, y) = d(y, x)$. So assume that

$$x \quad = \quad a \cos t_x + b \sin t_x, \tag{50}$$

$$y \quad = \quad a \cos t_y + b \sin t_y \tag{51}$$

with $0 \leq t_x < t_y < 2\pi$ and $t_y - t_x < \pi$. Then

$$d(x, y) = g(x \cdot y) = g\big(\cos(t_y - t_x)\big).$$

Put
$$\eta(t) := g(\cos t) \text{ for } 0 \leq t < \pi.$$

Observe that η is a function from $[0, \pi[$ into $\mathbb{R}_{\geq 0}$. Let α, β be non–negative real numbers with $\alpha + \beta < \pi$ and put

$$t_x = 0, \ t_y = \alpha, \ t_z = \alpha + \beta.$$

In view of (ii), we then get

$$\eta(\alpha + \beta) = \eta(\alpha) + \eta(\beta).$$

As in section 2.5 we hence have $\eta(t) = rt$ for all $t \in [0, \pi[$ with a constant $r \geq 0$. This implies that

$$d(x, y) = r \cdot \arccos(xy) \tag{52}$$

with $\arccos z \in [0, \pi[$ for $z \in \,]-1, 1]$.

PROPOSITION 11. *Suppose that d is a function* (46) *which satisfies (i) and (ii). Then there exists a non–negative real number r such that* (52) *holds true for all pairs x, y of points on closed lines satisfying* $y \neq -x$.

Proof.   This is already proved, since $d(x, y) = d(y, x)$ in the case that (50), (51) hold true with $0 \leq t_x < t_y < 2\pi$ and $t_y - t_x < \pi$. We should also mention that, as in the case of open lines, r does not depend on the underlying line, provided it is a closed line. To finish the proof of Proposition 11, we take this argument into account and also the following. Replacing (42) by

$$\{a\cos(t + \alpha) + b\sin(t + \alpha) \,|\, 0 \leq t < 2\pi\}$$

with a fixed real α, we get the closed line

$$\{A\cos t + B\sin t \,|\, 0 \leq t < 2\pi\}$$

since

$$A = a\cos\alpha + b\sin\alpha,$$
$$B = -a\sin\alpha + b\cos\alpha$$

also leads to $A^2 = 1 = B^2$ and $AB = 0$ from (43).   □

The main result on distances in de Sitter's world is now the following

THEOREM 12. *All solutions* $d : S^n \times S^n \to \mathbb{R}_{\geq 0}$ *of functional equations (i), (ii) are given precisely as follows*

$$d(x, y) = \begin{cases} k \cdot \text{arg}\cosh(xy) & for \quad xy > 1 \\ r \cdot \arccos(xy) & for \quad xy \in \,]-1, 1] \\ g(x \cdot y) & for \quad y \neq -x \text{ and } xy \leq -1 \\ s & for \quad y = -x \end{cases}$$

where k, r, s *are non–negative constants, where g is an arbitrary function from* $] - \infty, -1]$ *into* $\mathbb{R}_{\geq 0}$, *and where* arg cosh, arccos *are chosen in* $\mathbb{R}_{\geq 0}$, $[0, \pi[$, *respectively.*

Proof.   That d must be a function as described follows mainly from Propositions 9, 10, 11 and Theorem 6. That, on the other hand, d as written there solves (i) and (ii), is obvious.   □

If one follows the idea that a concept of distance between distinct points x, y requires first of all a uniquely determined connecting line for x, y, one could leave $d(x, y)$ undefined in all cases where $xy \le -1$. So a good notion of distance in de Sitter's geometry is certainly

$$d(x, y) = \begin{cases} \operatorname{arg\,cosh}(xy) & \text{for } xy > 1 \\ \arccos(xy) & \text{for } -1 < xy \le 1. \\ \text{undefined} & \text{otherwise} \end{cases} \qquad (53)$$

4.9 Stabilizers

One gets the $(\nu - 1)$–dimensional subspaces of n–dimensional de Sitter's world, $\nu = 2, \ldots, n + 1$, as branches of intersections of S^n with ν–dimensional affine subspaces of $\mathbb{R}^{n+1}$ which contain the origin. Intersecting S^n with

$$[\mathbb{R}^3] := \{x \in \mathbb{R}^{n+1} \mid x_3 = \ldots = x_n = 0\},$$

we get all points of $[\mathbb{R}^3]$ satisfying

$$x_1^2 + x_2^2 - x_{n+1}^2 = 1.$$

Up to notation, this is of course S^2. We shall call S^2 *de Sitter's plane*. In this section we will study only the structure of S^2. We first of all would like to determine the stabilizer of a given line l of S^2. This is the subgroup $\Delta^2(l)$ of Δ^2 which consists of all $\delta \in \Delta^2$ satisfying $\delta(l) = l$. Since Δ^2 operates transitively on each of the sets L_c, L_0, L_∞ we only need to determine $\Delta^2(l)$ for cases (28), (29), (30). For if l is any other line, say a closed line, and if $l = \delta(l_c)$ with $\delta \in \Delta^2$ where l_c is the line (28), then

$$\Delta^2(l) = \delta \cdot \Delta^2(l_c) \cdot \delta^{-1}. \qquad (54)$$

PROPOSITION 13. *The stabilizer of the null–line* (29) *when* $n = 2$ *is given by*

$$\{L(k, a) \mid k, a \in \mathbb{R} \text{ with } k \ne 0\},$$

where we put

$$L(k, a) := \begin{pmatrix} 1 & a & a \\ -\dfrac{a}{k} & \dfrac{k^2 - a^2 + 1}{2k} & \dfrac{k^2 - a^2 - 1}{2k} \\ \dfrac{a}{k} & \dfrac{k^2 + a^2 - 1}{2k} & \dfrac{k^2 + a^2 + 1}{2k} \end{pmatrix}.$$

REMARK. We already encountered $L(k,a)$ with $k > 0$ almost at the end of section 2.6: there we have to put $n = 2$.

Proof of Proposition 13.   Denote the line (29) by l_0 and the Lorentz transformation
$$x \rightarrow x \cdot L(k,a)$$
by δ. Then $\delta(l_0) = l_0$: obviously,

$$\delta(1,t,t) = (1, a + kt, a + kt).$$

Therefore $\delta(l_0) \subseteq l_0$ and $(1, t', t')$ has the pre–image $(1, r, r)$ with $a + kr := t'$. Assume now that the Lorentz matrix

$$L = \begin{pmatrix} l_{11} & l_{12} & l_{13} \\ l_{21} & l_{22} & l_{23} \\ l_{31} & l_{32} & l_{33} \end{pmatrix}$$

preserves the null–line l_0. Since $(1,0,0)$ has its image in l_0, we get

$$l_{11} = 1 \text{ and } l_{12} = l_{13} =: a. \tag{55}$$

Observe also that the image of $(1,1,1)$ is in l_0:

$$l_{31} = -l_{21} =: b, \tag{56}$$
$$l_{22} + l_{32} = l_{23} + l_{33}. \tag{57}$$

Assume that $b = 0$. Then

$$a = l_{11}l_{12} + l_{21}l_{22} - l_{31}l_{32} = 0$$

and

$$\begin{pmatrix} l_{22} & l_{23} \\ l_{32} & l_{33} \end{pmatrix}$$

is one of the Lorentz matrices a), c) of section 1.4 because of (57). For a) we get

$$L = L(e^\alpha, 0),$$

and for c),

$$L = L(-e^{-\alpha}, 0).$$

Suppose now that $b \neq 0$. This implies that $a \neq 0$, since otherwise

$$-b = l_{11}l_{21} + l_{12}l_{22} - l_{13}l_{23} = 0.$$

Put $kb := a$. Hence $k \neq 0$. Multiplying the first two columns of L leads to

$$k = l_{22} + l_{32}, \tag{58}$$

and the multiplication of the first two rows implies

$$\frac{1}{k} = l_{22} - l_{23}. \tag{59}$$

Multiplying the second column with itself yields

$$a^2 + l_{22}^2 - l_{32}^2 = 1.$$

This equation together with (58) implies

$$2kl_{22} = k^2 - a^2 + 1.$$

From (58) we get l_{32}, from (59), l_{23}, and finally, from (57), l_{33}. $\square$

REMARK. We have

$$L^{-1}(k, a) = L\left(\frac{1}{k}, -\frac{a}{k}\right)$$

and

$$L(k, a) \cdot L(l, b) = L(kl, la + b)$$

for $k, a, l, b \in \mathbb{R}$ with $kl \neq 0$. The stabilizer Δ_0^2 of a null–line of S^2 is therefore isomorphic to the affine group of mappings

$$x \to kx + a$$

of the real line, from (54).

PROPOSITION 14. *The stabilizer of the closed line* (28) *for the case* $n = 2$ *is given by all mappings*

$$x \quad \to \quad \left(\begin{array}{cc|c} & & 0 \\ & A & \\ & & 0 \\ \hline 0 & 0 & \varepsilon \end{array}\right), \tag{60}$$

where A *is an orthogonal matrix of* $\mathbb{R}^2$ *and where* $\varepsilon^2 = 1$. *The stabilizer of the open line* (30) *when* $n = 2$ *is given by all mappings*

$$x \to \begin{pmatrix} l_{11} & 0 & l_{13} \\ 0 & \varepsilon & 0 \\ l_{31} & 0 & l_{33} \end{pmatrix} \tag{61}$$

where

$$A := \begin{pmatrix} l_{11} & l_{13} \\ l_{31} & l_{33} \end{pmatrix}$$

is a Lorentz matrix with $l_{11} \geq 1$ and where $\varepsilon^2 = 1$.

Proof.   Put

$$\xi = \begin{pmatrix} 1 & 0 & 0 \\ 0 & -1 & 0 \\ 0 & 0 & 1 \end{pmatrix}, \; \eta = \begin{pmatrix} 1 & 0 & 0 \\ 0 & 1 & 0 \\ 0 & 0 & -1 \end{pmatrix}$$

and

$$A(\alpha) = \begin{pmatrix} \cos \alpha & \sin \alpha & 0 \\ -\sin \alpha & \cos \alpha & 0 \\ 0 & 0 & 1 \end{pmatrix}$$

for $\alpha \in [0, 2\pi[$. It is obvious what those mappings do with (28) when $n = 2$: the mappings ξ, η are classical reflections, and $A(\alpha)$ is a simple rotation. They all preserve (28). Suppose now that L leaves invariant the closed line (28). Since the image of $(1, 0, 0)$ has 0 as its third coordinate, it follows that $l_{13} = 0$. Also the third coordinate of the image of $(0, 1, 0)$ is 0. This implies that $l_{23} = 0$. Hence

$$l_{13}^2 + l_{23}^2 - l_{33}^2 = -1$$

leads to $l_{33} =: \varepsilon$ with $\varepsilon^2 = 1$. The equation

$$l_{31}^2 + l_{32}^2 - l_{33}^2 = -1$$

then leads to $l_{31} = l_{32} = 0$. — All mappings (61) transform (30) onto itself:

$$(\cosh t, 0, \sinh t) \begin{pmatrix} \cosh \alpha & 0 & \sinh \alpha \\ 0 & \varepsilon & 0 \\ \pm \sinh \alpha & 0 & \pm \cosh \alpha \end{pmatrix}$$

is namely the point $\left(\cosh(\alpha \pm t), 0, \sinh(\alpha \pm t) \right)$. If, on the other hand, L preserves (30), we get $l_{12} = 0$ and $l_{32} = 0$ by considering the images of points with $t = 0$ and $t = 1$. Hence $l_{22}^2 = 1$, i.e. $l_{22} =: \varepsilon$ with $\varepsilon^2 = 1$. Now observe that

$$l_{21}^2 + 1 - l_{23}^2 = 1,$$
$$l_{11}l_{21} - l_{13}l_{23} = 0,$$
$$l_{11}^2 - l_{13}^2 = 1.$$

This implies that $l_{21} = l_{23} = 0$. Since

$$\cosh t \cdot l_{11} + \sinh t \cdot l_{31} \geq 1$$

for all $t \in \mathbb{R}$, we get $l_{11} \geq 1$ for $t = 0$.   □

REMARK. The mappings (60) can be written as

$$(\alpha, i, j) := A(\alpha) \cdot \xi^i \cdot \eta^j \tag{62}$$

with $\alpha \in [0, 2\pi[$ and $i, j \in \{1, 2\}$. Then $\xi A(\beta) = A(-\beta)\xi$ implies

$$(\alpha, i, j) \cdot (\beta, \nu, \mu) = (\alpha + (-1)^i \beta, i + \nu, j + \mu),$$

where we add mod 2π in the first coordinate, and mod 2 in the other components. The mappings (61) can be written

$$[\alpha, i, j] := B(\alpha) \cdot \xi^i \cdot \eta^j \tag{63}$$

with $\alpha \in \mathbb{R}$ and $i, j \in \{1, 2\}$, where

$$B(\alpha) := \begin{pmatrix} \cosh \alpha & 0 & \sinh \alpha \\ 0 & 1 & 0 \\ \sinh \alpha & 0 & \cosh \alpha \end{pmatrix}.$$

Here we have

$$[\alpha, i, j] \cdot [\beta, \nu, \mu] = [\alpha + (-1)^j \beta, i + \nu, j + \mu],$$

where we add in the first coordinate as usual, but add mod 2 in the other components.

REMARK. The groups $\Delta_0^2, \Delta_c^2, \Delta_\infty^2$ are pairwise not isomorphic. Here Δ_c^2 denotes the stabilizer of a closed line which is uniquely determined (in view of (54)) up to isomorphism and which can be defined as group of mappings (62). The situation is similar for Δ_∞^2. There is an element of order 3 in Δ_∞^2, namely $\left(\frac{2\pi}{3}, 2, 2\right)$. Since there is no element of order 3 in Δ_0^2 or in Δ_∞^2, Δ_c^2 cannot be isomorphic to one of the other groups. Also $\Delta_0^2, \Delta_\infty^2$ cannot be isomorphic, since every element of Δ_∞^2 is a product of involutions, but there exists an element of Δ_0^2 which cannot be written as a product of involutions: the element

$$[\alpha, i, j] = [0, 2, 1] \cdot [-\alpha, 2, 1] \cdot [0, i, j]$$

is the product of involutions of Δ_∞^2 and the affine mapping $x \to 2x$ of $\mathbb{R}$ cannot be written as such a product of involutions

$$x \to -x + a,$$

since otherwise an equation of the form

$$\begin{pmatrix} 2 & 0 \\ 0 & 1 \end{pmatrix} = \begin{pmatrix} -1 & a_1 \\ 0 & 1 \end{pmatrix} \cdots \begin{pmatrix} -1 & a_\lambda \\ 0 & 1 \end{pmatrix} =: \begin{pmatrix} (-1)^\lambda & b \\ 0 & 1 \end{pmatrix}$$

would hold true.

4.10   The Minkowski model of de Sitter's plane

We shall define the real Minkowski plane II: *points* are

(1) the elements of $\mathbb{R}^2$,

(2) the lines of $\mathbb{R}^2$ of slope $+1$ or -1,

(3) the symbol ∞.

Circles are defined as sets of points. Every hyperbola of $\mathbb{R}^2$, together with its two asymptotes, is called a *circle* whenever the asymptotes are of type (2). Every line l of $\mathbb{R}^2$, together with ∞, is also called a *circle*, provided that l is not of type (2). The following mapping σ is an injective mapping from S^2 into the set Φ^2 of points of the real Minkowski plane II:

$$\sigma(x_1, x_2, x_3) \quad := \quad \left(\frac{x_2}{1+x_1}, \frac{x_3}{1+x_1} \right) \in \mathbb{R}^2 \tag{64}$$

for $x_1 \neq -1$,

$$\sigma\left(-1, \frac{1}{p-q}, \frac{1}{p-q} \right) \quad := \quad l_+(p,q) \tag{65}$$

for $p \neq q$, and

$$\sigma\left(-1, \frac{1}{p+q}, -\frac{1}{p+q} \right) \quad := \quad l_-(p,q) \tag{66}$$

for $p \neq -q$, where $l_+(p,q)$, $l_-(p,q)$ denote the line of $\mathbb{R}^2$ through (p,q) of slope $+1,-1$, respectively. Finally put $\sigma(-1,0,0) := \infty$.

In fact, suppose that

$$(x_1, x_2, x_3) \text{ and } (y_1, y_2, y_3)$$

are points of S^2 with $x_1 \neq -1 \neq y_1$ and

$$\left(\frac{x_2}{1+x_1}, \frac{x_3}{1+x_1} \right) = \left(\frac{y_2}{1+y_1}, \frac{y_3}{1+y_1} \right). \tag{67}$$

Then

$$\frac{1-x_1}{1+x_1} = \frac{x_2^2 - x_3^2}{(1+x_1)^2} = \frac{y_2^2 - y_3^2}{(1+y_1)^2} = \frac{1-y_1}{1+y_1},$$

i.e. $x_1 = y_1$ and hence $x_2 = y_2$ and $x_3 = y_3$, according to (67). Observe that

$$\eta^2 - \xi^2 \neq 1 \tag{68}$$

when $x_1 \neq -1$ and

$$\xi = \frac{x_2}{1 + x_1}, \quad \eta = \frac{x_3}{1 + x_1}$$

with $(x_1, x_2, x_3) \in S^2$. Hence

$$\sigma^{-1}(\xi, \eta) = \left(\frac{1 - \xi^2 + \eta^2}{1 + \xi^2 - \eta^2}, \frac{2\xi}{1 + \xi^2 - \eta^2}, \frac{2\eta}{1 + \xi^2 - \eta^2} \right) \tag{69}$$

for $(\xi, \eta) \in \mathbb{R}^2$ with $\eta^2 - \xi^2 \neq 1$. — We are now interested in all points $(x_1, x_2, x_3) \in S^2$ with $x_1 = -1$. Those points are given by

$$(-1, \alpha, \alpha) \text{ and } (-1, \alpha, -\alpha)$$

with $\alpha \in \mathbb{R}$. The image of $(-1, 0, 0)$ is ∞ and we have furthermore that

$$\sigma(-1, \alpha, \alpha) = l_+ \left(\frac{1}{\alpha}, 0 \right) \tag{70}$$

$$\sigma(-1, \alpha, -\alpha) = l_- \left(\frac{1}{\alpha}, 0 \right) \tag{71}$$

for $\alpha \neq 0$. Observe that

$$l_+(p, q) = l_+(a, b)$$

implies that $p - q = a - b$ and observe also that the euclidean lines $l_+(0, 0)$ and $l_-(0, 0)$ do not occur as images under the mapping σ. Let ω be the circle which consists of the two points $l_+(0, 0)$, $l_-(0, 0)$ and of all points

$$(\xi, \eta) \text{ with } \eta^2 - \xi^2 = 1.$$

Then σ is a bijective mapping from S^2 onto $\Phi^2 \backslash \omega$. We will call ω the circle at infinity of Π. Every set $l \backslash \omega$ is said to be an *affine circle* of Π iff $l \neq \omega$ is a circle of Π.

Suppose that

$$ax_1 + bx_2 + cx_3 = 0$$

with $(a, b, c) \neq (0, 0, 0)$ is the equation of a plane π of $\mathbb{R}^3$. We would like to determine the image of $\pi \cap S^2$ under σ. On account of (69), we get

$$a(1 - \xi^2 + \eta^2) + 2b\xi + 2c\eta = 0 : \tag{72}$$

this equation gives us all points $(\xi, \eta) \in \mathbb{R}^2 \backslash \omega$ with

$$(\xi, \eta) \in \sigma(\pi \cap S^2).$$

As far as the other points are concerned, the situation is the following:

1. $\infty \in \sigma(\pi \cap S^2) \Leftrightarrow (-1,0,0) \in \pi \Leftrightarrow a = 0$,

2. $l_+\left(\dfrac{1}{\alpha},0\right) \in \sigma(\pi \cap S^2) \Leftrightarrow (-1,\alpha,\alpha) \in \pi \Leftrightarrow \alpha(b+c) = a$ for $\alpha \neq 0$,

3. $l_-\left(\dfrac{1}{\alpha},0\right) \in \sigma(\pi \cap S^2) \Leftrightarrow (-1,\alpha,-\alpha) \in \pi \Leftrightarrow \alpha(b-c) = a$ for $\alpha \neq 0$.

REMARK. The mapping σ has the following background: suppose that $x = (x_1, x_2, x_3)$ is a point of S^2 such that $x_1 \neq -1$. Denote by l_x the euclidean line of $\mathbb{R}^3$ through x and $(-1,0,0)$. The point of intersection of l_x and the plane of equation $x_1 = 0$ is then

$$\left(0, \frac{x_2}{1+x_1}, \frac{x_3}{1+x_1}\right).$$

The mapping σ is thus a so-called stereographic projection as far as the points x of S^2 with $x_1 \neq -1$ are concerned.

All null–lines of S^2 are given by

$$N_-(t) := (\cos t, \sin t, 0) + \mathbb{R}(\sin t, -\cos t, 1),$$
$$N_+(t) := (\cos t, \sin t, 0) + \mathbb{R}(\sin t, -\cos t, -1)$$

with $t \in [0, 2\pi[$.

The images of the null–lines are given by

$$\sigma(N_-(0)) = \{(\xi, -\xi) \mid \xi \in \mathbb{R}\},$$
$$\sigma(N_+(0)) = \{(\xi, \xi) \mid \xi \in \mathbb{R}\},$$
$$\sigma(N_-(\pi)) = \{\infty\} \cup \{l_+(\xi, 0) \mid \xi \in \mathbb{R}\setminus\{0\}\},$$
$$\sigma(N_+(\pi)) = \{\infty\} \cup \{l_-(\xi, 0) \mid \xi \in \mathbb{R}\setminus\{0\}\},$$
$$\sigma(N_-(t)) = \left\{l_-\left(\frac{\sin t}{1+\cos t}, 0\right)\right\} \cup \left\{\left(\xi, -\xi + \frac{\sin t}{1+\cos t}\right) \;\middle|\; \xi \in \mathbb{R}\setminus\{\varphi_t\}\right\},$$
$$\sigma(N_+(t)) = \left\{l_+\left(\frac{\sin t}{1+\cos t}, 0\right)\right\} \cup \left\{\left(\xi, \xi - \frac{\sin t}{1+\cos t}\right) \;\middle|\; \xi \in \mathbb{R}\setminus\{\varphi_t\}\right\}$$

with $t \in]0, 2\pi[\setminus\{\pi\}$ and $\varphi_t = -\frac{\cos t}{\sin t}$.

It might be useful to look a little bit closer at one of the sets $\sigma\big(N_-(t)\big)$ or $\sigma\big(N_+(t)\big)$ in case $t \neq \pi$ and $t \in]0, 2\pi[$. So for instance

$$\sigma\big(N_-(t)\big) = \left\{ l_-\left(\tan\frac{t}{2}, 0\right)\right\} \cup \left\{ \left(\xi, -\xi + \tan\frac{t}{2}\right) \;\middle|\; -\frac{\cos t}{\sin t} \neq \xi \in \mathbb{R}\right\}$$

consists of all points of the euclidean line with equation

$$\xi + \eta = \tan\frac{t}{2} \tag{73}$$

with exception of the intersection point with ω, and it contains the point

$$l_-\left(\tan\frac{t}{2}, 0\right)$$

which as a euclidean line coincides with line (73). *The images of null–lines are therefore easy to describe: they are exactly the so-called generators of* Π, *of course each without the intersection point with* ω. The generators of Π are defined as the following sets of points:

(i) $\{\infty\} \cup \{l_+(\xi, 0) \mid \xi \in \mathbb{R}\}$,

(ii) $\{\infty\} \cup \{l_-(\xi, 0) \mid \xi \in \mathbb{R}\}$,

(iii) $\{l_-(\alpha, 0)\} \cup \{(\xi, -\xi + \alpha) \mid \xi \in \mathbb{R}\}$,

(iv) $\{l_+(\alpha, 0)\} \cup \{(\xi, \xi - \alpha) \mid \xi \in \mathbb{R}\}$

with $\alpha \in \mathbb{R}$.

In order to get the images of the other lines of S^2, we notice that two of the three interesting cases for a plane π,

$$ax_1 + bx_2 + cx_3 = 0, \quad (a, b, c) \neq (0, 0, 0), \tag{74}$$

should be still considered: $\pi \cap S^2$ consists of two null–lines when

$$a^2 + b^2 = c^2.$$

$\pi \cap S^2$ is an ellipse for

$$a^2 + b^2 < c^2, \tag{75}$$

and a hyperbola whenever

$$a^2 + b^2 > c^2. \tag{76}$$

Suppose that (75) holds true. Put $m = -\dfrac{b}{c}$ when $a = 0$. In view of (72) we get

$$\sigma(\pi \cap S^2) = \{\infty\} \cup \{(\xi, m\xi) \mid \xi \in \mathbb{R}\}.$$

Observe that $|m| < 1$ because of (75). In the case $a \neq 0$, equation (72) can be written as

$$(\eta - q)^2 - (\xi - p)^2 = q^2 - p^2 - 1 > 0 \tag{77}$$

with $pa := b$ and $qa := -c$.

The II–circle (77) (of course, together with its two asymptotes) has nothing in common with ω. This circle is therefore precisely the image of $\pi \cap S^2$ when $\pi \cap S^2$ is an ellipse not passing through (-1,0,0).

In the remaining case (76), equation (72) has the form

$$\xi = m\eta \text{ with } a = 0, m := -\frac{c}{b} \text{ and } |m| < 1 \tag{78}$$

or the form

$$(\xi - p)^2 - (\eta - q)^2 = 1 + p^2 - q^2 > 0 \tag{79}$$

with $a \neq 0$, $pa := b$ and $qa := -c$.

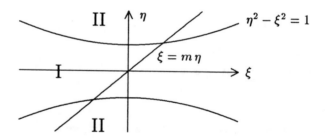

The branch of $\pi \cap S^2$ through (1,0,0) for (78) has as image under σ that part of

$$l := \{(m\eta, \eta) \mid \eta \in \mathbb{R}\}$$

which is also in

$$I := \{(p, q) \in \mathbb{R}^2 \mid 1 + p^2 - q^2 > 0\}.$$

The branch of $\pi \cap S^2$ through (-1,0,0) has as image

$$\{\infty\} \cup (l \cap II)$$

with

$$II := \{(p, q) \in \mathbb{R}^2 \mid 1 + p^2 - q^2 < 0\}.$$

Suppose that $(p, q) \in I$. Then exactly one of the following cases hold true:

(1) $p = q = 0$,

(2) $p = q \neq 0$,

(3) $p = -q \neq 0$,

(4) $p^2 \neq q^2$.

The Π–circle (79) (together, of course, with its two asymptotes) has exactly two distinct points in common with ω. These points are in the different cases

(1') $l_+(0,0)$, $l_-(0,0)$,

(2') $l_+(0,0)$, $\left(\dfrac{p^2 - 1}{2p}, \dfrac{p^2 + 1}{2p} \right)$,

(3') $l_-(0,0)$, $\left(\dfrac{p^2 - 1}{2p}, -\dfrac{p^2 + 1}{2p} \right)$,

(4') $\left(\dfrac{p + \varepsilon q \sqrt{1 + p^2 - q^2}}{q^2 - p^2}, \dfrac{q + \varepsilon p \sqrt{1 + p^2 - q^2}}{q^2 - p^2} \right)$, $\varepsilon \in \{1, -1\}$.

Denote by H the set of all $(\xi, \eta) \in \mathbb{R}^2$ satisfying (79). Our plane π of (74) is now of the form

$$\pi : x_1 + px_2 - qx_3 = 0. \tag{80}$$

The images of the two branches of $\pi \cap S^2$ for (1) are given by

$$\{(\xi, \eta) \in H \mid \xi < 0\} \text{ and } \{(\xi, \eta) \in H \mid \xi > 0\}.$$

The images are, for (2) and $p > 0$

$$\{(\xi, \eta) \in H \cap I \mid \xi < p\}$$

and

$$\{(\xi, \eta) \in H \cap I \mid \xi > p\} \cup \{l_-(2p, 0)\} \cup (H \cap II);$$

if $p < 0$ interchange $\xi < p$ and $\xi > p$ in both formulas. The images are quite similar in the case (3). They are here given by

$$\{(\xi, \eta) \in H \cap I \mid \xi < p\}$$

and

$$\{(\xi, \eta) \in H \cap I \mid \xi > p\} \cup \{l_+(2p, 0)\} \cup (H \cap II)$$

if $p > 0$; if $p < 0$, $\xi < p$ and $\xi > p$ must again be interchanged in both formulas.

In the case (4) we start to walk along H with its two asymptotes, from one of the points (4') on, say from A on, agreeing that this is possible as indicated in the picture, up to the other point B of (4'). This part traversed will be then the image of one branch of $\pi \cap S^2$ under σ. Walking from A up to B in the opposite direction, leads to the image of the other branch of $\pi \cap S^2$.

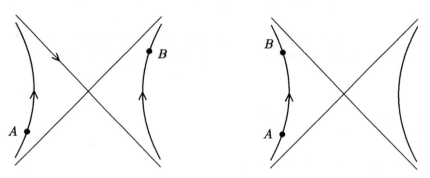

Obviously, this rule also holds true in cases (1), (2), (3).

4.11   Ring coordinates

The ring $\mathbb{A}$ which will play a role in this section is the ring of *double numbers*. A double number is a matrix

$$\begin{pmatrix} a & b \\ b & a \end{pmatrix}$$

with $a, b \in \mathbb{R}$. We add and multiply double numbers as we add and multiply matrices. Instead of

$$\begin{pmatrix} 1 & 0 \\ 0 & 1 \end{pmatrix}$$

we shall simply write 1 and instead of

$$\begin{pmatrix} 0 & 1 \\ 1 & 0 \end{pmatrix}$$

just j. Then

$$\begin{pmatrix} a & b \\ b & a \end{pmatrix} = a + bj.$$

Moreover, $j^2 = 1$ and

$$\begin{aligned} (a + bj) + (c + dj) &= (a + c) + (b + d)j \\ (a + bj) \cdot (c + dj) &= (ac + bd) + (ad + bc)j \end{aligned}$$

for $a, b, c, d \in \mathbb{R}$. $\mathbb{A}$ is a commutative ring with identity element 1. It is easy to check that $\mathbb{A}$ contains exactly four ideals, namely $\{0\}, \mathbb{A}$ and

$$
\begin{aligned}
I_+ &:= \mathbb{R} \cdot (1+j) := \{r(1+j) \mid r \in \mathbb{R}\}, \\
I_- &:= \mathbb{R} \cdot (1-j).
\end{aligned}
$$

The group U of units of $\mathbb{A}$ is given by (see section 5.6.5)

$$
U = \{a + bj \mid a, b \in \mathbb{R} \text{ with } a^2 \neq b^2\}.
$$

Observe that $j \in U$. The mapping

$$
a + bj \rightarrow \overline{a + bj} := a - bj
$$

is an automorphism of $\mathbb{A}$ of order 2.

To every point of the real Minkowski plane II we shall now associate coordinates coming from $\mathbb{A}$.

To $(\xi, \eta) \in \mathbb{R}^2$ we associate

$$
U(\xi + \eta j, 1) := \Big\{ (u(\xi + \eta j), u) \mid u \in U \Big\}.
$$

Moreover

$$
\begin{aligned}
l_+(v, 0) &\rightarrow U\big((v+1) - (v-1)j, 1 - j\big), \\
l_-(v, 0) &\rightarrow U\big((v+1) + (v-1)j, 1 + j\big), \\
\infty &\rightarrow U(1, 0).
\end{aligned}
$$

Observe that

$$
U(z_1, z_2) = U(uz_1, uz_2)
$$

holds true for $u \in U$ and that

$$
z_1, z_2 \in I_+ \text{ or } z_1, z_2 \in I_- \tag{81}
$$

is not possible when $U(z_1, z_2)$ are coordinates of a point of II. On the other hand, assuming that (81) is not satisfied for $z_1, z_2 \in \mathbb{A}$ implies that there is exactly one point in II with coordinates $U(z_1, z_2)$.

In fact, if $z_2 \in U$, then

$$
U(z_1, z_2) = U(z_1 z_2^{-1}, 1) =: U(\xi + \eta j, 1).
$$

If $z_2 \notin U$, then $z_2 \in I_+ \cup I_-$. When

$$
z_2 = r \cdot (1+j), \ r \in \mathbb{R},
$$

we have $r = 0$ or $r \neq 0$. If $r = 0$, then $z_1 \in U$ since (81) does not hold true. Hence $U(z_1 z_1^{-1}, 0)$ are coordinates of ∞. If $r \neq 0$, we get

$$U(z_1, z_2) = U(z_1 r^{-1}, 1 + j) =: U(\alpha + \beta j, 1 + j)$$

with $\alpha \neq \beta$ since $z_1 \notin I_+$. Observe that

$$[(1 - k) + kj](1 + j) = 1 + j$$

and $(1 - k) + kj \in U$ for $k \neq \frac{1}{2}$. Now

$$[(1 - k) + kj](\alpha + \beta j) = (v + 1) + (v - 1)j$$

with $k := \frac{1}{2} + \frac{1}{\beta - \alpha}$ and $v := \frac{1}{2}(\alpha + \beta)$. Since

$$U\big((v + 1) + (v - 1)j, 1 + j\big) = U\big((w + 1) + (w - 1)j, 1 + j\big),$$

and since $v, w \in \mathbb{R}$ implies $v = w$, we get the coordinates of

$$l_-(v, 0) = l_- \left(\frac{\alpha + \beta}{2}, 0 \right).$$

All circles of Π are given in the form

$$(z_1 z_2)\, M\, (\overline{z}_1 \overline{z}_2)^T = 0, \tag{82}$$

where

$$M = \begin{pmatrix} m_{11} & m_{12} \\ m_{21} & m_{22} \end{pmatrix}$$

is a matrix over $\mathbb{A}$ satisfying $\det M \neq 0$ and

$$M = \overline{M}^T := \begin{pmatrix} \overline{m_{11}} & \overline{m_{12}} \\ \overline{m_{21}} & \overline{m_{22}} \end{pmatrix}^T.$$

Notice that $M = \overline{M}^T$ implies that

$$a := m_{11} \in \mathbb{R}, \ d := m_{22} \in \mathbb{R}$$

and

$$\overline{m}_{21} = m_{12} =: b + cj$$

with $b, c \in \mathbb{R}$. Hence

$$M = \begin{pmatrix} a & b + cj \\ b - cj & d \end{pmatrix} \tag{83}$$

with $0 \neq \det M = ad - b^2 + c^2$. The points $U(x + yj, 1)$ of (82) are thus given by

$$0 = (z_1 z_2) M \begin{pmatrix} \overline{z_1} \\ \overline{z_2} \end{pmatrix} = \left(a(x^2 - y^2) + 2bx + 2cy + d\right). \tag{84}$$

Obviously, $U(1, 0)$ is on (82) if and only if $a = 0$. There are no other points on (82) when $a = 0$, besides $U(1, 0)$ and the solutions $U(x + yj, 1)$ of (84). When $a \neq 0$, the points on (82) besides the solutions $U(x + yj, 1)$ of (84) are

$$U\left((v + 1) - (v - 1)j, 1 - j\right) \text{ and } U\left((w + 1) + (w - 1)j, 1 + j\right)$$

with

$$v = -\frac{b + c}{a} \text{ and } w = -\frac{b - c}{a},$$

i.e. they are the two asymptotes

$$l_+ \left(-\frac{b + c}{a}, 0\right) \text{ and } l_- \left(-\frac{b - c}{a}, 0\right).$$

Comparing (84) with (72) yields that the circles which play a role in the model of de Sitter's plane are characterized by

$$\text{trace}\,(M) := m_{11} + m_{22} = a + d = 0.$$

If $\det M > 0$, we have the image of a closed line, and if $\det M < 0$, the image of two open lines of S^2. Generators as defined in the previous section are also easy to describe in terms of ring coordinates: the two generators through ∞, i.e. $U(1, 0)$, are given by the point solutions $U(z_1, z_2)$ of

$$\begin{vmatrix} 1 & 0 \\ z_1 & z_2 \end{vmatrix} \in I_+, \quad \begin{vmatrix} 1 & 0 \\ z_1 & z_2 \end{vmatrix} \in I_-,$$

respectively. The two generators through $(\alpha, 0)$, $\alpha \in \mathbb{R}$, i.e. $U(\alpha + 0j, 1)$, are given as the point solutions $U(z_1, z_2)$ of

$$\begin{vmatrix} \alpha & 1 \\ z_1 & z_2 \end{vmatrix} \in I_+, \quad \begin{vmatrix} \alpha & 1 \\ z_1 & z_2 \end{vmatrix} \in I_-,$$

respectively.

It is easy to see that

$$U(z_1', z_2') = U(z_1, z_2) \cdot \begin{pmatrix} a_{11} & a_{12} \\ a_{21} & a_{22} \end{pmatrix} \tag{85}$$

where $a_{ij} \in \mathbb{A}$ and $a_{11}a_{22} - a_{12}a_{21} \in U$ is a bijection of the set Φ^2 of points of
II such that images and pre–images of circles of II are circles of II. Two points
$A, B \in \Phi^2$ are called *parallel* if there exists a generator through A, B. Through
three pairwise non parallel points there is exactly one circle of II (see section
6.2.3). The group Γ of mappings (85) operates sharply transitively on the set
of ordered triples (A, B, C) of pairwise non–parallel points A, B, C.

We must get other models of de Sitter's plane by replacing ω by any other
circle of II. Especially simple will be the model we get by replacing ω by the
circle through $U(1,0)$, $U(0,1)$, $U(1,1)$. This can be performed by a mapping
(85) which transforms ω onto ϱ, say by

$$U(z_1', z_2') = U(z_1, z_2) \begin{pmatrix} 1 & -j \\ j & 1 \end{pmatrix} = U(z_1 + jz_2, z_2 - jz_1).$$

However, we prefer to go another way. Observe that ϱ is also given by

$$\varrho = \{(\xi, 0) \mid \xi \in \mathbb{R}\} \cup \{\infty\}.$$

The mapping

$$\tau(x_1, x_2, x_3) := \left(\frac{x_1}{x_2 + x_3}, \frac{1}{x_2 + x_3} \right) \tag{86}$$

for $(x_1, x_2, x_3) \in S^2$ with $x_2 + x_3 \neq 0$,

$$\tau(1, \alpha, -\alpha) := l_+(-\alpha, 0), \tag{87}$$
$$\tau(-1, \alpha, -\alpha) := l_-(\alpha, 0) \tag{88}$$

for $\alpha \in \mathbb{R}$, is a bijection between S^2 and $\Phi^2 \backslash \varrho$. It is also based on a stereographic
projection with center in the projective closure of S^2:

$$p \cdot (x_1, x_2, x_3, 1) + q \cdot (0, 1, -1, 0) = r \cdot (\xi, \frac{1}{2}, \frac{1}{2}, \eta) \tag{89}$$

with $r \neq 0$ leads to

$$(\xi, \eta) = \left(\frac{x_1}{x_2 + x_3}, \frac{1}{x_2 + x_3} \right).$$

Formula (86) implies

$$\tau^{-1}(\xi, \eta) = \left(\frac{\xi}{\eta}, \frac{1 - \xi^2 + \eta^2}{2\eta}, \frac{1 + \xi^2 - \eta^2}{2\eta} \right) \tag{90}$$

for $\eta \neq 0$. We therefore get all (ξ, η) in $\tau(\pi \cap S^2)$, where π is the plane of
equation (74), by means of

$$(c - b)(\xi^2 - \eta^2) + 2a\xi + (c + b) = 0. \tag{91}$$

Remembering formulas (75), (76), we know that $\pi \cap S^2$

(i) is an ellipse,

(ii) is a hyperbola,

(iii) are two null–lines

whenever

(i') $a^2 + b^2 < c^2$,

(ii') $a^2 + b^2 > c^2$,

(iii') $a^2 + b^2 = c^2$

respectively. Since the null–lines are going over again into generators (here, of course, without the point of intersection with ϱ) we only have to deal with cases (i) and (ii). $c - b = 0$ thus belongs to (ii), i.e. $a \neq 0$. According to the rule presented at the end of section 4.10

$$2a\xi + (c + b) = 0, \text{i.e.}$$

$$\left\{ \left(-\frac{c+b}{2a}, \eta \right) \mid \eta \in \mathbb{R}\backslash\{0\} \right\}$$

carries the images of two branches of a hyperbola.

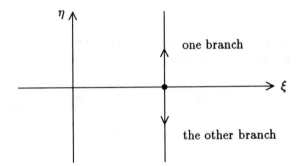

If $c \neq b$, (91) reads

$$\left(\xi - \frac{a}{b-c} \right)^2 - \eta^2 = \frac{a^2 + b^2 - c^2}{(b-c)^2}. \tag{92}$$

For case (i') there is no intersection point with ϱ, so that then we have the image of a closed line of S^2.

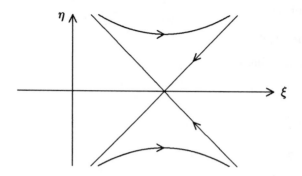

For case (ii'), again two open lines are represented.

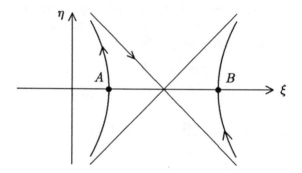

It might also be worthwhile to look for the notion of distance, (53), in our model. For this purpose notice that

$$x_1 y_1 + x_2 y_2 - x_3 y_3 = 1 - 2 \frac{(\xi_1 - \eta_1)^2 - (\xi_2 - \eta_2)^2}{(1 + \xi_1^2 - \xi_2^2)(1 + \eta_1^2 - \eta_2^2)}$$

holds true when $x, y \in S^2$ have images $(\xi_1, \xi_2), (\eta_1, \eta_2)$ in Φ^2.

4.12 Fundamental Theorem of de Sitter's plane

We would like to determine all bijections of the set of points of de Sitter's plane such that images and pre-images of null–lines are null–lines. Fundamental for our considerations now will be the model of S^2 which we developed in section 4.11. Let σ be a bijection as described above,

$$\sigma : \hat{S}^2 \to \hat{S}^2,$$

with $\mathbb{R}_2 := \mathbb{R}^2 \backslash \{(\xi, 0) \mid \xi \in \mathbb{R}\}$ and

$$\begin{aligned}
\hat{S}^2 &:= \mathbb{R}_2 \cup L_+ \cup L_-, \\
L_+ &:= \{l_+(v, 0) \mid v \in \mathbb{R}\}, \\
L_- &:= \{l_-(v, 0) \mid v \in \mathbb{R}\}.
\end{aligned}$$

Denote by γ the null–line

$$\{(\xi, \xi) \mid \xi \in \mathbb{R}^*\} \cup \{l_+(0, 0)\}$$

with $\mathbb{R}^* := \mathbb{R} \backslash \{0\}$. In view of Theorem 1, there exists a motion which maps the null–line $\sigma(\gamma)$ back to γ. So up to a motion of S^2, we may assume that $\sigma(\gamma) = \gamma$. The stabilizer of a null–line still operates transitively on the set of points of this line, according to Proposition 13: observe that the image of the null–line (29) (for $n = 2$) under τ is exactly γ with $\tau(1, 0, 0) = l_+(0, 0)$. There hence exists a motion which transforms $(1, 0, 0)$ in $(1, t, t)$, $t \in \mathbb{R}$, namely $L(k, t)$, $k \neq 0$. We thus may also assume that σ fixes $l_+(0, 0)$. There are exactly two null–lines through $l_+(0, 0)$, namely γ and L_+. Hence $\sigma(L_+) = L_+$. Put

$$\sigma(t, t) =: \big(\varphi(t), \varphi(t) \big)$$

and

$$\sigma\big(l_+(v, 0) \big) =: l_+\big(\psi(v), 0 \big).$$

Then φ, ψ are bijections of $\mathbb{R}^*, \mathbb{R}$, respectively. Let (x, y) be a point of $\mathbb{R}_2$ such that $x^2 \neq y^2$. Then (x, y) and $\dfrac{x + y}{2}(1, 1)$ are on a common null–line and so are (x, y) and $l_+(x - y, 0)$. This carries over to the images. Hence $\sigma(x, y)$ and $\sigma\left(\dfrac{x + y}{2}, \dfrac{x + y}{2} \right)$ are on a common null–line, say on δ, and $\sigma(x, y)$ and $l_+\big(\psi(x - y), 0 \big)$ are also on a common null–line, say on ε. δ must be a null–line $\neq \gamma$ through

$$\sigma\left(\frac{x + y}{2}, \frac{x + y}{2} \right) \in \gamma \backslash \{l_+(0, 0)\},$$

and ε must be a null–line $\neq L_+$ through $l_+\big(\psi(x - y), 0 \big)$. Hence

$$\sigma(x, y) = \varphi\left(\frac{x + y}{2} \right) \cdot (1, 1) + \frac{1}{2}\psi(x - y) \cdot (1, -1). \tag{93}$$

This formula applies also to the case $x = y$ since $\psi(0) = 0$ holds true in view of the fact that $l_+(0, 0)$ remains fixed under σ. The second coordinate of the point (93) must be unequal to 0. Hence

$$\varphi\left(\frac{x + y}{2} \right) \neq \frac{1}{2}\psi(x - y)$$

for all $x, y \in \mathbb{R}$ with $x \neq -y \neq 0$. Put

$$2t := x - y \text{ and } 2s := x + y.$$

Then $2\varphi(s) \neq \psi(2t)$ for all $s, t \in \mathbb{R}$ with $0 \neq s \neq t$. Let $s \neq 0$ be a real number. Since ψ is a bijection of $\mathbb{R}$, there exists $\tau \in \mathbb{R}$ with $2\varphi(s) = \psi(2\tau)$. Hence $\tau = s$, because $\tau \neq s$ implies that $0 \neq s \neq \tau$ and thus $2\varphi(s) \neq \psi(2\tau)$. This implies that

$$\sigma(x, y) = \varphi\left(\frac{x+y}{2}\right) \cdot (1,1) + \varphi\left(\frac{x-y}{2}\right) \cdot (1,-1) \tag{94}$$

for all $x, y \in \mathbb{R}$ with $x \neq -y \neq 0$, where we also put $\varphi(0) := 0$. Moreover

$$\sigma\left(l_+(v,0)\right) = l_+\left(2\varphi\left(\frac{v}{2}\right), 0\right) \tag{95}$$

for all $v \in \mathbb{R}$. φ is a bijection of $\mathbb{R}$. Let $v \neq 0$ be a real number. The image of

$$\left\{ (x, v - x) \mid x \in \mathbb{R} \backslash \{v\} \right\} \tag{96}$$

under σ is

$$\left\{ \left(y, 2\varphi\left(\frac{v}{2}\right) - y\right) \mid y \in \mathbb{R} \backslash \left\{ 2\varphi\left(\frac{v}{2}\right) \right\} \right\}. \tag{97}$$

(96), (97) are null–lines together with $l_-(v, 0)$, $l_-\left(2\varphi\left(\frac{v}{2}\right), 0\right)$. Hence

$$\sigma\left(l_-(v,0)\right) = l_-\left(2\varphi\left(\frac{v}{2}\right), 0\right) \tag{98}$$

for all $v \neq 0$. But since $\sigma(L_-)$ must also be a null–line, we get, in view of (98), that

$$\sigma\left(l_-(0,0)\right) = l_-(0,0)$$

holds true. (98) is thus also satisfied for $v = 0$. Together with this we finally get that (94) holds true also in the case $x = -y \neq 0$. We have thus proved

THEOREM 15. *All bijections σ of the set of points of de Sitter's plane with*

$$\sigma(\gamma) = \gamma, \ \sigma\left(l_+(0,0)\right) = l_+(0,0)$$

and such that images and pre–images of null–lines are null–lines, are given precisely by

$$\sigma(x, y) = \varphi\left(\frac{x+y}{2}\right) \cdot (1,1) + \varphi\left(\frac{x-y}{2}\right) \cdot (1,-1), \tag{99}$$

$$\sigma\left(l_+(x,0)\right) = l_+\left(2\varphi\left(\frac{x}{2}\right), 0\right), \tag{100}$$

$$\sigma\left(l_-(x,0)\right) = l_-\left(2\varphi\left(\frac{x}{2}\right), 0\right) \tag{101}$$

for all $x, y \in \mathbb{R}$ with $y \neq 0$, where $\varphi : \mathbb{R} \to \mathbb{R}$ is an arbitrary bijection with $\varphi(0) = 0$.

REMARK. Let Σ be an arbitrary bijection of S^2 such that images and pre–images of null–lines are null–lines. Take a motion μ of S^2 such that

$$\mu\big(\Sigma(\gamma)\big) = \gamma,$$
$$\mu\big(\Sigma(l_+(0,0))\big) = l_+(0,0)$$

holds true. Then $\mu \cdot \Sigma$ is a mapping σ of Theorem 15. Hence $\Sigma = \mu^{-1}\sigma$. All mappings Σ are thus given by the mappings of Theorem 15 up to motions.

REMARK. The stabilizer of γ is given up to isomorphism by the group of all $L(k,t)$, $k \neq 0$, as already mentioned. All $L(k,t)$ also fixing $l_+(0,0)$ are then given by

$$\{L(k,0) \mid k \neq 0\}.$$

These mappings correspond precisely to the mappings of Theorem 15 with

$$\varphi(x) := \frac{1}{k}x, \; x \in \mathbb{R}. \tag{102}$$

These functions φ are only special bijections of $\mathbb{R}$ with $\varphi(0) = 0$. There hence exists $2^{\aleph}$ mappings σ of Theorem 15 which are not motions of S^2 since there are exactly $2^{\aleph}$ permutations of $\mathbb{R}$ not of form (102).

The next Theorem 16 we will call the Fundamental Theorem of de Sitter's plane:

THEOREM 16. *All bijections of the set of points of de Sitter's plane such that images and pre–images of null–lines are null–lines and such that images of open lines are open lines are motions.*

Proof.   Let σ be a mapping as described. Without loss of generality we may assume that $\sigma(\gamma) = \gamma$ and that

$$\sigma\big(l_+(0,0)\big) = l_+(0,0).$$

For the mapping σ we thus have formulas (99), (100), (101). In terms of the motions belonging to functions (102) we may also assume that the underlying function φ of σ satisfies $\varphi(1) = 1$. An open line in our model which is not part of a hyperbola must go over into an open line of the same type, since otherwise the image would contain an asymptote, whereas asymptotes are only images of asymptotes in view of (100) and (101): the *asymptotes* are here the points $l_+(x,0)$ and $l_-(x,0)$. For the open line

$$l(x) := \{(x,y) \in \mathbb{R}_2 \mid y > 0\}$$

we thus get

(i) $\varphi\left(\dfrac{x+y}{2}\right) + \varphi\left(\dfrac{x-y}{2}\right) =: \omega(x),$

(ii) $\mathrm{sgn}\left[\varphi\left(\dfrac{x+y}{2}\right) - \varphi\left(\dfrac{x-y}{2}\right)\right] =: \delta(x)$

for all $y > 0$ and suitable functions

$$\omega : \mathbb{R} \to \mathbb{R}, \ \delta : \mathbb{R} \to \{+1, -1\}.$$

This implies that $\varphi(x) = kx$ for all $x \in \mathbb{R}$ with a constant $k \neq 0$, in view of Theorem 17 (section 4.13). But then σ must be the identity, according to (99) and $\varphi(1) = 1$.   □

REMARK. The group Γ, generated by

$$U(z_1', z_2') = U(\bar{z}_1, \bar{z}_2)$$

and the mappings (85), is exactly the group of bijections of Φ^2 of Π such that images and pre-images of circles are circles (see section 6.2.3). The stabilizer of the circle ϱ, i.e.

$$\{\xi \in \Gamma \mid \xi(\varrho) = \varrho\},$$

is the group of motions of de Sitter's plane. The geometry of Π is widely known (see W. Benz [2]). All notions in Π like angles, reflections, etc. then also apply to S^2.

4.13 A conditional functional equation

In this section we would like to solve the functional equations problem (i), (ii) of section 4.12 under the assumption that φ is a bijection of $\mathbb{R}$ with $\varphi(0) = 0$. (i) is an equation in two unknown functions φ, ω which is supposed to hold true under an additional condition, namely (ii) with an other unknown function δ.

THEOREM 17. *Let φ be a bijection of $\mathbb{R}$ with $\varphi(0) = 0$ and let $\omega : \mathbb{R} \to \mathbb{R}$ and $\delta : \mathbb{R} \to \{+1, -1\}$ be functions such that (i), (ii) hold true for all $x, y \in \mathbb{R}$ with $y > 0$. Then there exists a constant $k \neq 0$ with*

$$\delta(x) = \operatorname{sgn} k \text{ and } \varphi(x) = \omega(x) = kx$$

for all $x \in \mathbb{R}$.

Proof. We put

$$\frac{x+y}{2} =: t \text{ and } \frac{x-y}{2} =: s.$$

Then (i) reads

$$\varphi(t) + \varphi(s) = \omega(t + s). \tag{103}$$

This equation holds true for all $t, s \in \mathbb{R}$ such that $t > s$ since $t - s = y > 0$. Equation (103) is symmetric in t and s. For $s > t$ we get, from (103),

$$\varphi(s) + \varphi(t) = \omega(s + t).$$

Equation (103) thus holds true for all $t, s \in \mathbb{R}$ with $t \neq s$. Put $s = 0$ in (103). Then $\varphi(t) = \omega(t)$ for all $t \neq 0$, in view of $\varphi(0) = 0$. This together with (103) implies that

$$\varphi(t) + \varphi(s) = \varphi(t + s) \tag{104}$$

for all $t, s \in \mathbb{R}$ with $t \neq \pm s$. We shall now apply (104) to equation (i). This leads to

$$2\varphi\left(\frac{x}{2}\right) + \varphi\left(\frac{y}{2}\right) + \varphi\left(-\frac{y}{2}\right) = \varphi(x) \tag{105}$$

for all $x, y \in \mathbb{R}$ with $x \notin \{0, y, -y\}$ and $y > 0$. Let y_1, y_2 be positive real numbers. Then

$$\varphi\left(\frac{y_1}{2}\right) + \varphi\left(-\frac{y_1}{2}\right) = \varphi\left(\frac{y_2}{2}\right) + \varphi\left(-\frac{y_2}{2}\right) =: a.$$

Otherwise take a real $x \notin \{0, \pm y_1, \pm y_2\}$ and look at (105) in the two cases $y = y_1$ and $y = y_2$. We now would like to show that a is equal to 0. Since φ is bijective, there exists a uniquely determined $r \in \mathbb{R}$ with $a = \varphi(r)$. Assume that $a \neq 0$ and hence $r \neq 0$. Take $y > 0$ and

$$x \notin \{0, \pm 2r, -r, \pm y\}.$$

Then (105) holds true, i.e.

$$\begin{aligned}
\varphi(x) &= \varphi\left(\frac{x}{2}\right) + \varphi\left(\frac{x}{2}\right) + \varphi(r) \\
&= \varphi\left(\frac{x}{2}\right) + \varphi\left(\frac{x}{2} + r\right) \\
&= \varphi\left(\frac{x}{2} + \frac{x}{2} + r\right) = \varphi(x + r),
\end{aligned}$$

in view of (104). Hence $r = 0$ since φ is bijective. This contradicts our assumption that $r \neq 0$. We thus have

$$\varphi\left(\frac{y}{2}\right) + \varphi\left(-\frac{y}{2}\right) = 0$$

for all $y > 0$ and hence $\omega(0) = 0$ and

$$\varphi(t) + \varphi(s) = \varphi(t + s)$$

for all $t, s \in \mathbb{R}$ with $t = -s$.

Take real numbers $x \neq 0$ and $y \neq \pm x$. Then (105) holds true. Hence

$$\varphi\left(\frac{x}{2}\right) + \varphi\left(\frac{x}{2}\right) = \varphi\left(\frac{x}{2} + \frac{x}{2}\right)$$

for all $x \neq 0$. Equation (104) thus holds true for all $t, s \in \mathbb{R}$. This together with (ii) implies that

$$\text{sgn } \varphi(y) = \delta(x) \tag{106}$$

for all $x, y \in \mathbb{R}$ with $y > 0$. The function $\delta(x) \in \{+1, -1\}$ is hence a constant δ_0. Define

$$f(y) := \delta_0 \varphi(y)$$

for $y \geq 0$. Then $f(y) > 0$ for $y > 0$. Since

$$f(x + y) = f(x) + f(y)$$

holds true for all $x, y \geq 0$, we get $f(x) = k_0 x$ with a constant $k_0 > 0$, in view of Theorem 5 of chapter 1. Put $k := k_0 \cdot \delta_0$. Hence

$$\varphi(y) = ky \tag{107}$$

for all $y \geq 0$ with a constant $k \neq 0$. (106) yields $\delta(x) = \text{sgn } k$ for all $x \in \mathbb{R}$. We also have for $y < 0$,

$$\varphi(y) = -\varphi(-y) = -k \cdot (-y) = ky.$$

$\square$

4.14   De Sitter's world and Lie geometry

Since S^n is part of $\mathbb{R}^{n+1}$, we may speak of parallel null–lines: null–lines are also lines of $\mathbb{R}^{n+1}$, and therefore the notion of parallelism of lines of $\mathbb{R}^{n+1}$ might be applied.

Lemma 18. *Let g, h be null–lines of S^n, $n \geq 3$, with $g \cap h = \emptyset$. Then $g \parallel h$ if and only if there is no null–line l with*

$$l \cap g \neq \emptyset \text{ and } l \cap h \neq \emptyset.$$

Proof.   Motions of S^n are defined as special affine mappings of $\mathbb{R}^{n+1}$ which of course preserve parallelism of lines. Because of Theorem 1 we hence may assume that g is null–line (29), without loss of generality. Thus

$$g = \{a + \lambda p \mid \lambda \in \mathbb{R}\}$$

with $a := (1, 0, \ldots, 0)$ and $p := (0, 1, 0, \ldots, 0, 1)$. Assume that $g \parallel h$ with $g \cap h = \emptyset$,

$$h = \{b + \mu p \mid \mu \in \mathbb{R}\} \subset S^n,$$

and $b \in S^n$. If there existed a null–line l with

$$l \cap g = \{a + \alpha p\}$$

and

$$l \cap h = \{b + \beta p\},$$

then

$$0 = (a + \alpha p - b - \beta p)^2 = (a - b)^2 + 2(\alpha - \beta) p (a - b)$$

by applying scalar product (27). Then $ap = 0$ and also $bp = 0$, in view of $h \subset S^n$. Hence

$$0 = (a - b)^2 = 2(1 - ab),$$

i.e. $b_1 = 1$, i.e. $b \in g$ because of $bp = 0$. But this contradicts $g \cap h = \emptyset$. — Assume now that $g \nparallel h$ with $g \cap h = \emptyset$,

$$h = \{b + \mu q \mid \mu \in \mathbb{R}\} \subset S^n,$$

$b \in S^n$. Then $q \neq 0 = q^2$ and $bq = 0$. We have

$$p \cdot q \neq 0,$$

since otherwise p, q would be linearly dependent, since

$$(p_1 q_1 + \ldots + p_n q_n)^2 = (p_{n+1} \, q_{n+1})^2 = (p_1^2 + \ldots + p_n^2)(q_1^2 + \ldots + q_n^2).$$

But then

$$0 = (a + \alpha p - b - \beta q)^2 = (a - b)^2 - 2\alpha bp - 2\beta aq - 2\alpha\beta pq$$

has a solution $\alpha, \beta \in \mathbb{R}$: put $\beta = 0$ when $bp \neq 0$ and $\alpha = 0$ when $bp = 0 \neq aq$. If $bp = 0 = aq$, we need only observe that $p \cdot q \neq 0$.   □

We are now interested in all projective points of type

$$\mathbb{R}(x_0, x_1, \ldots, x_n, x_{n+1}), \quad x_0 = 0 \tag{108}$$

of the Lie quadric L^{n-1} of equation (see section 3.8)

$$x_1^2 + \ldots + x_n^2 - x_{n+1}^2 = x_0^2. \tag{109}$$

The affine points of (109), i.e. the points with $x_0 \neq 0$, are the points of S^n. The remaining points (108) of (109) can be identified with the parallel classes of null–lines. In fact, let $\mathbb{R}(p_i)$ be a point (108) satisfying (109). Then $p_{n+1} \neq 0$. Without loss of generality, put $p_{n+1} = 1$. Then

$$p_1^2 + \ldots + p_n^2 = 1.$$

Take $(x_1, \ldots, x_n) \in \mathbb{R}^n$ with

$$x_1^2 + \ldots + x_n^2 = 1$$

and

$$p_1 x_1 + \ldots + p_n x_n = 0.$$

Then

$$\{(x_1, \ldots, x_n, 0) + \lambda(p_1, \ldots, p_n, 1) \mid \lambda \in \mathbb{R}\}$$

is a null–line of S^n. The null–line

$$\{b + \lambda q \mid \lambda \in \mathbb{R}\} \subset S^n,$$

on the other hand, represents the point

$$\mathbb{R}(0, q_1, \ldots, q_{n+1})$$

of the Lie quadric.

THEOREM 19. *Let P^n be the set of all parallel classes of null–lines of S^n, $n \geq 3$. There exists a bijection ψ from $S^n \cup P^n$ onto L^{n-1} such that $\psi(x)$ and $\psi(y)$ are in contact with each other for $x, y \in S^n \cup P^n$ if and only if there exists a null–line $l \ni x, y$ when $x, y \in S^n$, or there exists a null–line l in y through x when x is in S^n and y is a parallel class. The mapping*

$$\psi(x) := \begin{cases} \mathbb{R}(1, x_1, \ldots, x_{n+1}) & x \in S^n \\ & for \\ \mathbb{R}(0, x_1, \ldots, x_{n+1}) & x \in P^n \end{cases}$$

*is such a bijection, where a class $x \in P^n$ is represented by any $(x_1, \ldots, x_{n+1})$
with*

$$\{b + \lambda \cdot (x_1, \ldots, x_{n+1}) \mid \lambda \in \mathbb{R}\} \in x$$

for a suitable $b \in S^n$.

Proof.   Let x, y be distinct elements of S^n. Then $\psi(x)$ and $\psi(y)$ are in contact iff

$$x_1 y_1 + \ldots + x_n y_n - x_{n+1} y_{n+1} = 1 \cdot 1.$$

But this is equivalent to the fact that there exists a null–line through x, y, namely

$$\{x + \lambda(y - x) \mid \lambda \in \mathbb{R}\}.$$

As we already know from the proof of Lemma 18, $p \cdot q \neq 0$ is satisfied for linearly independent

$$(p_1, \ldots, p_{n+1}), \ (q_1, \ldots, q_{n+1})$$

with $p_1^2 + \ldots + p_n^2 - p_{n+1}^2 = 0 = q_1^2 + \ldots + q_n^2 - q_{n+1}^2$. Therefore there do not exist distinct $x, y \in P^n$ such that $\psi(x), \psi(y)$ are in contact with each other. Suppose finally that x is in S^n and that y is a parallel class. Now

$$x_1 y_1 + \ldots + x_n y_n - x_{n+1}\, y_{n+1} = 1 \cdot 0$$

is equivalent to the fact that

$$\{x + \lambda(y_1, \ldots, y_{n+1}) \mid \lambda \in \mathbb{R}\}$$

is a null–line. $\square$

4.15   Fundamental Theorem of de Sitter's space

As a consequence of Theorem 19 we get a theorem which is due to J. Lester [4] (see also E.M. Schröder [2] for a generalization).

THEOREM 20. *Every bijection σ of S^n, $n \geq 3$, such that images and pre-images of null–lines are null–lines, must be a motion of S^n.*

Proof.   Let σ be a mapping as described and let g, h are null–lines of S^n. It is a consequence of Lemma 18 that $g \parallel h$ then holds true if and only if $\sigma(g) \parallel \sigma(h)$ is satisfied. The restriction $\sigma \mid P^n$ is thus a permutation of P^n and $\psi \sigma \psi^{-1}$ is a Lie transformation of L^{n-1}, in view of Theorem

19. Lie transformations of L^{n-1} are restrictions on L^{n-1} of projective transformations of the $(n+1)$–dimensional real projective space (see GT, 194). They must be affine since $\sigma|P^n$ permutes P^n: the hyperplane of equation $x_0 = 0$ namely remains fixed as a whole, since it is the span of the classes $(1,0,\ldots,0,1)$, $(0,1,0,\ldots,0,1)$, $\ldots$, $(0,\ldots,0,1,1)$, $(1,1,0,\ldots,0,\sqrt{2})$ of P^n. Since $\sigma(S^n) = S^n$ they are even Lorentz–transformations of $\mathbb{R}^{n+1}$ leaving the origin invariant. They are thus motions of S^n.   □

REMARK. There are precisely $\aleph$ mappings σ as described in Theorem 20 in the case $n \geq 3$, but $2^\aleph$ mappings in the case $n = 2$.

EXERCISES

1. Let L be the set of all ordered triples (l_1, l_2, p) where l_1, l_2 are lines of (S^2, Δ^2) through the point p, and let $W \neq \emptyset$ be a set. Find all functions

$$f : L \to W$$

such that $f(l_1, l_2, p) = f(\delta(l_1), \delta(l_2), \delta(p))$ holds true for all $\delta \in \Delta^2$ and for all $(l_1, l_2, p) \in L$.

2. Determine all 3–point–invariants of (S^2, Δ^2).

3. Let l be a line of (C^2, Δ^2). Determine all $f \in \Delta^2$ with $f(p) = p$ for all points p of l.

4. Determine all bijections of S^2 such that images and pre–images of lines are lines.

5. Determine all bijections of S^n preserving all distances (53).

6. Determine all homomorphisms $\sigma : \mathbb{A} \to \mathbb{A}$ with $\sigma(1) = 1$ and such that the mapping $x \to Re[\sigma(x)]$ $(x \in \mathbb{R})$ is continuous in 0.

Chapter 5

FUNDAMENTAL GEOMETRIES

Until the end of the 18. century, geometry mainly was euclidean geometry. Since that time several other geometries were developed which play a fundamental role in mathematics and its applications. We mention Projective Geometry, but also the geometries of Möbius, Laguerre, Lie, Plücker, Minkowski, Hjelmslev, and also of course the geometries of Bolyai, Gauß, Lobatschewskij, and Riemann. In the next two chapters we would like to present some important geometries (first of all euclidean geometry) and we would like to study some of their specific features. Since we intend to cover several geometries, we are forced to restrict ourselves to special topics in each case. Here, as in the previous chapters, we prefer to present newer results, whenever we think that this is possible.

5.1 Euclidean geometry

5.1.1 Theorem of Beckman and Quarles

Let S be the set $\mathbb{R}^n$ with an integer $n \geq 1$ and let

$$d : \mathbb{R}^n \times \mathbb{R}^n \to \mathbb{R}$$

be the function

$$d(x,y) = \sqrt{\sum_{i=1}^{n}(x_i - y_i)^2}$$

for elements $x = (x_1, \ldots, x_n)$ and $y = (y_1, \ldots, y_n)$ of $\mathbb{R}^n$. The group $G := G(d)$ is then given (see section 1.2) by all mappings

$$f(x) = xQ + a \tag{1}$$

for real matrices $a = (a_1 \ldots a_n)$ and

$$Q = \begin{pmatrix} q_{11} & \cdots & q_{1n} \\ \vdots & & \\ q_{n1} & \cdots & q_{nn} \end{pmatrix} \tag{2}$$

such that $QQ^T = E := (\delta_{ij})$. The geometry $(\mathbb{R}^n, G)$ is called the n–dimensional *euclidean geometry*.

A fundamental theorem in euclidean geometry is the following result of Beckman and Quarles [1]:

THEOREM 1. *Let $k > 0$ be a fixed real number and let*

$$f : \mathbb{R}^n \to \mathbb{R}^n \ (n \geq 2)$$

be a mapping satisfying

$$\forall_{x,y \in \mathbb{R}^n} \quad d(x,y) = k \Rightarrow d(f(x), f(y)) = k.$$

Then f has the form (1) such that $QQ^T = E$ holds true for Q.

REMARK. An easy and accesible proof of the Theorem of Beckman and Quarles can be found in our book GT, chapter 1.

5.1.2 A theorem of June Lester

When the author of this book visited Iran in 1978, he presented there the following problem to one of his former Ph.D. students who was a professor in Teheran:

Special version: Let $f : \mathbb{R}^2 \to \mathbb{R}^2$ be a mapping satisfying

$$\forall_{a,b,c \in \mathbb{R}^2} \quad \triangle(a,b,c) = 1 \Rightarrow \triangle(f(a), f(b), f(c)) = 1$$

where $\triangle(a,b,c)$ denotes the area of the triangle with vertices a, b, c. Prove then that f is equiaffine, i.e. affine with determinant ± 1.

General version: Generalize the special version to higher dimensions and to the ring case (compare section 5.3.1).

The special version was solved by G. Martin (unpublished, see section 5.3.1). For the general version June Lester [5] proved the following

THEOREM 2. *Let $f : \mathbb{R}^n \to \mathbb{R}^n$, $n \geq 3$, be a mapping satisfying*

$$\forall_{a,b,c \in \mathbb{R}^n} \quad \Delta(a,b,c) = 1 \Rightarrow \Delta(f(a), f(b), f(c)) = 1.$$

Then f is a euclidean motion, i.e. a mapping of the form (1) with orthogonal Q.

Proof.   (a) The mapping f must be injective. If $a \neq b$ there exists c with $\Delta(a,b,c) = 1$. Hence $\Delta(a', b', c') = 1$ and thus $a' \neq b'$. Here x' denotes $f(x)$ for $x \in \mathbb{R}^n$.

(b) $\Delta(a,b,c) = 1$ iff

$$(a - c)^2(b - c)^2 = 4 + \left[(a - c) \cdot (b - c)\right]^2 \tag{3}$$

holds true, where we put

$$x \cdot y = (x_1, \ldots, x_n)(y_1, \ldots, y_n) = \sum_{i=1}^{n} x_i y_i$$

for $x, y \in \mathbb{R}^n$.

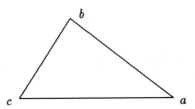

Observe that

$$\left[(a - c) \cdot (b - c)\right]^2 = (a - c)^2(b - c)^2 - 4\left[\Delta(a,b,c)\right]^2. \tag{4}$$

The proof of (4) is based on elementary geometry. However, from a strict point of view it seems to be better to define the area $\Delta(a,b,c) \geq 0$ by means of (4). (For a characterization of $\Delta(a,b,c)$ see section 5.3.3.)

(c) Suppose that

$$\| a - c \| = \| b - c \| = \sqrt{2} \text{ and } (a - c) \cdot (b - c) = 0$$

hold true for $a, b, c \in \mathbb{R}^n$ where $\| x \|$ denotes the non–negative square root of x^2 for $x \in \mathbb{R}^n$. Then there exist $p, q, r \in \mathbb{R}^n$ such that the following triangles have area 1:

  i) $cap, caq, car, cbp, cbq, cbr,$

  ii) $paq, qar, pcq, qcr, pbq, qbr.$

In order to prove this statement we may assume $c = 0$. Choose $s \in \mathbb{R}^n$ with

$$s^2 = \frac{3}{2} \text{ and } as = 0 = bs,$$

and define

$$2(p - s) := a - b =: 2(s - r), \ 2(q - s) := a + b.$$

Then p, q, r satisfy the required conditions in view of (b).

  (d) For $a, p, q \in \mathbb{R}^n$ assume that all triangles $0\,a\,p, \ 0\,a\,q, \ p\,0\,q, \ p\,a\,q$ have area 1. Then

$$p + q = a \text{ or } \| p - q \| = \| a \| .$$

Proof.   Let ω, σ be real numbers such that

$$s := p - \omega a \perp a \text{ and } t := q - \sigma a \perp a$$

hold true, where $x \perp y$ is defined by $x \cdot y = 0$. Since $0ap$ and $0aq$ have area 1, we get

$$a^2 s^2 = 4 = a^2 t^2,$$

in view of (3). Hence $t^2 = s^2 =: \varrho > 0$. Thus $\lambda^2 \le \varrho^2$ with $\lambda := ts$, since $(ts)^2 \le t^2 s^2$. This implies that $\varrho \ge |\lambda|$, i.e. $\varrho + \lambda$ and $\varrho - \lambda$ are non–negative. Since $p0q, paq$ also have area 1, we obtain

$$4 = \varrho^2 - \lambda^2 + 4\omega^2 + 4\sigma^2 - 2\omega\sigma\lambda a^2 \tag{5}$$

and

$$4 = \varrho^2 - \lambda^2 + 4(\omega - 1)^2 + 4(\sigma - 1)^2 - 2(\omega - 1)(\sigma - 1)\lambda a^2.$$

This implies that $(\omega + \sigma - 1)(\varrho - \lambda) = 0$ since $4 = \varrho a^2$. Assume that $\varrho = \lambda$. Then

$$(t - s)^2 = t^2 - 2ts + s^2 = 0,$$

i.e. $t = s$. Hence

$$4 = 4\omega^2 + 4\sigma^2 - 2\omega\sigma \cdot 4$$

from (5), i.e. $(\omega - \sigma)^2 = 1$, i.e. $\| p - q \| = \| a \|$ since $p - q = (\omega - \sigma)a$.

Assume $\varrho = -\lambda \neq \lambda$. Then $\omega + \sigma - 1 = 0$ and

$$(t + s)^2 = t^2 + 2ts + s^2 = 0,$$

i.e. $t = -s$. Thus $p + q = a$.

Finally assume that $\varrho \notin \{\lambda, -\lambda\}$. From (5) and $\omega + \sigma = 1$, we obtain $\varrho(\varrho - \lambda) = 8\omega\sigma$, i.e.

$$(p - q)^2 = (s - t)^2 + (\omega - \sigma)^2 a^2 = 2(\varrho - \lambda) + (1 - 4\omega\sigma)a^2 = a^2.$$

(e) Assume that all the triangles $0\,a\,b,\ 0\,b\,p,\ 0\,b\,q,\ 0\,a\,p,\ p\,b\,q$ have area 1 and that $p + q = a$ holds true. Then $ab = b^2$.

Proof. Since $0ab$ has area 1, the elements a, b are linearly independent. Let $r \in \mathbb{R}^n$ be an element $\neq 0$ with $ar = 0 = br$, and put

$$p =: \alpha a + \beta b + s, \quad q := \gamma a + \delta b + t$$

with suitable multiples s and t of r and real numbers $\alpha, \beta, \gamma, \delta$. From $p + q = a$ follows $\alpha + \gamma = 1$, $\delta = -\beta$, $s + t = 0$ and hence $t^2 = s^2 = -st$. The triangles $0ab, 0bp, 0bq$ have area 1, i.e.

$$a^2 b^2 = 4 + (ab)^2, \quad b^2 p^2 = 4 + (bp)^2, \quad b^2 q^2 = 4 + (bq)^2.$$

Hence $4(1 - \alpha^2) = b^2 s^2 = 4(1 - \gamma^2)$, i.e. $\alpha^2 = \gamma^2$. This together with $\alpha + \gamma = 1$ implies that $\alpha = \gamma = \frac{1}{2}$, i.e. $b^2 s^2 = 3$. — Since $0ap, pbq$ have area 1, we obtain

$$4(1 - \beta)^2 = a^2 s^2 = 4(1 - \beta^2) - 4s^2 b \cdot (b - a),$$

i.e. $(a - b) \cdot b = 0$, since $s^2 \neq 0$ from $b^2 s^2 = 3$.

(f) Assume that the following triangles have area 1:

i) $c\,a\,p,\ c\,a\,q,\ c\,a\,r,\ c\,b\,p,\ c\,b\,q,\ c\,b\,r,$

ii) $p\,a\,q,\ q\,a\,r,\ p\,c\,q,\ q\,c\,r,\ p\,b\,q,\ q\,b\,r,$

iii) $a\,b\,c.$

Then $\| a - c \| = \| b - c \|$.

Proof. Without loss of generality we may take $c = 0$. If $p + q = a$, then $p + q \neq b$ and $ab = b^2$. This implies that $b^2 \neq a^2$ since $a^2 b^2 = 4 + (ab)^2$.

Since then $ab \neq a^2$ we get $q + r \neq b$ (see part (e) with a, b interchanged and p replaced by r). Thus $\| q - r \| = \| b \|$ (see part (d) with a and b interchanged and p replaced by r). But $q + r \neq a$ (otherwise $p = r$), so $\| q - r \| = \| a \|$ (see part (d) with p replaced by r). Hence $\| a \| = \| b \|$, which is impossible since $a^2 \neq b^2$. Thus our assumption that $p + q = a$ does not hold true. Then $\| p - q \| = \| a \|$ by (d) and similarly, $\| p - q \| = \| b \|$. Hence $\| a \| = \| b \|$.

(g) In order now to prove Theorem 2, consider a, b and c in $\mathbb{R}^n$ with

$$\| a - c \| = \| b - c \| = \sqrt{2} \text{ and } (a - c)(b - c) = 0.$$

Then there exist p, q, r in $\mathbb{R}^n$ satisfying the conditions i), ii) of (c). The images of these elements under $x \to x' = f(x)$ then satisfy the conditions i), ii), iii) of (f). Thus $\| a' - c' \| = \| b' - c' \|$.

Let $a_1, a_2, c \in \mathbb{R}^n$ be elements with

$$\| a_1 - c \| = \| a_2 - c \| = \sqrt{2}.$$

Then obviously there exists a $b \in \mathbb{R}^n$ since $n \geq 3$ such that

$$\| b - c \| = \sqrt{2}, \quad (b - c)(a_1 - c) = 0 = (b - c)(a_2 - c).$$

Thus, from the previous argument,

$$\| a_1' - c' \| = \| b' - c' \| = \| a_2' - c' \|.$$

Now let a, b, c, d be elements of $\mathbb{R}^n$ with

$$\| a - b \| = \| c - d \| = \sqrt{2}.$$

Since any two line segments of length $\sqrt{2}$ in $\mathbb{R}^n$ can be joined by a chain of line segments of length $\sqrt{2}$ concatenated end to end, we get from the previous argument that

$$\| a' - b' \| = \| c' - d' \| =: k > 0.$$

The mapping $x \to g(x) := \frac{\sqrt{2}}{k} f(x)$ preserves distance $\sqrt{2}$. Because of Theorem 1, g has the form (1) with orthogonal Q. But since $f(x) = \frac{k}{\sqrt{2}} g(x)$ preserves triangle area 1, $k = \sqrt{2}$. $\qquad \Box$

REMARK. H. Lenz [2] proves the following result: If $f : \mathbb{R}^n \to \mathbb{R}^n$ ($3 < n < \infty$) is an injective mapping which preserves the area of equilateral triangles of side length 1, then f has form (1) with orthogonal Q. For $n = 3$ the same also holds if the area of triangles with side lengths $1, 1, 1$ or $1, 1, \sqrt{2}$ is preserved.

5.1.3   All 2–point–invariants

We would like to determine all functions

$$f : \mathbb{R}^n \times \mathbb{R}^n \to W$$

into an abstract set $W \neq \emptyset$ such that

$$f(x, y) = f\big(\gamma(x), \gamma(y)\big) \tag{6}$$

holds true for all $x, y \in \mathbb{R}^n$ and all mappings $\gamma : \mathbb{R}^n \to \mathbb{R}^n$ of the form

$$\gamma(x) = xQ + t, \; QQ^T = E, \tag{7}$$

with a real matrix $t = (t_1 \ldots t_n)$ and a real $n \times n$–matrix Q.

LEMMA 3. *Let a, b, c, d be points of $\mathbb{R}^n$. Then there exists a mapping* (7) *with*

$$\gamma(a) = c \text{ and } \gamma(b) = d$$

if and only if $(a - b)^2 = (c - d)^2$ is satisfied.

Proof.   For a mapping of the form (7),

$$\big[\gamma(a) - \gamma(b)\big]\big[\gamma(a) - \gamma(b)\big]^T = (a - b)QQ^T(a - b)^T$$

holds true, i.e. $(c - d)^2 = (a - b)^2$. — Now let a, b, c, d be elements of $\mathbb{R}^n$ satisfying

$$(c - d)^2 = (a - b)^2. \tag{8}$$

$a = b$ implies $c = d$. Then $\gamma(x) = x + (c - a)$ is a mapping with $\gamma(a) = c$ and $\gamma(b) = d$. Assume that $a \neq b$. Define

$$\frac{a - b}{\| a - b \|} =: (v_{11}, \ldots, v_{1n}) \text{ and } \frac{c - d}{\| c - d \|} =: (w_{11}, \ldots, w_{1n})$$

and take orthogonal $n \times n$–matrices V, W the first rows of which are

$$(v_{11}, \ldots, v_{1n}), \; (w_{11}, \ldots, w_{1n}),$$

respectively. Then

$$\frac{a - b}{\| a - b \|} = (1, 0, \ldots, 0)V, \; \frac{c - d}{\| c - d \|} = (1, 0, \ldots, 0)W,$$

and hence $\gamma(x) := (x - a)V^{-1}W + c$ is a required mapping.   □

Let $W \neq \emptyset$ be a set and define $K := \mathbb{R}_{\geq 0}$.

THEOREM 4. *Suppose that g is a mapping from K into W. Then*

$$f(x, y) := g(\, \| x - y \| \,) \qquad (9)$$

is a solution of (6). If on the other hand,

$$f : \mathbb{R}^n \times \mathbb{R}^n \to W$$

is a solution of (6), then there exists a mapping

$$g : K \to W$$

such that (9) holds true.

Proof.   Let γ be a mapping of the form (7). Then

$$\| x - y \| = \| x' - y' \|$$

holds true for $x' = \gamma(x)$ and $y' = \gamma(y)$ in view of Lemma 3. Hence

$$f(x, y) = g(\, \| x - y \| \,) = g(\, \| x' - y' \| \,) = f(x', y').$$

Assume now that f satisfies (6). For $r \in K$, define $g(r)$ as follows: take elements $x, y \in \mathbb{R}^n$ such that $\| x - y \| = r$ holds true. Then put $g(r) := f(x, y)$. Such elements x, y exist, for instance $x = y = 0$ if $r = 0$ and

$$x = r \cdot \frac{a}{\| a \|}, \quad y = 0$$

if $r > 0$ where $a \neq 0$ is an element of $\mathbb{R}^n$ (observe that $n \geq 1$). Moreover, g is well-defined: if u, v are also elements of $\mathbb{R}^n$ such that $\| u - v \| = r$ holds true, then

$$(x - y)^2 = r^2 = (u - v)^2$$

implies the existence of a mapping of the form (7), say γ, with

$$\gamma(x) = u \text{ and } \gamma(y) = v.$$

Hence

$$f(x, y) = f(\gamma(x), \gamma(y)) = f(u, v).$$

From the definition of g, we thus get $f(x, y) = g(r) = g(\| x - y \|)$.   □

We now would like to characterize euclidean distances:

THEOREM 5. *Let $f : \mathbb{R}^n \times \mathbb{R}^n \to \mathbb{R}_{\geq 0}$ be a mapping such that*

(i) $f(x,y) = f(\gamma(x),\gamma(y))$ *holds true for all* $x,y \in \mathbb{R}^n$ *and all mappings of the form* (7),

(ii) *if* x,z *and* $y = \lambda x + (1-\lambda)z$ *with* $0 \leq \lambda \leq 1$ *are elements of* $\mathbb{R}^n$, *then*

$$f(x,z) = f(x,y) + f(y,z), \tag{10}$$

(iii) there exists an $a \neq 0$ *in* $\mathbb{R}^n$ *with* $f(0,a) = \| a \|$.

Then

$$f(x,y) = \sqrt{\sum_{i=1}^{n}(x_i - y_i)^2}$$

holds true for all $x,y \in \mathbb{R}^n$.

Proof.   Let $a \neq 0$ be an element of $\mathbb{R}^n$ with $f(0,a) = \| a \|$. Equation (10) yields $f(0,0) = 0$ for $x = y = z = 0$. Because of (i) and Theorem 4,

$$f(x,y) = g(\| x - y \|) \geq 0$$

for all $x,y \in \mathbb{R}^n$. Hence $g(0) = 0$ and

$$g(\alpha + \beta) = g(\alpha) + g(\beta)$$

for all $\alpha, \beta \in \mathbb{R}_{\geq 0}$ such that $0 \in \{\alpha, \beta\}$. Let α, β be positive real numbers and put

$$x = \frac{(\alpha + \beta) \cdot a}{\| a \|}, \quad z = 0, \quad \lambda = \frac{\alpha}{\alpha + \beta}$$

and $y = \lambda x + (1-\lambda)z$. Then (10) implies

$$g(\alpha + \beta) = g(\beta) + g(\alpha).$$

Because of Theorem 5, chapter 2, we have that $g(t) = kt$ for all $t \geq 0$ with a constant $k \geq 0$. Finally

$$\| a \| = f(0,a) = g(\| a \|) = k \cdot \| a \|,$$

i.e. $k = 1$. Hence $f(x,y) = g(\| x - y \|) = \| x - y \|$. $\square$

5.1.4   All 3–point–invariants

We already encountered an important 3–point–invariant in section 5.1.2, namely $\triangle(a,b,c)$. More precisely it is the function

$$\triangle : \mathbb{R}^n \times \mathbb{R}^n \times \mathbb{R}^n \to \mathbb{R}_{\geq 0}$$

satisfying (4). This invariant is a defining one, even a strong one, when $n \geq 3$ in view of Theorem 2. In the case $n = 2$ of course, $\triangle$ cannot be a defining invariant for euclidean geometry. — It might be mentioned that (4) offers an obvious geometric interpretation of the Cauchy–Schwarz–inequality:

$$\left[2\triangle(x,y,0)\right]^2 = \sum_{i=1}^{n} x_i^2 \cdot \sum_{i=1}^{n} y_i^2 - \left(\sum_{i=1}^{n} x_i y_i\right)^2 .$$

The question to characterize all 3–point–invariants of euclidean geometry is of course connected with the question of congruence of two triangles. Here there are different (but equivalent) answers possible.

LEMMA 6. *Let $a_1, a_2, a_3, b_1, b_2, b_3$ be points of $\mathbb{R}^n$. Then there exists a mapping (7) with*

$$\gamma(a_i) = b_i \ for \ all \ i \in \{1,2,3\} \tag{11}$$

if and only if

$$\| \, a_i - a_j \, \| = \| \, b_i - b_j \, \| \tag{12}$$

is satisfied for all $i, j \in \{1,2,3\}$ with $i < j$.

Proof.   If γ is a mapping of the form (7) such that (11) holds true, then (12) also holds true because of Lemma 3. Now let $a_1, \ldots, b_3$ be points such that (12) is satisfied. In all the cases where

$$\#\{a_1, a_2, a_3\} \leq 2,$$

there exists γ as needed, in view of (12) and Lemma 3. Assume that a_1, a_2, a_3 are pairwise distinct. Then b_1, b_2, b_3 are also pairwise distinct, because of (12). If a_1, a_2, a_3 are on a common line l, then b_1, b_2, b_3 are also on a common line in view of (12). In this case we may assume without loss of generality that a_2 is on l between a_1 and a_3. Because of Lemma 3, there exists a mapping γ of the form (7) satisfying

$$\gamma(a_1) = b_1 \ and \ \gamma(a_3) = b_3. \tag{13}$$

Now

$$a_2 = \lambda a_1 + (1 - \lambda)a_3 \text{ with } \lambda = \frac{\| a_2 - a_3 \|}{\| a_1 - a_3 \|}$$

implies that

$$\gamma(a_2) = \lambda\gamma(a_1) + (1 - \lambda)\gamma(a_3),$$

and hence $\gamma(a_2) = b_2$, because of (13) and (12). If finally a_1, a_2, a_3 are not on a common line, then b_1, b_2, b_3 are also not collinear, i.e. they are not on a common line. Observe that this implies that $n \geq 2$. Put

$$\| a_2 - a_1 \| =: p_3, \; \| a_3 - a_2 \| =: p_1, \; \| a_1 - a_3 \| =: p_2.$$

Since $p_i + p_j > p_k$ for $\{i, j, k\} = \{1, 2, 3\}$, we get

$$2p_2p_3 > \left| - p_1^2 + p_2^2 + p_3^2 \right|,$$

i.e. $p_2^2 > q_1^2$, where we put

$$q_1 := \frac{p_2^2 + p_3^2 - p_1^2}{2p_3}.$$

Define $q_2 > 0$ by $q_2^2 = p_2^2 - q_1^2$. For the points

$$c_1 := 0, \; c_2 := (p_3, 0, \ldots, 0), \; c_3 := (q_1, q_2, 0, \ldots, 0)$$

we then have

$$\| c_i - c_j \| = \| a_i - a_j \| \text{ for } i, j \in \{1, 2, 3\}.$$

Define

$$v_1 := \frac{a_2 - a_1}{p_3} \text{ and } w_1 := \frac{a_3 - a_1}{q_2} - \frac{q_1}{q_2} \frac{a_2 - a_1}{p_3}.$$

Since $v_1^2 = 1 = w_1^2$ and $v_1w_1 = 0$ hold true, there exists a real orthogonal $n \times n$–matrix Q_1 such that v_1, w_1 are the first and second row of Q_1 respectively. Hence

$$\gamma_1(c_i) = a_i \text{ for } i = 1, 2, 3$$

where we put $\gamma_1(x) = xQ_1 + a_1$. Similarly, with

$$v_2 := \frac{b_2 - b_1}{p_3} \text{ and } w_2 := \frac{b_3 - b_1}{q_2} - \frac{q_1}{q_2} \frac{b_2 - b_1}{p_3}$$

we get $\gamma_2(c_i) = b_i$ for $i = 1, 2, 3$. Hence

$$\gamma_2\gamma_1^{-1}(a_i) = b_i \text{ for } i = 1, 2, 3. \square$$

Let $W \neq \emptyset$ be a set and define

$$K = \{(r_1, r_2, r_3) \in \mathbb{R}^3 \mid \forall_{\{i,j,k\}=\{1,2,3\}} 0 \leq r_i \leq r_j + r_k\}.$$

We would like to determine all functions

$$f : \mathbb{R}^n \times \mathbb{R}^n \times \mathbb{R}^n \to W$$

such that

$$f(x, y, z) = f\big(\gamma(x), \gamma(y), \gamma(z)\big) \tag{14}$$

holds true for all $x, y, z \in \mathbb{R}^n$ and all mappings γ of the form (7).

THEOREM 7. *Suppose that g is a mapping from K into W. Then*

$$f(x, y, z) := g\big(\| y - z \|,\ \| z - x \|,\ \| x - y \| \big) \tag{15}$$

is a solution of the functional equation (14). *If on the other hand,*

$$f : \mathbb{R}^n \times \mathbb{R}^n \times \mathbb{R}^n \to W,\ n \geq 2 \tag{16}$$

is a solution of (14), *then there exists a mapping*

$$g : K \to W$$

such that (15) *holds true.*

Proof. Obviously, (15) is a solution of (14). — Assume now that (16) satisfies (14). For $(r_1, r_2, r_3) \in K$ define $g(r_1, r_2, r_3)$ as follows: take elements $x, y, z \in \mathbb{R}^3$ such that

$$r_1 = \| y - z \|,\ r_2 = \| z - x \|,\ r_3 = \| x - y \|$$

holds true. Then put

$$g(r_1, r_2, r_3) := f(x, y, z).$$

Such elements x, y, z exist: they can easily be found if at least one of the components of $(r_1, r_2, r_3) \in K$ is zero, since then the other two must coincide. In the remaining cases put $x = 0$, $y = (r_3, 0, \ldots, 0)$ and $z = (t_1, t_2, 0, \ldots, 0)$ (observe that $n \geq 2$) such that $\| y - z \| = r_1$ and $\| z - x \| = r_2$ (observe that $r_1 + r_2 \geq r_3$). Moreover, g is well–defined: if u, v, w are also elements of $\mathbb{R}^n$ with

$$\| v - w \| = r_1,\ \| w - u \| = r_2,\ \| u - v \| = r_3,$$

then according to Lemma 6, there exists a γ of the form (7) such that

$$\gamma(x) = u,\ \gamma(y) = v,\ \gamma(z) = w$$

hold true. But then

$$f(x, y, z) = f\big(\gamma(x), \gamma(y), \gamma(z)\big) = f(u, v, w).$$

We hence have

$$f(x, y, z) = g(\| y - z \|, \| z - x \|, \| x - y \|)$$

for all $x, y, z \in \mathbb{R}^n$. $\qquad\qquad\qquad\qquad\qquad\qquad\qquad\qquad$ $\square$

In order to write the 3–point–invariant $\triangle(x, y, z)$ in the form (15), we observe that

$$[(x - z) - (y - z)]^2 = (x - z)^2 - 2(x - z)(y - z) + (y - z)^2 \qquad (17)$$

and hence, in view of (4),

$$\triangle(x, y, z) = \frac{1}{2}\sqrt{(x - z)^2(y - z)^2 - \frac{1}{4}[(x - z)^2 + (y - z)^2 - (x - y)^2]^2}.$$

Thus $\triangle(x, y, z) = g(\| y - z \|, \| z - x \|, \| x - y \|)$ with

$$g(r_1, r_2, r_3) = \frac{1}{2}\sqrt{r_1^2 \, r_2^2 - \frac{1}{4}(r_1^2 + r_2^2 - r_3^2)^2}$$

for all $(r_1, r_2, r_3) \in K$.

We have already mentioned that there are different (but equivalent) answers possible to the problem of finding all 3–point–invariants. Thinking of the side–angle–side theorem for congruent triangles, we might try to characterize 3–point–invariants in form of

$$f(x, y, z) = \bar{g}\left(\| x - z \|, \| y - z \|, \frac{(x - z)(y - z)}{\| x - z \| \cdot \| y - z \|}\right).$$

But this seems not to be a good expression, since the cases $x = z$ or $y = z$ are not included. So it might be better to try with

$$f(x, y, z) = h(\| x - z \|, \| y - z \|, (x - z)(y - z)).$$

The characterization is now possible by means of Theorem 7 because the equations

$$(x - z)(y - z) = \tfrac{1}{2}(\| x - z \|^2 + \| y - z \|^2 - \| x - y \|^2),$$
$$\| x - y \| = \sqrt{\| x - z \|^2 + \| y - z \|^2 - 2(x - z)(y - z)}$$

hold true from (17), which imply that a function in

$$\| x - z \|, \| y - z \|, (x - z)(y - z)$$

is also a function in

$$\| x - z \|, \| y - z \|, \| x - y \|$$

and vice versa.

5.2   Similarity transformations

5.2.1   Mappings preserving euclidean circles

By a *circle* of $\mathbb{R}^n$, $n \geq 2$, we mean in this section an euclidean circle, i.e. the set of all points in a 2–dimensional plane E of $\mathbb{R}^n$ having a fixed distance $r > 0$ from a given point $m \in E$.

THEOREM 8. *Let $f : \mathbb{R}^n \to \mathbb{R}^n$, $n \geq 2$, be a bijection such that the image of every circle of $\mathbb{R}^n$ is contained in a circle. Then there exists a real $k > 0$ and a mapping γ of the form (7) such that*

$$f(x) = k \cdot \gamma(x) \tag{18}$$

holds true for all $x \in \mathbb{R}^n$. Every mapping of the form (18) is on the other hand a bijective mapping of $\mathbb{R}^n$ such that images and pre–images of circles are circles.

Proof.   (a) The latter statement of Theorem 8 is obvious, since the inverse of a mapping (18) is again of the form (18), since f maps planes onto planes and since γ keeps distances invariant.

(b) Define $\varphi := f^{-1}$ and observe that φ is a bijection of $\mathbb{R}^n$. Let p_1, p_2, p_3 be three distinct points of $\mathbb{R}^n$ on a line l. We would like to show that then $\varphi(p_1)$, $\varphi(p_2)$, $\varphi(p_3)$ are also collinear points. Assume that there is no line containing $\varphi(p_1)$, $\varphi(p_2)$, $\varphi(p_3)$. Then there exists a euclidean circle c through these points and, since $f(c)$ is contained in a euclidean circle c', the points

$$f\big[\varphi(p_i)\big] = p_i, \; i = 1, 2, 3,$$

must be in c'. But this is not true since a euclidean circle cannot contain three distinct and collinear points. The points $\varphi(p_i)$, $i = 1, 2, 3$, are hence collinear. According to A.3.1, GT 104 ff, and to Proposition 3 of the present chapter 1, φ must be of the form

$$\varphi(y) = yR + b \tag{19}$$

with real matrices $b = (b_1 \ldots b_n)$ and

$$R = \begin{pmatrix} r_{11} & \cdots & r_{1n} \\ \vdots & & \\ r_{n1} & \cdots & r_{nn} \end{pmatrix}$$

with $\det R \neq 0$. Put $\varphi(y) =: x$. Then $f(x) = y$ and thus

$$f(x) = xR^{-1} - bR^{-1}$$

in view of (19). With $R^{-1} = Q$ and $-bR^{-1} =: a$ we shall write

$$f(x) = xQ + a \qquad (20)$$

with real matrices $a = (a_1 \ldots a_n)$ and

$$Q = \begin{pmatrix} q_{11} & \cdots & q_{1n} \\ \vdots & & \\ q_{n1} & \cdots & q_{nn} \end{pmatrix}$$

with $\det Q \neq 0$.

Denote the i-th row of Q by q_i. Let $i \neq j$ be fixed integers in $\{1, \ldots, n\}$ and consider the circle $x(t)$, $t \in [0, 2\pi[$, of $\mathbb{R}^n$ with

$$x_\nu(t) = \begin{cases} \cos t & \nu = i \\ \sin t & \text{for} \quad \nu = j \\ 0 & \nu \neq i, j \end{cases}$$

for $\nu \in \{1, \ldots, n\}$. Denote by m the center and by r the radius of the image circle. Then according to (20),

$$(q_i \cdot \cos t + q_j \cdot \sin t + a - m)^2 = r^2$$

for all $t \in [0, 2\pi[$. Applying this equation for the pairs

$$t \in \{0, \pi\}, \ t \in \left\{\frac{1}{2}\pi, \frac{3}{2}\pi\right\}, \ t \in \left\{\frac{1}{4}\pi, \frac{7}{4}\pi\right\}$$

we get $q_i^2 = q_j^2$ and $q_i q_j = 0$. Hence

$$p := q_1^2 = \ldots = q_n^2 > 0$$

and $q_i q_j = 0$ for all $i \neq j$ in $\{1, \ldots, n\}$. Put $p =: k^2$ with $k > 0$ and $kQ_1 := Q$. Then

$$f(x) = k \cdot \left[xQ_1 + \frac{1}{k}a\right]$$

with $Q_1 Q_1^T = E$. Hence f is of the form (18). $\qquad \square$

The mappings (18) are called the similarity transformations of $\mathbb{R}^n$. They all are characterized by Theorem 8 as the automorphism group of the block space consisting of $\mathbb{R}^n$, $n \geq 2$, as the set of points and with the circles of $\mathbb{R}^n$ as blocks. A *block space* is a set $S \neq \emptyset$, the elements of which are called *points*, and a set $\mathbb{B}$ of subsets of S, the elements of which are called *blocks*. *Automorphisms* of $(S, \mathbb{B})$ are bijections of S such that images and pre–images of blocks are blocks.

Similarity transformations are products of mappings γ of the form (7), called *congruent mappings*, and *dilatations*, i.e. mappings of the form

$$x \to \lambda x + t$$

with a real $\lambda \neq 0$ and a matrix $t = (t_1 \ldots t_n)$.

For the remaining part of this section 5.2 we denote by G the group of similarity transformations of $\mathbb{R}^n$. We are interested in the geometry $(\mathbb{R}^n, G)$ which we will call the n–dimensional geometry of similarity transformations. The set of circles of $\mathbb{R}^n$ is an invariant notion of $(\mathbb{R}^n, G)$, and even a defining one in view of Theorem 8.

5.2.2   All 2–line–invariants

LEMMA 9. *Let $a_1, a_2, a_3, b_1, b_2, b_3$ be points of $\mathbb{R}^n$. Then there exists a mapping (18) with*

$$f(a_i) = b_i \text{ for all } i \in \{1, 2, 3\}$$

if and only if there exists a real $k > 0$ such that

$$k \cdot \| a_i - a_j \| = \| b_i - b_j \|$$

is satisfied for all $i, j \in \{1, 2, 3\}$ with $i < j$.

Proof.   If f is the mapping (18) with $f(a_i) = b_i$ for $i = 1, 2, 3$, then

$$\| f(a_i) - f(a_j) \| = \| k\gamma(a_i) - k\gamma(a_j) \| = k \cdot \| a_i - a_j \|,$$

since γ preserves distances. — If on the other hand,

$$k \cdot \| a_i - a_j \| = \| b_i - b_j \| \text{ for } i, j \in \{1, 2, 3\}$$

holds true, apply Lemma 6 to the points

$$ka_1, ka_2, ka_3, b_1, b_2, b_3.$$

Then there exists a mapping of the form (7),

$$\gamma(x) = xQ + t, \ QQ^T = E,$$

with

$$\gamma(ka_i) = b_i \text{ for } i = 1, 2, 3.$$

Put $f(x) := k \cdot \left(xQ + \frac{1}{k}t\right)$. Then $f(a_i) = b_i$ for $i = 1, 2, 3$ and f is moreover of type (18).   □

LEMMA 10. *Let l_1, l_2, l_3, l_4 be lines of $\mathbb{R}^n$, $n \geq 2$, with*

$$l_i = \{p_i + \lambda v_i \mid \lambda \in \mathbb{R}\}, \ i = 1, 2, 3, 4.$$

There exists a mapping $f \in G$ with

$$f(l_1) = l_3 \text{ and } f(l_2) = l_4$$

if and only if

$$\varepsilon(l_1, l_2) = \varepsilon(l_3, l_4) \quad and \quad \frac{(v_1 v_2)^2}{v_1^2 \, v_2^2} = \frac{(v_3 v_4)^2}{v_3^2 \, v_4^2} \qquad (21)$$

hold true, where we put

$$\varepsilon(l_1, l_2) = \begin{cases} 0 \\ 1 \end{cases} \quad for \quad \begin{matrix} l_1 \cap l_2 = \emptyset \\ l_1 \cap l_2 \neq \emptyset \end{matrix} \ .$$

Proof.   Let f be a mapping of the form (18) such that $f(l_1) = l_3$ and $f(l_2) = l_4$ hold true. If $l_1 \cap l_2 = \emptyset$ then $f(l_1) \cap f(l_2) = \emptyset$ and vice versa. Hence $\varepsilon(l_1, l_2) = \varepsilon(l_3, l_4)$. Also, the remaining part of (21) holds true. — Suppose now that l_1, l_2, l_3, l_4 are lines satisfying (21).

Case 1: $\varepsilon(l_1, l_2) = 1$. Assume $l_1 = l_2$. Then (21) yields

$$(v_3 v_4)^2 = v_3^2 \, v_4^2$$

and hence that v_3, v_4 are linearly dependent. This implies that $l_3 = l_4$, since $\varepsilon(l_3, l_4) = 1$. Take two points $a \neq b$ on l_1 and two points $c \neq d$ on l_3 with $\| a - b \| = \| c - d \|$. Then there exists a γ of the form (7) with $\gamma(a) = c$, $\gamma(b) = d$ and thus with $\gamma(l_1) = l_3$. Assume $l_1 \neq l_2$. This implies that $l_3 \neq l_4$, since otherwise $(v_1 v_2)^2 = v_1^2 \, v_2^2$, i.e. $l_1 = l_2$. Define

$$a_3 :\in l_1 \cap l_2 \text{ and } b_3 :\in l_3 \cap l_4$$

and take points $a_1 \in l_1$, $a_2 \in l_2$, $b_1 \in l_3$, $b_2^* \in l_4$ with

$$1 = \| a_1 - a_3 \| = \| b_1 - b_3 \| \quad \text{and} \quad 1 = \| a_2 - a_3 \| = \| b_2^* - b_3 \| .$$

Now (21) implies that $\left[(a_1 - a_3)(a_2 - a_3)\right]^2 = \left[(b_1 - b_3)(b_2^* - b_3)\right]^2$. Choose

$$b_2 \in \{b_2^*,\ 2b_3 - b_2^*\}$$

such that $(a_1 - a_3)(a_2 - a_3) = (b_1 - b_3)(b_2 - b_3)$. Then $b_2 \in l_4 \backslash \{b_3\}$, $\| b_2 - b_3 \|$
$= \| b_2^* - b_3 \|$ and thus

$$(a_1 - a_2)^2 = (a_1 - a_3)^2 + (a_2 - a_3)^2 - 2(a_1 - a_3)(a_2 - a_3) = (b_1 - b_2)^2.$$

Because of Lemma 6 there exists a γ of the form (7) with $\gamma(a_i) = b_i$ for
$i = 1, 2, 3$. Hence $\gamma(l_1) = l_3$ and $\gamma(l_2) = l_4$.

Case 2: $\varepsilon(l_1, l_2) = 0$. This together with $\varepsilon(l_3, l_4) = 0$ implies that $l_1 \cap l_2 = \emptyset$
and $l_3 \cap l_4 = \emptyset$. Assume that $v_i^2 = 1$ for $i = 1, 2, 3, 4$. Then

$$w_1 := v_2 - (v_1\, v_2)v_1 = 0 \tag{22}$$

if and only if

$$w_3 := v_4 - (v_3\, v_4)v_3 = 0 \tag{23}$$

from (21). The lines l_1, l_2 are parallel iff (22) holds true.

We may assume that without loss of generality $v_1 v_2 = v_3 v_4$ since if $v_1 v_2 = -v_3 v_4$ in (21), v_4 could be replaced by $-v_4$. There exist points $a_1 \in l_1$, $a_2 \in l_2$
with

$$(a_1 - a_2)v_i = 0 \text{ for } i = 1, 2,$$

and points $b_1 \in l_3$, $b_2 \in l_4$ with

$$(b_1 - b_2)v_i = 0 \text{ for } i = 3, 4.$$

In view of Lemma 9 there exists an $f \in G$ if $l_1 \parallel l_2$ with

$$f(a_1) = b_1,\ f(a_2) = b_2,\ f(a_1 + v_1) = b_1 + kv_3$$

and $k \cdot \| a_1 - a_2 \| := \| b_1 - b_2 \|$. Hence $f(l_1) = l_3$ and $f(l_2) = l_4$ since
parallelism is preserved by f. — Finally assume that $l_1 \nparallel l_2$. Then $w_1 \neq 0$ in
(22) and hence $w_3 \neq 0$. Thus $\| w_1 \| = \| w_3 \|$, in view of (21). Put

$$e_1 := v_1,\ e_2 := \frac{w_1}{\| w_1 \|},\ e_3 := \frac{a_1 - a_2}{\| a_1 - a_2 \|}$$

and

$$E_1 := v_3, \; E_2 := \frac{w_3}{\| \, w_3 \, \|}, \; E_3 := \frac{b_1 - b_2}{\| \, b_1 - b_2 \, \|}.$$

Observe that $e_i e_j = E_i E_j$ for $i, j \in \{1, 2, 3\}$. Let

$$\gamma(x) = xQ$$

be a mapping with $QQ^T = E$ and $\gamma(e_i) = E_i$ for $i = 1, 2, 3$. Define

$$f(x) = k \cdot (x - a_1)Q + b_1, \; k \cdot \| \, a_1 - a_2 \, \| := \| \, b_1 - b_2 \, \|,$$

which has the form (18). Then $f(a_1) = b_1$, $f(a_2) = b_2$ and

$$f(a_1 + v_1) = b_1 + kv_3, \; f(a_2 + v_2) = b_2 + kv_4$$

by observing (note that $\| \, w_1 \, \| = \| \, w_3 \, \|$ and $v_1 v_2 = v_3 v_4$) that

$$v_2 Q = [w_1 + (v_1 v_2)v_1] \, Q = w_3 + (v_3 \, v_4)v_3 = v_4.$$

Hence $f(l_1) = l_3$ and $f(l_2) = l_4$.   □

Denote by M^n the set of all lines of $\mathbb{R}^n$ and define

$$K := \{0, 1\} \times [0, 1].$$

Let $W \neq \emptyset$ be a set. We would like to determine all functions

$$h : M^n \times M^n \to W \tag{24}$$

such that

$$h(l_1, l_2) = h\big(f(l_1), f(l_2)\big) \tag{25}$$

holds true for all $l_1, l_2 \in M^n$ and all mappings f of the form (18).

THEOREM 11. *Suppose that g is a mapping from K into W. Then*

$$h(l_1, l_2) := g\left(\varepsilon(l_1, l_2), \frac{(v_1 v_2)^2}{v_1^2 \, v_2^2} \right) \tag{26}$$

is a solution of the functional equation (25) where

$$l_i = \{p_i + \lambda v_i \mid \lambda \in \mathbb{R}\}, \; i = 1, 2. \tag{27}$$

If on the other hand, (24) with $n \geq 3$ is a solution of (25), then there exists a mapping

$$g : K \to W$$

such that (26) *holds true.*

   Proof.   Obviously, (26) satisfies (25). — Now let (24) be a solution of
(25). For $(r_1, r_2) \in K$, define $g(r_1, r_2)$ as follows: Take lines l_1, l_2 with

$$\varepsilon(l_1, l_2) = r_1 \text{ and } \frac{(v_1\, v_2)^2}{v_1^2\, v_2^2} = r_2.$$

Then put $g(r_1, r_2) := h(l_1, l_2)$. Such lines exist: set

$$p_1 = 0, \ v_1 = (1, 0, \ldots, 0), \ v_2 = \left(\sqrt{r_2}, \sqrt{1 - r_2}, 0 \ldots, 0\right)$$

and

$$p_2 = \begin{cases} 0 & r_1 = 1 \\ & \text{for} \\ (0, 0, 1, 0, \ldots, 0) & r_1 = 0 \end{cases}.$$

The function g is well–defined. If l_3, l_4 are lines of $\mathbb{R}^n$ with

$$\varepsilon(l_3, l_4) = r_1 \text{ and } \frac{(v_3 v_4)^2}{v_3^2\, v_4^2} = r_2,$$

then, according to Lemma 10, there exists a mapping f of the form (18) with
$f(l_1) = l_3$ and $f(l_2) = l_4$. But then

$$h(l_1, l_2) = h\big(f(l_1), f(l_2)\big) = h(l_3, l_4).$$

Hence $g(r_1, r_2) = h(l_3, l_4)$.   □

   REMARK. Put

$$\frac{v_1 v_2}{\sqrt{v_1^2}\sqrt{v_2^2}} =: \cos \alpha \text{ with } \alpha \in [0, \pi]$$

for the elements $v_1 \neq 0$ and $v_2 \neq 0$ of $\mathbb{R}^n$. The important values for the lines
l_1, l_2 of (27) are hence $\varepsilon(l_1, l_2)$ and $\cos^2 \alpha$ i.e. $\varepsilon(l_1, l_2)$ and $\{\alpha, \pi - \alpha\}$ since
$\cos^2 \alpha = \cos^2(\pi - \alpha)$.

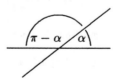

5.2.3 The set of angles as invariant notion

In order to avoid the ambiguity $\alpha, \pi - \alpha$ for the angle between two lines, we proceed as follows: an ordered pair of half–lines with the same endpoint is called an *angle* where a half–line with endpoint p is defined as point set

$$h := \{p + \lambda v \mid \lambda \in \mathbb{R}_{\geq 0}\}$$

with $v \neq 0$. The set of half–lines of $\mathbb{R}^n$ is an invariant notion of $(\mathbb{R}^n, G)$ and the set of angles is an invariant notion of $(\mathbb{R}^n, G)$ as well. Let two angles

$$(h_1, h_2, p) \text{ and } (h_3, h_4, q) \tag{28}$$

be given.

LEMMA 12. *There exists an $f \in G$ such that*

$$f(h_1) = h_3, \ f(h_2) = h_4, \ f(p) = q$$

holds true if and only if

$$\frac{v_1 v_2}{\sqrt{v_1^2 \, v_2^2}} = \frac{v_3 v_4}{\sqrt{v_3^2 \, v_4^2}}$$

is satisfied, where we put

$$h_i = \{p_i + \lambda v_i \mid \lambda \geq 0\}$$

with $p_1 = p_2 = p$ and $p_3 = p_4 = q$.

For the case $\varepsilon(l_1, l_2) = 1$ a proof of Lemma 12 can be given similar to the proof of Lemma 10.

The important invariant of an angle (h_1, h_2, p) is thus

$$\frac{v_1}{\sqrt{v_1^2}} \cdot \frac{v_2}{\sqrt{v_2^2}} =: \cos \alpha \tag{29}$$

with $\alpha \in [0, \pi]$. — If angle measures in $[0, 2\pi[$ should also play a role, we may define angles as objects

$$(h_1, h_2, p, A), \tag{30}$$

where A denotes an *angular space* of (h_1, h_2, p) when v_1, v_2 are linearly independent:

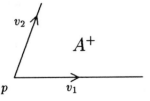
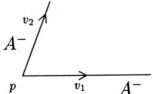

$$A^+ \quad := \quad \{p + \alpha_1 v_1 + \alpha_2 v_2 \mid \alpha_1 > 0 \text{ and } \alpha_2 > 0\},$$

$$A^- \quad := \quad \{p + \alpha_1 v_1 + \alpha_2 v_2 \mid \alpha_1, \alpha_2 \in \mathbb{R}\} \backslash (A^+ \cup h_1 \cup h_2).$$

The set ANG of objects (30) together with the objects

$$(h_1, h_2, p), \quad \text{if } \frac{v_1}{\sqrt{v_1^2}} = \frac{v_2}{\sqrt{v_2^2}}, \tag{31}$$

and

$$(h_1, h_2, p), \quad \text{if } \frac{v_1}{\sqrt{v_1^2}} = -\frac{v_2}{\sqrt{v_2^2}}, \tag{32}$$

is again an invariant notion. The important invariant is here the usual angle measure:

THEOREM 13. *Define for $(\mathbb{R}^n, G)$, $n \geq 2$,*

$$\sphericalangle(h_1, h_2, p, A) := \begin{cases} \alpha & A = A^+ \\ & for \\ 2\pi - \alpha & A = A^- \end{cases}$$

when v_1, v_2, are linearly independent, where $\alpha \in]0, \pi[$ is given by (29). Define the measure of (31), (32), as $0, \pi$, respectively. Suppose that g is a mapping from $[0, 2\pi[$ into the set $W \neq \emptyset$. Then

$$h(\omega) := g(\sphericalangle \omega) \text{ for } \omega \in ANG \tag{33}$$

is a solution $h : ANG \to W$ of the functional equation

$$\forall_{\omega \in ANG} \forall_{f \in G} \; h(\omega) = h(f(\omega)). \tag{34}$$

If on the other hand, $h : ANG \to W$ is a solution of (34), then there exists a

$$g : [0, 2\pi[\to W$$

such that (33) holds true.

Proof.   The image of $\{p + \lambda v \mid \lambda \geq 0\}$ under

$$f(x) = kxQ + t \tag{35}$$

with $QQ^T = E$ and $k > 0$ is

$$\{f(p + \lambda v) \mid \lambda \geq 0\},$$

i.e.

$$\{f(p) + \lambda \cdot kvQ \mid \lambda \geq 0\}.$$

The image of the angular space A^+ of (h_1, h_2, p) (here v_1, v_2 are linearly independent) is

$$f(A^+) = \{f(p) + \alpha_1 \cdot k v_1 Q + \alpha_2 \cdot k v_2 Q \mid 0 < \alpha_1, \alpha_2\},$$

i.e. $f(A^+)$ is the angular space A^+ of

$$\big(f(h_1),\ f(h_2),\ f(p)\big).$$

Hence $\sphericalangle(h_1, h_2, p, A) = \sphericalangle\big(f(h_1),\ f(h_2),\ f(p), f(A)\big)$. The function (33) is thus a solution of (34). — Conversely, if (33) is a solution of (34), we would like to define $g(\alpha)$ for $\alpha \in [0, 2\pi[$. Define $g(0)$, $g(\pi)$ respectively by

$$h\big(\sphericalangle(h_1, h_2, p)\big),$$

where (h_1, h_2, p) is given by (31), (32) respectively.

Now let α be a real number in $]0, \pi[$. Take (h_1, h_2, p) with (29). Then put

$$g(\alpha) := h(h_1, h_2, p, A^+).$$

In the case $\alpha \in]\pi, 2\pi[$, take (h_1, h_2, p) such that (29) again holds true. Now put

$$g(\alpha) := h(h_1, h_2, p, A^-).$$

In the case $\alpha \in]0, \pi[$, we must show that corresponding to

$$(h_1, h_2, p, A_{12}^+),\ (h_3, h_4, q, A_{34}^+)$$

with

$$\frac{v_1 v_2}{\sqrt{v_1^2}\, \sqrt{v_2^2}} = \frac{v_3 v_4}{\sqrt{v_3^2}\, \sqrt{v_4^2}}$$

there exists a mapping f of form (35) with

$$f(h_1) = h_3,\ f(h_2) = h_4,\ f(p) = q,\ f(A_{12}^+) = A_{34}^+.$$

But a mapping f of the form (35) that satisfies the first three of these equations, also satisfies $f(A_{12}^+) = A_{34}^+$, as we have seen at the beginning of this proof. $\quad\square$

We would like to return to the angles (28). The first observation is that corresponding to (h_1, h_2, p) there exists $f \in G$ with

$$f(h_1) = h_2,\ f(h_2) = h_1,\ f(p) = p.$$

This is a consequence of Lemma 12, since

$$\frac{v_1 v_2}{\sqrt{v_1^2}\, \sqrt{v_2^2}} = \frac{v_2 v_1}{\sqrt{v_2^2}\, \sqrt{v_1^2}}$$

holds true. Angles hence do not really depend on the order of h_1, h_2 in (h_1, h_2, p). Another observation is

THEOREM 14. *Let $f : \mathbb{R}^n \to \mathbb{R}^n$, $n \geq 2$, be a bijection such that the image of every half–line is subset of a half–line. Then the image $f(h)$ of a half–line h with endpoint p is a half–line with endpoint $f(p)$. If moreover*

$$\frac{v_1 v_2}{\sqrt{v_1^2\, v_2^2}} = \frac{v_3 v_4}{\sqrt{v_3^2\, v_4^2}} \tag{36}$$

holds true for every pair of angles (h_1, h_2, p) and (h_3, h_4, q) with

$$f(h_1) = h_3, \ f(h_2) = h_4, \ f(p) = q,$$

then $f \in G$.

Proof.   According to A.3.1 (GT 104) and Proposition 3, chapter 1,

$$f(x) = xQ + t$$

with $\det Q \neq 0$. The images of half–lines are hence half–lines and endpoints go over into endpoints. We will apply (36) in the cases

$$v_1, v_2 \in \big\{ (1,0,\ldots,0),\ (0,1,0,\ldots,0), \ldots, (0,\ldots,0,1) \big\}$$

by observing that

$$v_{i+2} = v_i Q \text{ for } i = 1, 2.$$

Call the rows of Q successively $q_1, \ldots, q_n$. Then $q_i q_j = 0$ for $i \neq j$ in $\{1, 2, \ldots, n\}$. Now apply (36) for an $i > 1$ for

$$v_1 = (v_{11}, \ldots, v_{1n}) \text{ and } v_2 = (v_{21}, \ldots, v_{2n})$$

with $v_{11} = v_{21} = 1 = v_{1i} = -v_{2i}$ and $v_{1j} = v_{2j} = 0$ otherwise. Then $q_1^2 = q_i^2$ for $i = 2, \ldots, n$. Thus $f \in G$.   □

5.2.4 Angle spaces

Let $M \neq \emptyset$ and W be sets and define

$$A := \big\{ (x, \{y, z\}) \mid x, y, z \in M \text{ with } x \notin \{y, z\} \big\}.$$

Suppose that ω is a mapping from A into W. Then

$$(M, A, W, \omega)$$

is called an *angle space*. What we have in mind by $(x, \{y, z\})$, say in the case $M := \mathbb{R}^n$, is the angle at x between the half–lines xy and xz, both with endpoint x. — Now let S be a fixed subset of A. Then the *problem of angle preservation* asks for all functions

$$f : M \to M$$

such that

$$\forall_{T \in S} \left[f(T) \in A \text{ and } \omega\big(f(T)\big) = \omega(T) \right] \tag{37}$$

holds true. Here $f(T)$ denotes $\big(f(x), \{f(y), f(z)\}\big)$ for $T = \big(x, \{y, z\}\big)$.

For the case $S = A$ (we call it the universal case) and for $M := \mathbb{R}^n$, $W := \mathbb{R}$, and

$$\omega\big(x, \{y, z\}\big) := \frac{(y - x)(z - x)}{\sqrt{(y - x)^2 (z - x)^2}} \tag{38}$$

for the euclidean scalar product, the functional equation is given by

$$\frac{\big(f(y) - f(x)\big)\big(f(z) - f(x)\big)}{\sqrt{\big(f(y) - f(x)\big)^2 \big(f(z) - f(x)\big)^2}} = \frac{(y - x)(z - x)}{\sqrt{(y - x)^2 (z - x)^2}}$$

for all $x, y, z \in \mathbb{R}^n$ such that $x \notin \{y, z\}$. The assumption that $f(T) \in A$ for $T \in A$ guarantees that $f(x) \notin \{f(y), f(z)\}$.

THEOREM 15. *Let Σ be the angle space*

$$(\mathbb{R}^n, A, \mathbb{R}, \omega), \ n \geq 2,$$

with ω as in (38). *Define*

$$S = \{T \in A \mid \omega(T) = 0\}.$$

The set of solutions of (37) *is then given by the group of similarities of $\mathbb{R}^n$.*

Proof.   (a) A solution f must be injective: let $x \neq y$ be elements of $\mathbb{R}^n$. Take $z \in \mathbb{R}^n$ with $T = \big(x, \{y, z\}\big) \in S$. Then $f(T) \in A$ implies that $f(x) \notin \{f(y), f(z)\}$.

(b) Let $x, p_1, q \in \mathbb{R}^n$ be distinct and collinear. Take points $p_2, \ldots, p_n$ such that

$$\omega\big(x, \{p_i, p_j\}\big) = 0$$

for all $i, j \in \{1, \ldots, n\}$ with $i \neq j$. Then we also get

$$\omega\big(x, \{p_i', p_j'\}\big) = 0$$

for $p_1' = q$ and $p_i' = p_i$ otherwise for all $i, j \in \{1, \ldots, n\}$ with $i \neq j$. Hence

$$\omega\big(f(x), \{f(p_i), f(p_j)\}\big) = 0 \tag{39}$$

and

$$\omega\big(f(x), \{f(p_i'), f(p_j')\}\big) = 0$$

for all $i, j \in \{1, \ldots, n\}$ with $i \neq j$. The points $f(x), f(p_1), f(q)$ must thus be collinear. The points $f(x), f(p_1), \ldots, f(p_n)$ are moreover not in a common hyperplane of $\mathbb{R}^n$ in view of (39). Now A.3.1 (GT 104) and Proposition 3, chapter 1, imply that

$$f(x) = xQ + t$$

with det $Q \neq 0$. Now proceed as in the proof of Theorem 14. $\square$

5.2.5 Additive angle measures

We have already mentioned that the important invariant of an angle (h_1, h_2, p) is given by

$$\frac{v_1 v_2}{\sqrt{v_1^2 \, v_2^2}} =: \cos \alpha, \ \alpha \in [0, \pi],$$

where we put

$$h_i = \{p + \lambda v_i \mid \lambda \geq 0\} \tag{40}$$

for $i = 1, 2$. In other words, all functions

$$h : ANG_{[0,\pi]} \to W, \tag{41}$$

where $ANG_{[0,\pi]}$ denotes the set of all (h_1, h_2, p) with (40) and where $W \neq \emptyset$ is a set satisfying

$$h(h_1, h_2, p) = h\big(f(h_1), f(h_2), f(p)\big) \tag{42}$$

for all $(h_1, h_2, p) \in ANG_{[0,\pi]}$ and all $f \in G$, are given by

$$h(h_1, h_2, p) = g\left(\frac{v_1 v_2}{\sqrt{v_1^2 \, v_2^2}}\right) \tag{43}$$

where g is a mapping from $[-1, 1]$ into W. Put $W := \mathbb{R}_{\geq 0}$ and consider the following property:

(∗) *If $h_3 = \{p + \lambda v_3 \mid \lambda \geq 0\}$ is part of $A^+ \cup h_1 \cup h_2$, where A^+ is defined with respect to (h_1, h_2, p), then*

$$h(h_1, h_2, p) = h(h_1, h_3, p) + h(h_3, h_2, p).$$

THEOREM 16. *A function of the form* (41) *with $W = \mathbb{R}_{\geq 0}$ and satisfying* (42) *and* (∗) *for all $f \in G$ and all half–lines h_1, h_2, h_3 through the point $p \in \mathbb{R}^n$, $n \geq 2$, is given by*

$$h(h_1, h_2, p) = k \cdot \alpha$$

where $k \geq 0$ is a fixed real number and where

$$\arccos \frac{v_1 v_2}{\sqrt{v_1^2 \, v_2^2}} =: \alpha \in [0, \pi].$$

Proof.   Put $g(\cos t) =: \varphi(t)$ for $0 \leq t \leq \pi$. Let $t_1, t_2 \in [0, \pi]$ be real numbers such that $t_1 + t_2 \leq \pi$. Set $p = 0$ and

$$
\begin{aligned}
v_1 &= (1, 0, \ldots, 0), \\
v_2 &= (\cos(t_1 + t_2), \sin(t_1 + t_2), 0, \ldots, 0), \\
v_3 &= (\cos t_1, \sin t_1, 0, \ldots, 0).
\end{aligned}
$$

Then (∗) and (43) imply

$$\varphi(t_1 + t_2) = \varphi(t_1) + \varphi(t_2).$$

As in section 3.5, we then get $\varphi(t) = k \cdot t$.   □

5.3   Equiaffine geometry

5.3.1   A theorem of G. Martin

THEOREM 17. *Let $f : \mathbb{R}^2 \to \mathbb{R}^2$ be a mapping satisfying*

$$\forall_{a, b, c \in \mathbb{R}^2} \; \triangle(a, b, c) = 1 \Rightarrow \triangle(f(a), f(b), f(c)) = 1$$

where $\triangle(a, b, c)$ denotes the area of the triangle with vertices a, b, c. Then there exist real numbers

$$a_{ij}, \; i, j \in \{1, 2\}, \quad \text{and} \quad a_1, a_2$$

with $(a_{11}a_{22} - a_{12}a_{21})^2 = 1$ such that

$$f(x) = x \begin{pmatrix} a_{11} & a_{12} \\ a_{21} & a_{22} \end{pmatrix} + (a_1 a_2)$$

holds true for all $x \in \mathbb{R}^2$.

Proof.   (a) The mapping f must be injective. (Use the argument of part (a) of the proof of Theorem 2.)

(b) Let p_1, p_2, p_3 be distinct points on the line l of $\mathbb{R}^2$. We would like to show that p_1', p_2', p_3' are then collinear as well, where z' denotes $f(z)$ for $z \in \mathbb{R}^2$. Assume that p_1', p_2', p_3' are not collinear. For $x \in \mathbb{R}^2 \backslash l$ choose $y(x)$ on the line l_x through x and parallel to l with $\triangle(x, y, p_1) = 1$. Then $\triangle(x, y, p_i) = 1$ for $i = 1, 2, 3$. Thus $\triangle(x', y', p_i') = 1$. There hence exists an $i \in \{1, 2, 3\}$ with $x', y' \in m_i$ where m_i is the line parallel to the line l_{jk} through p_j', p_k' with $\{1, 2, 3\} = \{i, j, k\}$ such that the distance between m_i, l_{jk} is the same as that between m_i and p_i'. Hence

$$f(\mathbb{R}^2 \backslash l) \subseteq m_1 \cup m_2 \cup m_3. \tag{44}$$

Now take a fixed $x \in \mathbb{R}^2 \backslash l$ and a fixed $y(x)$ as described above. Let $l_- \neq l$ be the line parallel to l with $\triangle(x, y, q) = 1$ for all $q \in l_-$. Then

$$\triangle(x', y', z') = 1$$

for all $z \in l_-$ and thus $z' \in l_{jk} \cup l_{jk,i}$ where $l_{jk,i}$ is the line through p_i' and parallel to l_{jk}. Hence

$$f(l_-) \subseteq (m_1 \cup m_2 \cup m_3) \cap (l_{jk} \cup l_{jk,i}) \tag{45}$$

in view of (44). The mapping f is injective and $f(l_-)$ thus contains infinitely many points, whereas the right hand side of (45) only contains three points.

(c) Put $a = 0$, $b = (1, 0)$, $c = (0, 2)$. Then $\triangle(a', b', c') = 1$, i.e. $f(\mathbb{R}^2)$ is not collinear. Now A.3.1 in GT 104 implies that

$$x' = x \cdot \begin{pmatrix} a_{11} & a_{12} \\ a_{21} & a_{22} \end{pmatrix} + (a_1 a_2)$$

for all $x \in \mathbb{R}^2$. Looking at the image triangle of $(0,0)$, $(1,0)$, $(0,2)$ which has area 1, we get $(a_{11}a_{22} - a_{12}a_{21})^2 = 1$.   □

For the elements

$$a = (a_1, a_2), \ b = (b_1, b_2), \ c = (c_1, c_2)$$

of $\mathbb{R}^2$ define

$$F(a,b,c) := \begin{vmatrix} a_1 & a_2 & 1 \\ b_1 & b_2 & 1 \\ c_1 & c_2 & 1 \end{vmatrix}.$$

Put $\alpha_i := a_i - c_i$ and $\beta_i := b_i - c_i$ for $i = 1, 2$. Then (4) implies

$$4\triangle^2 = (\alpha_1^2 + \alpha_2^2)(\beta_1^2 + \beta_2^2) - (\alpha_1\beta_1 + \alpha_2\beta_2)^2 = (\alpha_1\beta_2 - \beta_1\alpha_2)^2.$$

This, together with

$$F(a,b,c) := \begin{vmatrix} \alpha_1 & \alpha_2 & 0 \\ \beta_1 & \beta_2 & 0 \\ c_1 & c_2 & 1 \end{vmatrix},$$

yields

$$2 \cdot \triangle(a,b,c) = |F(a,b,c)|$$

since $\triangle \geq 0$.

We may pose the following problem, which is part of the problem in section 5.1.2, which we called there the *general version*: let R be a ring as described in the Remark of section 1.3 (we may even drop the assumption there that $1+1$ is not a zero divisor of R).

Determine now all functions

$$\varphi, \psi : R^2 \to R$$

such that

$$\left[F\big(f(a), f(b), f(c)\big) \right]^2 = 1$$

holds true for all $a, b, c \in R^2$ satisfying

$$\left[F(a,b,c) \right]^2 = 1$$

where we put $f(x) := \big(\varphi(x_1, x_2), \psi(x_1, x_2)\big)$ for $x = (x_1, x_2) \in R^2$.

Theorem 17 is the solution of this problem when $R := \mathbb{R}$.

5.3.2 n–dimensional equiaffine geometry

The mappings

$$f(x) = xQ + t$$

7*

with real matrices $t = (t_1 \ldots t_n)$ and

$$
Q = \begin{pmatrix} q_{11} & \cdots & q_{1n} \\ \vdots & & \vdots \\ q_{n1} & \cdots & q_{nn} \end{pmatrix}
$$

such that $[\det Q]^2 = 1$, are called *equiaffine mappings* of $\mathbb{R}^n$, $n \geq 1$. In the case $n = 2$ they have already occured in Martin's Theorem. In this section we denote by G the group of all equiaffine mappings of $\mathbb{R}^n$. The geometry (S, G) with $S = \mathbb{R}^n$ is called n–dimensional *equiaffine geometry*. For $n + 1$ points

$$
a_1 = (a_{11}, \ldots, a_{1n}), \ldots, a_{n+1} = (a_{n+1,1}, \ldots, a_{n+1,n})
$$

of $\mathbb{R}^n$ define

$$
F(a_1, \ldots, a_{n+1}) := \begin{vmatrix} a_{11} & \cdots & a_{1n} & 1 \\ a_{21} & \cdots & a_{2n} & 1 \\ \vdots & & & \\ a_{n+1,1} & \cdots & a_{n+1,n} & 1 \end{vmatrix}
$$

and

$$
V(a_1, \ldots, a_{n+1}) := |\, F(a_1, \ldots, a_{n+1}) \,| . \tag{46}
$$

$V(a_1, \ldots, a_{n+1})$ is the n–dimensional volume of the *parallelepiped* spanned by the vectors

$$
\overrightarrow{a_1 a_2}, \overrightarrow{a_1 a_3}, \ldots, \overrightarrow{a_1 a_{n+1}}
$$

and

$$
\Delta(a_1, \ldots, a_{n+1}) := \frac{1}{n!} V(a_1, \ldots, a_{n+1})
$$

is the n–dimensional volume of the *simplex* spanned by the vertices $a_1, \ldots, a_{n+1}$.

To prove that

$$
V : \mathbb{R}^n \times \ldots \times \mathbb{R}^n \to \mathbb{R}_{\geq 0}
$$

is an $(n + 1)$–point–invariant of (S, G), is not difficult: obviously,

$$
F(a_1, \ldots, a_{n+1}) := \begin{vmatrix} \alpha_{11} & \cdots & \alpha_{1n} & 0 \\ \vdots & & & \\ \alpha_{n1} & \cdots & \alpha_{nn} & 0 \\ a_{n+1,1} & \cdots & a_{n+1,n} & 1 \end{vmatrix} = \begin{vmatrix} \alpha_{11} & \cdots & \alpha_{1n} \\ \vdots & & \\ \alpha_{n1} & \cdots & \alpha_{nn} \end{vmatrix} ,
$$

where we put $\alpha_i := a_i - a_{n+1}$ for $i = 1, \ldots, n$. Moreover,

$$
f(a_i) - f(a_{n+1}) = \alpha_i Q
$$

holds true for $i = 1, \ldots, n$. Hence

$$F(f(a_1), \ldots, f(a_{n+1})) = F(a_1, \ldots, a_{n+1}) \cdot \det Q$$

and thus

$$V(f(a_1), \ldots, f(a_{n+1})) = V(a_1, \ldots, a_{n+1}).$$

THEOREM 18. *V is a defining invariant of n–dimensional equiaffine geometry.*

Proof.   Let $\gamma : \mathbb{R}^n \to \mathbb{R}^n$ be a mapping with

$$V(\gamma(a_1), \ldots, \gamma(a_{n+1})) = V(a_1, \ldots, a_{n+1})$$

for all $a_1, \ldots, a_{n+1} \in \mathbb{R}^n$. Put $e_{n+1} := (0, \ldots, 0)$ and

$$e_1 = (1, 0, \ldots, 0), \ldots, e_n = (0, \ldots, 0, 1).$$

Hence

$$\begin{vmatrix} b_{11} & \cdots & b_{1n} & 1 \\ \vdots & & & \\ b_{n1} & \cdots & b_{nn} & 1 \\ b_{n+1,1} & \cdots & b_{n+1,n} & 1 \end{vmatrix} = \pm \begin{vmatrix} 1 & \cdots & 0 & 1 \\ \vdots & & & \\ 0 & \cdots & 1 & 1 \\ 0 & \cdots & 0 & 1 \end{vmatrix} = \pm 1$$

with $b_i = (b_{i1}, \ldots, b_{in}) := \gamma(e_i)$ for $i = 1, \ldots, n + 1$. Define

$$Q = \begin{pmatrix} q_{11} & \cdots & q_{1n} \\ \vdots & & \\ q_{n1} & \cdots & q_{nn} \end{pmatrix}$$

and $f(x) = xQ + b_{n+1}$ such that

$$q_{i\nu} = b_{i\nu} - b_{n+1,\nu}$$

for $i, \nu \in \{1, \ldots, n\}$. Then $[\det Q]^2 = 1$ and $f(e_i) = b_i$ for $i = 1, \ldots, n+1$. Thus $f \in G$ and

$$V(\delta(a_1), \ldots, \delta(a_{n+1})) = V(a_1, \ldots, a_{n+1}) \tag{47}$$

for all $a_1, \ldots, a_{n+1} \in \mathbb{R}^n$, where we put $\delta := f^{-1} \cdot \gamma$. Observe that $\delta(e_i) = e_i$ for $i = 1, \ldots, n + 1$. Apply (47) for $a_i := e_i$, $i = 1, \ldots, n$, and $a_{n+1} := x \in \mathbb{R}^n$. Put $y := \delta(x)$. Then

$$\left| 1 - \sum_{i=1}^n x_i \right| = \left| 1 - \sum_{i=1}^n y_i \right|. \tag{48}$$

Apply (47) for $a_{n+1} = x$ and

$$a_\nu = \begin{cases} e_\nu & \nu \neq i \\ & \text{for} \\ e_{n+1} & \nu = i \end{cases}.$$

Hence $|x_i| = |y_i|$ for $i = 1, \ldots, n$. Points x of $\mathbb{R}^n$ with only one component $\neq 0$ thus remain fixed under δ, in view of (48). Take real numbers $r_1, \ldots, r_n$ unequal to 0 and put $a_{n+1} = x$, $y = \delta(x)$ and

$$a_i = r_i e_i, \ i = 1, \ldots, n.$$

Now (47) implies

$$\left| 1 - \sum_{i=1}^n \frac{x_i}{r_i} \right| = \left| 1 - \sum_{i=1}^n \frac{y_i}{r_i} \right|.$$

Squaring both sides of this equation yields

$$\sum_{k=1}^n \frac{(\varepsilon_k - 1)x_k}{r_k} = \sum_{i<j} \frac{(\varepsilon_i \varepsilon_j - 1)x_i x_j}{r_i r_j} \tag{49}$$

by observing that $|x_i| = |y_i|$, i.e. $y_i = \varepsilon_i x_i$, $\varepsilon_i^2 = 1$. We would now like to show that $y = x$, i.e. $\delta = \mathrm{id}$, i.e. $\gamma = f \in G$. If $x = e_{n+1}$ we already know that $y = x$. So we may assume that not all the components x_i of x are zero. Let

$$x_{i_1}, x_{i_2}, \ldots, x_{i_m} (i_1 < i_2 < \ldots < i_m)$$

be the non–zero components of x. If $m = 1$, we already know that $y = x$. So assume that $m \geq 2$ and put

$$\xi_\mu := x_{i_\mu}, \sigma_\mu := \varepsilon_{i_\mu}, s_\mu := r_{i_\mu}.$$

Then

$$\sum_{k=1}^m \frac{(\sigma_k - 1)\xi_k}{s_k} = \sum_{\nu<\mu} \frac{(\sigma_\nu \sigma_\mu - 1)\xi_\nu \xi_\mu}{s_\nu s_\mu} \tag{50}$$

holds true for all $s_1, \ldots, s_\mu \in \mathbb{R}\backslash\{0\}$, in view of (49). If all the σ's are 1, then again $y = x$. Without loss of generality, we thus may assume that

$$\sigma_1 = \ldots = \sigma_t = -1 \text{ with } t \geq 1$$

and moreover, if $t < m$, $\sigma_{t+1} = \ldots = \sigma_m = 1$. Put

$$s_k := \begin{cases} -2\xi_k & \text{for } k = 1, \ldots, t \\ \xi_k & \text{otherwise} \end{cases}.$$

Then (50) yields $t = t \cdot (m - t)$, i.e. $m = t + 1$. Hence, in view of (50),

$$\left(1 - \frac{\xi_m}{s_m}\right) \cdot \sum_{k=1}^{m-1} \frac{\xi_k}{s_k} = 0$$

for all $s_1, \ldots, s_m \in \mathbb{R}\backslash\{0\}$. But this is not true in the case $s_m = -\xi_m$ and $s_k = \xi_k$ for $k = 1, \ldots, m - 1$. $\quad\square$

5.3.3 Characterization of volumes of simplexes

Let T be the set of all sets

$$A = \{a_1, \ldots, a_{n+1}\}$$

where $a_1, \ldots, a_{n+1}$ are points of $\mathbb{R}^n$ such that A is not contained in a hyperplane of $\mathbb{R}^n$. This set T is obviously an invariant notion of n–dimensional equiaffine geometry (S, G). More precisely, this invariant notion is (T, φ) with

$$\varphi(\gamma, A) := \{\gamma(a_1), \ldots, \gamma(a_{n+1})\} = \gamma(A)$$

for $\gamma \in G$. Let W be a set.

THEOREM 19. *Suppose that $f : T \to W$ is a function satisfying*

$$\forall_{\gamma \in G} \forall_{A \in T} \ f(\gamma(A)) = f(A). \tag{51}$$

Then there exists

$$g : \mathbb{R}_{>0} \to W \tag{52}$$

with $\mathbb{R}_{>0} := \mathbb{R}_{\geq 0}\backslash\{0\}$ and

$$f(\{a_1, \ldots, a_{n+1}\}) = g(V(a_1, \ldots, a_{n+1})) \tag{53}$$

for all $\{a_1, \ldots, a_{n+1}\} \in T$. If, on the other hand, g is a function of the form (52), then (53) must be a solution of (51).

Proof.   Let $f : T \to W$ be a solution of (51) and let

$$A = \{a_1, \ldots, a_{n+1}\}$$

be an element of T. Then $V(a_1, \ldots, a_{n+1}) > 0$. Define $V = V(a_1, \ldots, a_{n+1})$,

$$(q_{i1}, \ldots, q_{in}) = \begin{cases} a_i - a_{n+1} & i = 1, \ldots, n-1 \\ \dfrac{1}{V} \cdot (a_n - a_{n+1}) & i = n \end{cases} \text{ for }$$

and

$$Q := \begin{pmatrix} q_{11} & \cdots & q_{1n} \\ \vdots & & \\ q_{n1} & \cdots & q_{nn} \end{pmatrix}.$$

Then $[\det Q]^2 = 1$ and

$$\psi(e) = a_{n+1}, \psi(e_1) = a_1, \ldots, \psi(e_{n-1}) = a_{n-1}, \psi(Ve_n) = a_n$$

holds true for

$$\psi(x) := xQ + a_{n+1}$$

and

$$e = 0, \; e_1 = (1, 0, \ldots, 0), \; \ldots, \; e_n = (0, \ldots, 0, 1).$$

Hence

$$f(A) = f\big(\psi^{-1}(A)\big) = f\big(\{e, e_1, \ldots, e_{n-1}, Ve_n\}\big).$$

For $\xi > 0$ define

$$g(\xi) := f\big(\{e, e_1, \ldots, e_{n-1}, \xi e_n\}\big).$$

Thus (53) holds true.   □

Let $a_1, \ldots, a_{n+1}$ be points of $\mathbb{R}^n$ in general position, i.e.

$$A = \{a_1, \ldots, a_{n+1}\}$$

is assumed not to be contained in a hyperplane of $\mathbb{R}^n$.

LEMMA 20. *If $b_1, \ldots, b_{n+1}$ are also in general position, then there exists a $\gamma \in G$ with*

$$\gamma(a_i) = b_i \; for \; i = 1, \ldots, n+1 \tag{54}$$

if and only if there exists a $\delta \in G$ such that

$$\delta(A) = \{b_1, \ldots, b_{n+1}\}. \tag{55}$$

Proof.   If (54) holds then obviously so does (55) with $\delta := \gamma$. Assume now that (55) holds, i.e.

$$\delta(a_1) = b_{i_1}, \ldots, \delta(a_{n+1}) = b_{i_{n+1}}.$$

The problem is to find a $\varrho \in G$ with

$$\varrho(b_1) = b_{i_1}, \ldots, \varrho(b_{n+1}) = b_{i_{n+1}},$$

because then we may put $\gamma = \varrho^{-1}\delta$ to obtain (54). Let Q_i be the matrix with rows

$$b_{i_1} - b_{i_{n+1}}, \ldots, b_{i_n} - b_{i_{n+1}}$$

and let Q be the matrix with rows

$$b_1 - b_{n+1}, \ldots, b_n - b_{n+1}.$$

Put $f_i(x) = xQ_i + b_{i_{n+1}}$ and $f(x) = xQ + b_{n+1}$. Then

$$f_i(e_\nu) = b_{i_\nu} \text{ and } f(e_\nu) = b_\nu$$

for $\nu = 1, \ldots, n+1$ and

$$e_1 = (1, 0, \ldots, 0), \ldots, e_n = (0, \ldots, 0, 1), \ e_{n+1} = 0. \tag{56}$$

Now observe that

$$\det Q_i = \pm \begin{vmatrix} b_{11} & \cdots & b_{1n} & 1 \\ \vdots & & & \\ b_{n+1,1} & \cdots & b_{n+1,n} & 1 \end{vmatrix} = \pm \det Q$$

and put

$$\varrho(x) := xQ^{-1}Q_i + [b_{i_{n+1}} - b_{n+1}Q^{-1}Q_i].$$

Then $\varrho \in G$ and $\varrho(b_\nu) = b_{i_\nu}$ for $\nu = 1, \ldots, n+1$. $\qquad\Box$

THEOREM 21. *Let P be the set of all ordered $(n+1)$-tuples, $n \geq 2$,*

$$a_1, \ldots, a_{n+1}$$

of $\mathbb{R}^n$ which are in general position, and let

$$\Delta : P \to \mathbb{R}_{>0}$$

be a function satisfying

(i) $\Delta(a_1, \ldots, a_{n+1}) = \Delta(\gamma(a_1), \ldots, \gamma(a_{n+1}))$ for all $\gamma \in G$ and all $(a_1, \ldots, a_{n+1}) \in P$

(ii) $\Delta(a_1, b, a_3, \ldots, a_{n+1}) + \Delta(b, a_2, a_3, \ldots, a_{n+1}) = \Delta(a_1, a_2, \ldots, a_{n+1})$ for all $(a_1, \ldots, a_{n+1}) \in P$ and all $b = (1 - \lambda)a_1 + \lambda a_2$ with $0 < \lambda < 1$

(iii) $\Delta(e_1, \ldots, e_{n+1}) = \frac{1}{n!}$ *for the points* $e_1, \ldots, e_{n+1}$ *of (56).*

Then

$$\Delta(a_1, \ldots, a_{n+1}) = \frac{1}{n!} V(a_1, \ldots, a_{n+1})$$

holds true for all $(a_1, \ldots, a_{n+1}) \in P$.

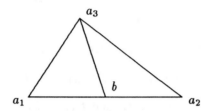

Proof.   Because of (i), Theorem 19 and Lemma 20, there exists a

$$g : \mathbb{R}_{>0} \to \mathbb{R}_{>0}$$

with

$$\Delta(a_1, \ldots, a_{n+1}) = g\bigl(V(a_1, \ldots, a_{n+1})\bigr) \qquad (57)$$

for all $(a_1, \ldots, a_{n+1}) \in P$. Let x and y be positive real numbers. Put

$$a_1 = 0, \ a_2 = (x + y)e_1, \ a_3 = e_2, \ldots, a_{n+1} = e_n$$

and

$$b = (1 - \lambda)a_1 + \lambda a_2 \text{ with } \lambda \cdot (x + y) := x.$$

Then (ii) yields

$$g(x + y) = g(x) + g(y). \qquad (58)$$

Put $g(0) = 0$. Then (58) holds true for all $x, y \in \mathbb{R}_{\geq 0}$. Theorem 5 of section 2.3 now implies that $g(x) = kx$ for a constant k which must be positive, since g maps $\mathbb{R}_{>0}$ into $\mathbb{R}_{>0}$. Hence

$$\Delta(a_1, \ldots, a_{n+1}) = \frac{1}{n!} V(a_1, \ldots, a_{n+1})$$

from (57) and (iii).   □

REMARK. A motivation for assumption (ii) seems to be obvious in view of the figure above, since for the areas of the triangles there we have

$$\Delta(a_1, a_2, a_3) = \Delta(a_1, b, a_3) + \Delta(b, a_2, a_3),$$

an equation which seems to be reasonable also for higher dimensions. — A short motivation for assumption (iii) could be the following: in the case of $\mathbb{R}^n$, we will write

$$\Delta(a_1, \ldots, a_{n+1}) = k_n V(a_1, \ldots, a_{n+1})$$

and instead of $e_1, \ldots, e_{n+1}$ for $\mathbb{R}^n$ we will write $E_1, \ldots, E_n$ for $\mathbb{R}^{n-1}$ (when $x_n = 0$). Then

$$k_n \cdot V(e_1, \ldots, e_{n+1}) = \int_0^1 k_{n-1} V(x_n E_1, \ldots, x_n E_{n-1}, E_n) dx_n,$$

i.e. $k_n = \int_0^1 k_{n-1} \, x_n^{n-1} \, dx_n = \frac{1}{n} k_{n-1}$, which seems to be reasonable, and furthermore $k_2 = \frac{1}{2}$.

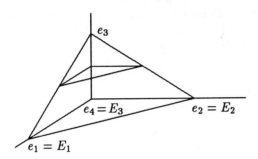

5.4 Affine geometry

5.4.1 The set of lines as defining notion

Let S be a real vector space of dimension at least 2. For elements $a, v \in S$ with $v \neq 0$, the set

$$l = \{a + \mu v \mid \mu \in \mathbb{R}\}$$

is called a *line* of S. Denote by N the set of all lines of S. Note that there is exactly one line through elements $a \neq b$ of S, namely $\{a + \mu \cdot (b - a) \mid \mu \in \mathbb{R}\}$.

THEOREM 22. *Let γ be a bijection of S with*

(∗) *Whenever l is a line of S, then so is $\gamma(l)$.*

Then there exists a bijective linear mapping λ of the vector space S such that

$$\gamma(x) = \lambda(x) + \gamma(0)$$

holds true for all $x \in S$.

Proof.   (a) A set $T \subset S$ is called *collinear* iff there exists a line $l \supseteq T$. Observe that

$$\lambda(x) := \gamma(x) - \gamma(0), \ \ x \in S,$$

is also bijective and satisfies (∗). Note that $\lambda(0) = 0$. Let v_1, v_2 be linearly independent elements of S. Define $w_i := \lambda(v_i)$, $i = 1, 2$. w_1, w_2 must also be linearly independent. Otherwise, $\{0, w_1, w_2\}$ would be collinear and hence so would $\{0, v_1, v_2\}$: let l_1, l_2, l, respectively, be lines containing $\{0, v_1\}$, $\{0, v_2\}$, $\{0, w_1, w_2\}$ respectively. This implies that

$$\lambda(l_1) = l = \lambda(l_2),$$

from (∗) (replace here γ by λ) and hence

$$l_1 = \lambda^{-1}(l) = l_2.$$

Define P, Q by

$$
\begin{aligned}
P &= \{\alpha_1 v_1 + \alpha_2 v_2 \mid \alpha_1, \alpha_2 \in \mathbb{R}\}, \\
Q &= \{\beta_1 w_1 + \beta_2 w_2 \mid \beta_1, \beta_2 \in \mathbb{R}\},
\end{aligned}
$$

respectively. $\lambda : P \to Q$ is a bijection. Here λ also denotes the restriction of the original mapping λ to P. In order to prove this statement, we only need to show that

$$\forall_{p \in P} \ \lambda(p) \in Q \ \text{ and } \ \forall_{q \in Q} \ \lambda^{-1}(q) \in P,$$

since λ is bijective. The image of the line ξ through $0, v_1$ is the line ξ' through $0, w_1$, and the image of the line η through $0, v_2$ is the line η' through $0, w_2$. For a given $p \in P$, choose $a \in \xi$ and $b \in \eta \backslash \{a\}$ such that a, b, p are collinear. Now $\lambda(a), \lambda(b), \lambda(p)$ are also collinear and since $\lambda(a) \in \xi'$, $\lambda(b) \in \eta'$ hold true, we get $\lambda(p) \in Q$. For the remaining statement observe that

(b) Whenever l is a line, then so is $\lambda^{-1}(l)$. If $a \neq b$ are elements of l, denote by l_0 the line through $\lambda^{-1}(a)$, $\lambda^{-1}(b)$. Then

$$l \ni a, b \in \lambda(l_0)$$

and thus $l = \lambda(l_0)$, i.e. $\lambda^{-1}(l) = l_0$.

(c) Write (α_1, α_2) instead of $\alpha_1 v_1 + \alpha_2 v_2$ and (β_1, β_2) instead of the element $\beta_1 w_1 + \beta_2 w_2$. The mapping $\lambda : P \to Q$ may then be considered to be a bijection λ' of $\mathbb{R}^2$ by putting

$$\lambda'(\alpha_1, \alpha_2) = (\beta_1, \beta_2)$$

iff $\lambda(\alpha_1 v_1 + \alpha_2 v_2) = \beta_1 w_1 + \beta_2 w_2$. The mapping λ' satisfies condition $(*)$ of Proposition 2 of section 1.2. In fact,

$$\lambda(a + \mathbb{R}v) = b + \mathbb{R}w$$

for

$$a = \alpha_1 v_1 + \alpha_2 v_2, \qquad v = \tau_1 v_1 + \tau_2 v_2 \neq 0,$$
$$b = \beta_1 w_1 + \beta_2 w_2, \qquad w = \sigma_1 w_1 + \sigma_2 w_2 \neq 0,$$
$$a + \mathbb{R}v := \{a + \mu v \mid \mu \in \mathbb{R}\}, \quad \ldots,$$

is equivalent to

$$\lambda'\big((\alpha_1, \alpha_2) + \mathbb{R}(\tau_1, \tau_2)\big) = (\beta_1, \beta_2) + \mathbb{R}(\sigma_1, \sigma_2).$$

Proposition 2 of section 1.2 hence implies that

$$\lambda'(\alpha_1, \alpha_2) = (\alpha_1, \alpha_2) \begin{pmatrix} a_{11} & a_{12} \\ a_{21} & a_{22} \end{pmatrix}$$

for real numbers a_{ij}, in view of $\lambda'(0) = 0$. In particular,

$$\lambda'(1, 0) = (a_{11}, a_{12}),$$
$$\lambda'(0, 1) = (a_{21}, a_{22}).$$

Hence $(a_{11}, a_{12}) = (1, 0)$ and $(a_{21}, a_{22}) = (0, 1)$ since

$$w_i = \lambda(v_i) = a_{i1} w_1 + a_{i2} w_2$$

for $i = 1, 2$. Thus $\lambda'(\alpha_1, \alpha_2) = (\alpha_1, \alpha_2)$, i.e.

$$\lambda(\alpha_1 v_1 + \alpha_2 v_2) = \alpha_1 w_1 + \alpha_2 w_2 = \alpha_1 \lambda(v_1) + \alpha_2 \lambda(v_2).$$

(d) Let p_1, p_2 be linearly dependent elements of S. In this case, we would also like to show that

$$\lambda(\alpha_1 p_1 + \alpha_2 p_2) = \alpha_1 \lambda(p_1) + \alpha_2 \lambda(p_2)$$

for $\alpha_1, \alpha_2 \in \mathbb{R}$. We may assume that $p_1 \neq 0$ without loss of generality. Then $p_2 = \varrho p_1$ with $\varrho \in \mathbb{R}$. Since the dimension of S is at least 2, there exists a $q \in S$ such that p_1, q are linearly independent. Hence, in view of (c),

$$\lambda(\alpha_1 p_1 + \alpha_2 p_2) = \lambda\big((\alpha_1 + \varrho \alpha_2)p_1 + 0 \cdot q\big) = (\alpha_1 + \varrho \alpha_2)\lambda(p_1)$$

and

$$\alpha_1\lambda(p_1) + \alpha_2\lambda(p_2) = \alpha_1\lambda(p_1 + 0 \cdot q) + \alpha_2\lambda(\varrho p_1 + 0 \cdot q)$$
$$= (\alpha_1 + \varrho\alpha_2)\lambda(p_1). \qquad \square$$

We denoted by N the set of all lines of S. The group $G(N)$ is called the *affine group* of S. It consists of all mappings γ given by

$$x \rightarrow \lambda(x) + t, \tag{59}$$

where λ is a bijective linear mapping of S and where t is an element of S. The geometry $\big(S, G(N)\big)$ is called *affine geometry*. When the dimension n of S is finite, (59) may be written in the form

$$\gamma(x) = xQ + t$$

with $t = (t_1 \ldots t_n)$ and

$$Q = \begin{pmatrix} q_{11} & \cdots & q_{1n} \\ \vdots & & \\ q_{n1} & \cdots & q_{nn} \end{pmatrix},$$

$\det Q \neq 0$. When $S = \mathbb{R}^n$, $n \geq 2$, the geometries of sections 5.1, 5.2, 5.3 are substructures (see section 1.3) of our present geometry $\big(S, G(N)\big)$ by choosing $S_0 := S$ and by observing that the groups of the geometries mentioned, are subgroups of the affine group. Note, that in view of Proposition 6, (section 1.3), all invariants and invariant notions of $\big(S, G(N)\big)$ are also invariants and invariant notions of the other geometries in question.

5.4.2 An affine invariant

Let S be a real vector space of dimension at least 2 again. Suppose that V is a subspace of the vector space S and that $a \in S$. Then

$$a + V := \{a + v \mid v \in V\}$$

is called an *affine subspace* of S of *dimension* m, where m is the dimension of the vector space V. Lines are thus 1–dimensional affine subspaces of S. Every element $a \in S$ may be written in the form

$$a + \{0\}$$

and is thus a 0–dimensional affine subspace of S. Elements of S are called points. Define T to be the set of all

$$(a, b, c) \in S \times S \times S, \quad a \neq b,$$

such that $\{a, b, c\}$ is collinear. Obviously, T is an invariant notion of the affine geometry (S, G), $G := G(N)$. Let (a, b, c) be an element of T and let l be the uniquely determined line (observe that $a \neq b$) through a, b, c. Then

$$c = a + \mu(b - a) \in a + \mathbb{R}(b - a) = l$$

for some real number μ. If

$$p + \mathbb{R}v$$

is another representation of l, and if

$$a = p + \alpha v, \; b = p + \beta v, \; c = p + \gamma v$$

holds true for real numbers, then

$$\mu = \frac{\alpha - \gamma}{\alpha - \beta} \tag{60}$$

with $\alpha \neq \beta$. In fact, $\alpha = \beta$ would imply theat $a = b$. Now observe that

$$p + \gamma v = c = a + \mu(b - a) = p + \alpha v + \mu(\beta - \alpha)v.$$

(60) is called the *affine ratio* $R(a, b, c)$ of

$$(a, b, c) \in T.$$

PROPOSITION 23. *The function $R : T \to \mathbb{R}$ is an invariant of the affine geometry (S, G) and moreover, a defining function.*

Proof.   (a) The image of $(a, b, c) \in T$ under (59) is

$$\left(\lambda(a) + t, \; \lambda(b) + t, \; \lambda(c) + t \right)$$

where λ is a bijective linear mapping of S. Now

$$c = a + \mu(b - c), \; \mu = R(a, b, c),$$

implies that $\lambda(c) = \lambda(a) + \mu[\lambda(b) - \lambda(c)]$ and hence

$$c' = a' + \mu(b' - c')$$

with $x' := \lambda(x) + t$ for $x \in S$. Thus

$$R(a', b', c') = \mu = R(a, b, c).$$

(b) A bijection of S preserving T maps lines onto lines and vice versa. Hence $G(N) = G(T)$. The group $G(R)$ is defined as a subgroup of $G(T)$. But according to (a), $G(N) = G \subseteq G(R)$.   □

$$\underset{a}{\underline{\quad R < 0 \qquad 0 < R(a, b, c) < 1 \qquad\; R > 1 \quad}} \atop b$$

5.4.3   The set of parabolas as defining notion

Let S be a real vector space of dimension at least 2 and let a, b be linearly independent elements of S. Put

$$P(a, b) := \{xa + x^2b \mid x \in \mathbb{R}\}. \tag{61}$$

Every image of $P(a, b)$ under a bijective mapping (59) is then called a *parabola* of S. The definition of the set of parabolas does not depend on a, b: Let a', b' also be linearly independent elements of S and suppose that $B \ni a, b$ and $B' \ni a', b'$ are bases of S. Since B and B' are of the same cardinality, there exists a bijection

$$\lambda_0 : B \to B'$$

with $\lambda_0(a) = a'$ and $\lambda_0(b) = b'$. Denote by λ the linear mapping of S which extends λ_0. The image of (61) under λ is then $P(a', b')$. This set is thus a parabola with respect to a, b and, vice versa, $P(a, b)$ is a parabola with respect to a', b'. The set of parabolas thus does not depend on a, b.

THEOREM 24. *Let S be a real vector space of dimension at least 2 and let γ be a bijection of S such that*

(∗) *The image $\gamma(p)$ of every parabola p of S is contained in a parabola.*

Then there exists a bijective linear mapping λ of the vector space S such that

$$\gamma(x) = \lambda(x) + \gamma(0)$$

holds true for all $x \in S$.

Proof.   (a) The set (61) does not contain three distinct and collinear elements of S. Otherwise there would exist an $\alpha \in \mathbb{R}$ and three distinct real numbers x, y, z with

$$\alpha(xa + x^2b) + (1 - \alpha)(ya + y^2b) = za + z^2b.$$

Hence

$$
\begin{array}{rcl}
\alpha \cdot 1 + (1 - \alpha) \cdot 1 + (-1) \cdot 1 & = & 0 \\
\alpha \cdot x + (1 - \alpha) \cdot y + (-1) \cdot z & = & 0 \\
\alpha \cdot x^2 + (1 - \alpha) \cdot y^2 + (-1) \cdot z^2 & = & 0,
\end{array}
$$

i.e.

$$0 \neq (x - y)(y - z)(z - x) = \begin{vmatrix} 1 & 1 & 1 \\ x & y & z \\ x^2 & y^2 & z^2 \end{vmatrix} = 0.$$

Of course, the property we just proved for the set (61), carries over to all images of (61) under bijective mappings of the form (59), and thus to all parabolas of S.

(b) Suppose that the dimension $n \geq 2$ of S is finite. Put $\varphi := \gamma^{-1}$ and observe that φ is bijective. Let p_1, p_2, p_3 be three distinct and collinear points. If $\varphi(p_1)$, $\varphi(p_2)$, $\varphi(p_3)$ were not collinear, we would take a parabola p through these points and $\gamma(p)$ would thus contain p_1, p_2, p_3 which contradicts what we proved in (a). According to A.3.1, GT 104 ff, and to Proposition 3 of the present chapter 1, φ (and thus also γ) must be of form (59).

(c) Suppose that the dimension n of S is at least 3. If p is a parabola of S, denote by $\overline{\gamma(p)}$ the (uniquely determined) parabola containing $\gamma(p)$. Now let

$$E = \{r + xa + yb \mid x, y \in \mathbb{R}\}$$

be a plane of S, i.e. a 2–dimensional affine subspace of S (compare section 5.4.2). Denote by p the parabola

$$p = \{r + xa + x^2b \mid x \in \mathbb{R}\}.$$

Put $\overline{\gamma(p)} =: \{s + xc + x^2d \mid x \in \mathbb{R}\}$ and denote by F the plane

$$F = \{s + xc + yd \mid x, y \in \mathbb{R}\}$$

which is the only plane containing $\overline{\gamma(p)}$. We would like to prove that

$$\gamma(E) \subseteq F$$

holds true. The idea is that the image $\gamma(q)$ of a parabola q which cuts p in four distinct points must be contained in F, and also the image $\gamma(q')$ of a parabola q' which cuts q in four distinct points must be part of F. By repeating this process, we get that every point of E is on a suitable parabola $q^* \subset E$ with $\gamma(q^*) \subset F$.

d) Let l be a line of S and let E be a plane of S through l. There exists an element $r \in S \backslash E$ such that $\gamma(r)$ is not in the uniquely determined plane $F \supseteq \gamma(E)$. We otherwise would have $\gamma(S) \subseteq F$ which contradicts dim $S \geq 3$ and the fact that γ is bijective. Let E' be the plane through l and r. Then

$$E \neq E' \text{ and } l = E \cap E'.$$

Let F' be the plane containing $\gamma(E')$. Since

$$\gamma(r) \in F' \backslash F$$

holds true,

$$F \neq F' \text{ and } \gamma(l) \subseteq F \cap F' =: g$$

must be satisfied. We would like to show that $\gamma(l)$ is equal to the line g. Assume there existed an element s on g which is not on $\gamma(l)$. Then $\gamma^{-1}(s) \notin l$. Take a parabola q through the element $\gamma^{-1}(s)$ and through two distinct and suitable elements of l. The parabola $\gamma(q)$ then would cut the line g in three distinct elements, which is impossible. Hence $\gamma(l) = g$. Theorem 22 now completes the proof. $\square$

REMARK. Essentially the same ideas as those in the proof of Theorem 24 lead to analogous results for ellipses or hyperbolas instead of parabolas. For real vector spaces S of finite dimension $n \geq 3$, one also may replace $(*)$ in Theorem 24 (for instance) by

$(*)$ The image $\gamma(e)$ of every ellipsoid e which is subset of a 3–dimensional affine subspace of S is contained in such an ellipsoid

in order to characterize again the bijective affine mappings (i.e. the bijective mappings of the form (59)) of S.

5.5   Euclidean geometry of normed spaces

Let S be a real vector space and let $\varphi : S \to \mathbb{R}$ be a mapping satisfying

  (i) $\varphi(x) = 0 \Rightarrow x = 0$,

 (ii) $\varphi(\lambda x) = |\lambda| \cdot \varphi(x)$,

(iii) $\varphi(x + y) \leq \varphi(x) + \varphi(y)$

for all $x, y, z \in S$ and $\lambda \in \mathbb{R}$. Then (S, φ) is called a real normed space. Instead of $\varphi(x)$ one usually writes $\|x\|$. This real number $\|x\|$ is called the norm of x. Obviously,

$$\|0\| = \|2 \cdot 0\| = 2 \cdot \|0\|$$

implies $\|0\| = 0$. The norm $\|x\|$ of $x \in S$ must moreover be a non–negative real number, since

$$0 = \|0\| = \|x + (-x)\| \leq \|x\| + \|(-1)x\| = 2 \cdot \|x\|.$$

The distance $d(x, y)$ of $x, y \in S$ is defined by

$$d(x, y) := \|x - y\|.$$

Let G be the group of all bijections of the distance space $(S, \mathbb{R}, d)$ (see section 1.2) which preserve distances. Then (S, G) is called the *euclidean geometry* over (S, φ). All elements of G are bijective affine mappings (59). This is a consequence of the following Theorem of Ulam and Mazur ([1]):

THEOREM 25. *Suppose that X, Y are real normed vector spaces and let $f : X \to Y$ be a surjective mapping satisfying*

$$\forall_{a,b \in X} \ \|a - b\| = \|f(a) - f(b)\|.$$

Then $x \to f(x) - f(0)$ must be linear.

For a proof of this Theorem of Ulam and Mazur we also refer to GT 44 ff. A real normed vecor space S is called *strictly convex* iff

$$\|a + b\| = \|a\| + \|b\|$$

for $a, b \in S$ implies that a, b are linearly dependent. The following Theorem was proved by W. Benz and H. Berens([1]):

THEOREM 26. *Let X, Y be real normed vector spaces such that Y is strictly convex and such that the dimension of X is at least 2. Let $\varrho > 0$ be a fixed real number and let $N > 1$ be a fixed integer. Suppose that $f : X \to Y$ is a mapping satisfying*

(i) $\|a - b\| = \varrho \Rightarrow \|f(a) - f(b)\| \leq \varrho$,

(ii) $\|a - b\| = N\varrho \Rightarrow \|f(a) - f(b)\| \geq N\varrho$

for all $a, b \in X$. Then

$$\forall_{a,b \in X} \ \|a - b\| = \|f(a) - f(b)\|$$

holds true and $x \to f(x) - f(0)$ must hence be linear.

REMARK. The last statement of Theorem 26 is due to J. A. Baker [1].

For a proof of Theorem 26 we refer also to GT 48 ff.

5.6 Projective geometry

5.6.1 Points, lines, hyperplanes

Let V be a real vector space of dimension at least 2. Let $S = S(V)$ be the set of all 1–dimensional subspaces of V and define $\mathbb{L} = \mathbb{L}(V)$ to be the set of all

2–dimensional subspaces of the vector space V. The elements of S are called *points* and the elements of $\mathbb{L}$ *lines*. Let p be a point and let l be a line. We say that p is on l or that l goes through p iff $p \subset l$. In this case we also say that p is incident with l or that l is incident with p. Lines may be considered as sets of points by identifying a line l with the set of points on l,

$$\{p \in S \mid p \subset l\}.$$

Projective transformations are defined when $\dim V \geq 3$ as bijections of S such that images and pre–images of lines are lines. We thus may speak of the group $G = G(V)$ of projective transformations. The geometry

$$\big(S(V), G(V)\big)$$

is called the *projective geometry* $\Pi(V)$ over V and $G(V)$ is called its *projective group*.

Let P, Q be distinct points of $S(V)$. Then there exists exactly one line l through P, Q. This is trivial since P, Q are distinct 1–dimensional subspaces of the vector space V, and since

$$l = \mathrm{span}\ \{p, q\}$$

for $P = \mathrm{span}\ \{p\}$, $Q = \mathrm{span}\ \{q\}$ is the uniquely determined 2–dimensional subspace of V containing P and Q. Often we shall denote by $\overline{PQ}$ the line joining P and $Q \neq P$.

A set $T \subseteq S(V)$ is called a *projective subspace* of $\Pi(V)$ iff T contains $\overline{PQ}$ for all $P, Q \in T$ with $P \neq Q$. Simple examples for projective subspaces of $\Pi(V)$ are given by $\emptyset, S(V)$, by every point, by every line.

LEMMA 27. *Let U be a subspace of the vector space V. The set of all 1–dimensional subspaces of U is then a projective subspace of $\Pi(V)$. There are no other projective subspaces of $\Pi(V)$.*

Proof.   The proof of the first part of the statement is of course trivial. Now let T be a projective subspace. When $T = \emptyset$ we can take $U = \{0\}$. So assume that $T \neq \emptyset$. Define U to be the union of all points

$$\mathrm{span}\ \{p\}$$

of T. Hence $p \in U$ implies that $\lambda \cdot p \in U$ for every real λ. Also $p, q \in U$ implies that $p + q \in U$: this is clear when p, q are linearly dependent. It is also clear if p, q are linearly independent since

$$\mathrm{span}\ \{p\},\ \mathrm{span}\ \{q\} \in T$$

implies span $\{p, q\} \subseteq T$. □

$H \subseteq S(V)$ is called a *hyperplane* of $\Pi(V)$ iff the following conditions hold true:

(i) H is a projective subspace of $\Pi(V)$,

(ii) $H \neq S(V)$,

(iii) If T is a projective subspace with $H \subseteq T \subseteq S(V)$ then $H = T$ or $T = S(V)$.

Let B be a basis of the vector space V and let b_0 be an element of B. Then the set H of all 1–dimensional subspaces of

$$\text{span } \left(B \backslash \{b_0\} \right)$$

is a hyperplane. In order to prove this statement, we only need to verify (iii) in the definition of a hyperplane. So assume that T is a projective subspace with

$$H \subsetneqq T \subsetneqq S(V).$$

Define U to be the union of all points

$$\text{span } \{p\}$$

of T. Then $B \backslash \{b_0\} \subset U$. Since $T \neq H$, the set $B \backslash \{b_0\}$ cannot be a basis of U. Take $t \in U$ such that

$$\left(B \backslash \{b_0\} \right) \cup \{t\}$$

is linearly independent. Since t can be linearly expressed in B, but not in $B \backslash \{b_0\}$, the element b_0 must be in

$$\text{span } \left[\left(B \backslash \{b_0\} \right) \cup \{t\} \right].$$

Hence $T = S(V)$.

The image of a hyperplane H of $\Pi(V)$ under a projective transformation γ of $\Pi(V)$ is again a hyperplane of $\Pi(V)$. This follows immediately from the definition of a hyperplane by observing that images and pre–images of projective subspaces are projective subspaces.

Let H be a hyperplane of $\Pi(V)$ and define

$$V_0 := S(V) \backslash H.$$

Let $N = \mathrm{span}\ \{n\}$ be a point of V_0 and let $B(H)$ be a basis of the vector space

$$U(H) := \bigcup_{P \in H} P.$$

Then $B := B(H) \cup \{n\}$ is a basis of V: otherwise we would have

$$H \subsetneqq T \subsetneqq S(V)$$

for the projective subspace T of all 1–dimensional subspaces of span B.

LEMMA 28. *Let h be an element of $U(H)$. Then*

$$\mathrm{span}\ \{h + n\} \in V_0. \tag{62}$$

Every point of V_0 can be written in the form (62). Two points

$$\mathrm{span}\ \{h + n\} \ and\ \mathrm{span}\ \{h' + n\}$$

with $h, h' \in U(H)$ are equal if and only if $h = h'$.

Proof.   If span $\{h + n\}$ with $h \in U(H)$ is not in V_0, then it is in H. Hence

$$h + n \in U(H), \quad \text{i.e. } n \in U(H).$$

This is not true since $B = B(H) \cup \{n\}$ is a basis of V. Now let span $\{p\}$ be a point of V_0. If we express p linearly in elements of B, we get

$$p = \alpha n + \alpha_1 b_1 + \ldots + \alpha_r b_r \tag{63}$$

with $\alpha, \alpha_1, \ldots, \alpha_r \in \mathbb{R}$ and $\{b_1, \ldots, b_r\}$ a finite subset of $B(H)$. The number α must be unequal to 0 because otherwise $p \in U(H)$, i.e. span $\{p\} \in H$. Hence

$$\mathrm{span}\ \{p\} = \ \mathrm{span}\ \{h + n\}$$

with

$$h = \sum_{i=1}^{r} \frac{\alpha_i}{\alpha}\ b_i \in U(H).$$

Assume that span $\{h + n\} = \mathrm{span}\ \{h' + n\}$ for $h, h' \in U(H)$. This implies

$$h' + n = \beta \cdot (h + n)$$

for a suitable real $\beta \neq 0$. If β were unequal to 1, then

$$n = \frac{1}{\beta - 1}(h' - \beta h) \in U(H)$$

which is a contradiction. □

The mapping

$$\omega(h) := \text{span } \{h + n\} \tag{64}$$

with $h \in U(H)$ is a bijection

$$\omega : U(H) \rightarrow V_0 \tag{65}$$

in view of Lemma 28. The points in V_0 are called the *affine points* of $\Pi(V)$ with respect to the hyperplane H. We are now interested in a description of points and lines of $\Pi(V)$ by means of V_0. In view of (64) and (65) *we shall identify V_0 with the vector space $U(H)$*. The points and lines of the affine geometry $U(H)$ in the sense of section 5.4.1 will be called *affine points* and *affine lines*. These (new) affine points are of course the affine points of $\Pi(V)$ with respect to H according to our identification (64), (65).

LEMMA 29. *If $l \in \mathbb{L}(V)$ is a line of $\Pi(V)$ which is not contained in H, then $l \cap H$ consists of exactly one point of $\Pi(V)$, and*

$$l_0 := l \backslash H$$

is an affine line. If

$$l_0 = \{a + \lambda v \mid \lambda \in \mathbb{R}\} \tag{66}$$

is an affine line with $a, v \in U(H)$, $v \neq 0$, then

$$l := l_0 \cup \{\text{span } \{v\}\} \tag{67}$$

is in $\mathbb{L}(V)$ with $l \cap H = \{\text{span } \{v\}\}$.

Proof.   (a) If $l \in \mathbb{L}(V)$ has at least two distinct points in common with H, then l is part of H since H is a projective subspace of $\Pi(V)$. — Assume there exists $l \in \mathbb{L}(V)$ with $l \cap H = \emptyset$. Take distinct points

$$\text{span } \{p\}, \text{ span } \{q\}$$

of l. Then

$$p - \alpha n \in U(H),$$

$$q - \beta n \in U(H)$$

for uniquely determined real coefficients α, β with $\alpha\beta \neq 0$. Since p, q are linearly independent, we get the contradiction

$$\text{span } \{\alpha^{-1}p - \beta^{-1}q\} \in l \cap H.$$

(b) Suppose that $l \in \mathbb{L}(V)$ is not contained in H. Let span $\{v\}$ be the point in $l \cap H$ and let span $\{p\}$ be a point in $l \backslash H$. If α is the uniquely determined real number with

$$p - \alpha n \in U(H),$$

then $\alpha \neq 0$. Put $a := \frac{p}{\alpha} - n \in U(H)$. Then

$$l_0 := l \backslash H = \{a + \lambda v \mid \lambda \in \mathbb{R}\}$$

in the notation of V_0, since the general point of $l \backslash H$ may be written in form

$$\text{span } \{p + \beta v\} = \text{span } \{\alpha(a + n) + \beta v\} = \text{span } \left\{a + \frac{\beta}{\alpha}v + n\right\}$$

for $\beta \in \mathbb{R}$.

(c) Let l_0 be the affine line (66). The points of l_0, written in terms of $S(V)$, are

$$\text{span } \{a + \lambda v + n\}, \lambda \in \mathbb{R}.$$

The projective line joining

$$\text{span } \{a + n\}, \text{ and span } \{a + n + v\}$$

is then l of (67). $\square$

We will call the line l of (67) the *projective extension* of the line (66) of V_0. Two lines

$$l_i = \{a_i + \lambda v_i \mid \lambda \in \mathbb{R}\}, \; i = 1, 2,$$

of V_0 are called *parallel* iff v_1, v_2 are linearly dependent in $U(H)$. The parallel-relation is an equivalence relation of the set of lines of V_0. Moreover the euclidean parallel axiom holds true: if p is a point of V_0 and if (66) is a line of V_0, then there exists exactly one line in V_0 through p which is parallel to l_0, namely

$$\{p + \lambda v \mid \lambda \in \mathbb{R}\}.$$

Two lines of V_0 are parallel iff their projective extensions intersect H in the same point.

If l_0 is a line of V_0, we denote by $[l_0]$ the set of all lines of V_0 which are parallel to l_0. We shall call $[l_0]$ a parallel class. If a, b are distinct points of V_0, we denote by (a, b) the line of V_0 joining them.

PROPOSITION 30. *The points of* $\Pi(V)$ *may be represented by the points of* V_0 *and by the parallel classes* $[l_0]$, l_0 *a line of* V_0. *The lines of* $\Pi(V)$ *are given by*

$$l_0 \cup \{[l_0]\},$$

l_0 *a line of* V_0, *and, if dim* $V \geq 3$, *by the sets*

$$(p, a, b) := \{[(p, x)] \mid x \in (a, b)\} \cup \{[(a, b)]\},$$

where p, a, b *are points of* V_0 *which are not collinear.*

Proof.   (a) Through every point span $\{v\}$ of H there can be drawn a line $l \in \mathbb{L}(V)$ with $l \not\subseteq H$, for instance

$$\{\lambda v \mid \lambda \in \mathbb{R}\} \cup \{\text{span } \{v\}\}.$$

The point span $\{v\}$ of H thus occurs in form of a parallel class $[l_0]$.

(b) Let $l \in \mathbb{L}(V)$ be a line contained in H, and let

$$\text{span } \{v\}, \quad \text{span } \{w\}$$

be distinct points of l. Hence $l = (0, v, w)$.

(c) (p, a, b) is a line in H, namely the line through

$$\text{span } \{p - a\} \text{ and span } \{p - b\}.$$

$\square$

Starting from a projective structure $\Pi(V)$, we were able to construct an affine structure $U(H)$ such that points and lines of $\Pi(V)$ are representable in terms of $U(H)$. Even the vector space V is, up to isomorphism, uniquely determined by $U(H)$, namely in the form of all pairs

$$(u, r), \ u \in U(H) \text{ and } r \in \mathbb{R},$$

with the operations

$$\lambda \cdot (u, r) := (\lambda u, \lambda r)$$

for $\lambda \in \mathbb{R}$, and

$$(u_1, r_1) + (u_2, r_2) := (u_1 + u_2, \ r_1 + r_2):$$

associate to

$$u + \alpha n \in V, \ u \in U(H), \ \alpha \in \mathbb{R},$$

the element (u, α). This is an isomorphism between the vector spaces V and $U(H) \times \mathbb{R}$.

Conversely, starting from a real vector space U of dimension at least 1, we may define the vector space

$$V := U \times \mathbb{R}$$

as above, and the hyperplane H of all 1–dimensional subspaces contained in the subspace

$$\{(u,0) \mid u \in U\}$$

of V. Then $V_0 := S(V) \backslash H$ may be identified with the original affine geometry over U by defining $n := (0,1) \in V$. The projective structure $\Pi(V)$ is called the *projective extension* of the affine structure U.

5.6.2 The projective extension of $\mathbb{R}^m$

Let m be a positive integer. Define

$$V := \mathbb{R}^m \times \mathbb{R} = \mathbb{R}^{m+1}$$

and let H be the hyperplane $\big($of $\Pi(V)\big)$ of all 1–dimensional subspaces contained in

$$U := \big\{(x_1, \ldots, x_m, 0) \in V \mid (x_1, \ldots, x_m) \in \mathbb{R}^m\big\}.$$

Hence $U(H) = U$. Putting $n := (0, \ldots, 0, 1) \in \mathbb{R}^m \times \mathbb{R}$ as in the previous section, an arbitrary point

$$X := \mathrm{span}\ \{x\} = \mathbb{R} \cdot x := \{rx \mid r \in \mathbb{R}\}$$

of $S(V)$ may be written in the form

$$X = \mathbb{R} \cdot (x_1, \ldots, x_m, x_{m+1}). \tag{68}$$

When $X \in H$, i.e. when $x \in U$, we have $x_{m+1} = 0$. When $X \notin H$, i.e. in the case $x \notin U$, we have $x_{m+1} \neq 0$ and hence

$$\mathrm{span}\ \{x\} = \ \mathrm{span}\ \left\{\left(\frac{x_1}{x_{m+1}}, \ldots, \frac{x_m}{x_{m+1}}, 0\right) + n\right\}.$$

In this case X is an affine point, namely the point

$$\left(\frac{x_1}{x_{m+1}}, \ldots, \frac{x_m}{x_{m+1}}\right) \in \mathbb{R}^m, \tag{69}$$

from (64), (65).

$x_1, \ldots, x_{m+1}$ in (68) are called *homogeneous coordinates* of X. They are determined up to a common factor $\varrho \neq 0$. One can immediately decide whether $X \in H$ (if $x_{m+1} = 0$) or not ($x_{m+1} \neq 0$). In the latter case, (69) are the affine coordinates (with respect to H) of X.

We now would like to determine an equation for an arbitrarily given hyperplane T of $\Pi(\mathbb{R}^{m+1})$. We shall try to find real numbers

$$t_1, \ldots, t_{m+1},$$

not all 0, such that

$$t_1 x_1 + \ldots + t_{m+1} x_{m+1} = 0 \tag{70}$$

holds true for all $\mathbb{R} \cdot (x_1, \ldots, x_{m+1})$ in T. Since the dimension of $U(T)$ must be m, (70) determines $t_1, \ldots, t_{m+1}$ up to a factor $\varrho \neq 0$. We may thus associate with the hyperplane T the coordinates

$$\mathbb{R} \cdot (t_1, \ldots, t_{m+1}).$$

All points $\mathbb{R} \cdot x$ of T then are given by equation (70).

5.6.3 The set of lines as defining notion

Let V be a real vector space of dimension at least 3. Let

$$f : S(V) \to S(V)$$

be a bijection of the set of points of $\Pi(V)$ satisfying

(∗) Whenever $l \in \mathbb{L}(V)$ is a line, then also

$$f(l) := \{f(P) \mid P \subset l\}.$$

It can easily be shown that f must be a projective transformation of $\Pi(V)$. In fact, we have to prove that if l is a line, then so is $f^{-1}(l)$: Let P, Q be distinct points of l and define

$$A := f^{-1}(P), \ B := f^{-1}(Q).$$

We have $A \neq B$ since f is bijective. There is a line g through A, B. In view of (∗), $f(g)$ must be a line containing P, Q. But there is exactly one line through P, Q. Hence $l = f(g)$ and thus

$$f^{-1}(l) = g \in \mathbb{L}(V).$$

Let H be a hyperplane. We already know from section 5.6.1 that

$$f(H) =: \overline{H}$$

is also a hyperplane of $\Pi(V)$, since f is a projective transformation of $\Pi(V)$. Let $B(H)$ be again a basis of $U(H)$ and let

$$N = \text{ span } \{n\}$$

be a point of $V_0 = S(V)\backslash H$. We already know from section 5.6.1 that

$$B := B(H) \cup \{n\}$$

must be a basis of V. Let $B(\overline{H})$ be a basis of $U(\overline{H})$ and span $\{\overline{n}\}$ be the point $f(N)$ of

$$\overline{V}_0 := S(V)\backslash \overline{H}.$$

Then

$$\overline{B} := B(\overline{H}) \cup \{\overline{n}\}$$

is also a basis of V. Hence the cardinalities of B and $\overline{B}$ coincide, and thus there exists a bijection

$$\tau : B(H) \rightarrow B(\overline{H}).$$

If we define

$$\tau \left(\sum_{i=1}^{r} \alpha_i b_i \right) := \sum_{i=1}^{r} \alpha_i \tau(b_i)$$

for every finite subset $\{b_1, \ldots, b_r\}$ of $B(H)$ and real numbers α_i, the mapping τ turns out to be an isomorphism between $U(H)$ and $U(\overline{H})$. Defining

$$\tau(u + \alpha n) = \tau(u) + \alpha \overline{n}$$

for $u \in U(H)$ and real α, we get even an automorphism of V. Put

$$\mu(\text{span } \{p\}) := \text{ span } \{\tau(p)\}$$

for every $p \neq 0$ of V. Then μ must be a projective transformation of $\Pi(V)$. We are now interested in the projective transformation

$$\varphi := \mu^{-1} f.$$

The following statements are easy to verify:

(i) $\varphi(N)$ $=$ $N,$
(ii) $\varphi(H)$ $=$ $H,$
(iii) $\varphi(V_0)$ $=$ $V_0,$
(iv)   Whenever l_0 is an affine line, then so is $\varphi(l_0).$

In view of Theorem 22 we may thus describe the restriction of φ on V_0 in the form

$$\varphi(x) = \lambda(x) + \varphi(0)$$

for all $x \in U(H)$, where λ is a bijective linear transformation of $U(H)$. Statement (i) implies that $\varphi(0) = 0$. Define

$$\lambda(x + \alpha n) := \lambda(x) + \alpha n \qquad (71)$$

for all $x \in U(H)$ and $\alpha \in \mathbb{R}$. We thus extended λ to a bijective linear transformation of V. Let

$$P = \text{span } \{p\}$$

be any point of $\Pi(V)$. We would like to show that

$$\varphi(P) = \text{span } \{\lambda(p)\}. \qquad (72)$$

If $P \in V_0$ we have

$$P = \text{span } \{u + n\}, \ u \in U(H),$$

i.e. $p = \varrho \cdot (u + n)$ for a suitable real $\varrho \neq 0$, and

$$\varphi(P) = \text{span } \{\lambda(u) + n\}.$$

Hence $\varphi(P) = \text{span } \{\lambda(p)\}$ from (71). If $P \in H$ we consider

$$\overline{NP} = l_0 \cup \{\text{span } \{p\}\}$$

with

$$l_0 = \{\varrho \cdot p \mid \varrho \in \mathbb{R}\}.$$

Since

$$\varphi(l_0) = \{\varrho \cdot \lambda(p) \mid \varrho \in \mathbb{R}\}$$

we get $\varphi(P) = \text{span } \{\lambda(p)\}$. Since $\varphi = \mu^{-1} f$ we obtain

$$f(P) = \text{span } \{\tau \lambda(p)\}$$

for $P = \text{span } \{p\}$ for all $P \in S(V)$. Since τ, λ are bijective linear mappings of
V, so are $\tau \cdot \lambda$. We have thus proven

THEOREM 31. *Let V be a real vector space of dimension at least 3 and
let γ be a bijection of $S(V)$ satisfying*

(*) *Whenever $l \in \mathbb{L}(V)$ is a line, then also $\gamma(l)$.*

Then there exists a bijective linear mapping σ of V such that

$$\gamma\big(\text{span } \{p\}\big) = \text{span } \{\sigma(p)\} \qquad (73)$$

*holds true for all $p \neq 0$ in V. On the other hand (73) is a projective transfor-
mation of $\Pi(V)$ when σ is a bijective linear mapping of V.*

5.6.4   An intrinsic characterization

Let $\mathbb{P}$ be a set and let $\mathbb{L}$ be a set of subsets of $\mathbb{P}$. We shall call the elements of $\mathbb{P}$ *points* and the elements of $\mathbb{L}$ *lines*. If $P \in \mathbb{P}$ is a point and $l \in \mathbb{L}$ a line such that $P \in l$ holds true, we shall say that P is on l or that l goes through P. In this case we shall also say that P is incident with l or that l is incident with P. Of course, $P \notin l$ will mean P is *not* on l and so on. The structure

$$\mathrm{II} = (\mathbb{P}, \mathbb{L})$$

is said to be a *projective space* if and only if the following properties (PS1), (PS2), (PS3) hold true.

(PS1) *If P, Q are distinct elements of $\mathbb{P}$, then there exists exactly one element l in $\mathbb{L}$ with $P, Q \in l$.*

    The line l through the points $P \neq Q$ will be denoted by $\overline{PQ}$. A subset T of $\mathbb{P}$ will be called *collinear* iff there exists a line containing T.

(PS2) *Let P, Q, R be three distinct points which are not collinear and let l be a line. If l has exactly two distinct points in common with*

$$\overline{PQ} \cup \overline{QR},$$

    then $l \cap \overline{RP} \neq \emptyset$.

(PS3) *Every line contains at least three distinct points.*

    Let $F = F(+, \cdot)$ be a (not necessarily commutative) field and let V be a *vector space* over F. This is an abelian group

$$V = V(+)$$

together with a multiplication

$$".":F \times V \to V$$

satisfying

$$
\begin{aligned}
\lambda \cdot (x + y) &= \lambda x + \lambda y \\
(\lambda + \mu) \cdot x &= \lambda x + \mu x \\
(\lambda \mu) \cdot x &= \lambda \cdot (\mu x) \\
1 \cdot x &= x
\end{aligned}
$$

for all $\lambda, \mu \in F$ and all $x, y \in V$.

If $p \neq 0$ is an element of V, then

$$Fp := \{\lambda p \mid \lambda \in F\}$$

is called a *point*. Denote the set of all points based on V by

$$\mathbb{P} = \mathbb{P}(V).$$

Let p, q be elements of $V \backslash \{0\}$ such that $q \notin Fp$. The set $l(p, q)$ of all points contained in

$$\hat{l}(p, q) := \{\lambda p + \mu q \mid \lambda, \mu \in F\}$$

is then called a *line*. We denote the set of all lines which are based on V by

$$\mathbb{L} = \mathbb{L}(V).$$

Of course, when $F := \mathbb{R}$ we get the already defined points and lines of section 5.6.1.

PROPOSITION 32. *Let F be a field and let V be a vector space over F. The structure*

$$\Pi(V) = \left(\mathbb{P}(V), \mathbb{L}(V)\right)$$

is then a projective space.

Proof.   a) If Fp, Fq are distinct points, then $q \notin Fp$ and $l(p, q)$ must hence be a line containing Fp, Fq. Now let $l(a, b)$ be a line through Fp, Fq. This implies that

$$p = \alpha a + \beta b \text{ and } q = \gamma a + \delta b$$

for suitable $\alpha, \beta, \gamma, \delta \in F$ and thus

$$
\begin{aligned}
a &= \alpha^{-1}p - \alpha^{-1}\beta b & (74) \\
(\delta - \gamma\alpha^{-1}\beta)b &= -\gamma\alpha^{-1}p + q
\end{aligned}
$$

when $\alpha \neq 0$. Observe that $\delta - \gamma\alpha^{-1}\beta \neq 0$ since $q \notin Fp$. Hence

$$\hat{l}(a, b) \subseteq \hat{l}(p, q) \subseteq \hat{l}(a, b),$$

i.e. $l(a, b) = l(p, q)$. If $\alpha = 0$ we have $\gamma \neq 0$ since $q \notin Fp$, and moreover

$$b \in Fp, \ a = \gamma^{-1}q - \gamma^{-1}\delta b$$

and thus $\hat{l}(a, b) \subseteq \hat{l}(p, q) \subseteq \hat{l}(a, b)$.

(b) $Fp, Fq, F(p + q)$ are three distinct points on $l(p, q)$.

(c) Let $P = Fp$, $Q = Fq$, $R = Fr$ be three distinct points, not on a common line. If the line l has exactly two distinct points in common with

$$\overline{PQ} \cup \overline{QR},$$

then $\#l \cap \overline{PQ} = 1 = \#l \cap \overline{QR}$ with

$$\{A\} = l \cap \overline{PQ} \neq l \cap \overline{QR} = \{B\}$$

in view of (b) and (PS1). Hence

$$A = F(\alpha p + \beta q),$$

$$B = F(\gamma q + \delta r)$$

with suitable $\alpha, \beta, \gamma, \delta$ in F such that $\alpha\delta \neq 0$. Take $\xi, \eta \in F$, not both 0, satisfying

$$\xi\beta + \eta\gamma = 0.$$

Put $s := \xi(\alpha p + \beta q) + \eta(\gamma q + \delta r)$ and $S = Fs$. Now observe that $s \neq 0$, S is on l and S is on $\overline{RP}$. $\square$

Two projective spaces

$$\Pi = (\mathbb{P}, \mathbb{L}) \text{ and } \Pi' = (\mathbb{P}', \mathbb{L}')$$

are called *isomorphic* iff there exists a bijection

$$\sigma : \mathbb{P} \to \mathbb{P}'$$

such that $l \in \mathbb{L}$ holds true iff $\sigma(l) \in \mathbb{L}'$ is satisfied.

THEOREM 33. *Let $\Pi = (\mathbb{P}, \mathbb{L})$ be a projective space such that there exist lines $l_1, l_2 \in \mathbb{L}$ with $l_1 \cap l_2 = \emptyset$. Then there exists a field F and a vector space V over F such that Π and $\Pi(V)$ are isomorphic.*

Theorems like this one belong to a discipline in geometry which is called *Foundations of Geometry*, a title which was chosen by David Hilbert (see his book [1]). Proofs of Theorem 33 can be found in many books, see for instance R. Lingenberg [1] or E.M. Schröder [1], volume 2. A really nice introductory book in this connection is the book by P. Scherk, R. Lingenberg [1]. Concerning the characterization of classes of geometries compare also H. Karzel, H.–J. Kroll [1] and W. Benz [3], where surveys are presented.

REMARK. Let m be a positive integer and let S_m be the set of all m-dimensional (see the beginning of section 5.6.5) projective subspaces of a projective space $\Pi(V)$ (see section 5.6.1) over a vector space V of dimension $> m+1$. If $G \geq G(V)$ is a subgroup of Perm S_m we may consider the geometry (S_m, G) which is called a Grassmann geometry (see W.–L. Chow [1]).

5.6.5 The projective line

Let V be a real vector space of dimension at least 2. If the dimension of V is finite and equal to $n+1$, then the *projective dimension* of the projective space $\Pi(V)$ is defined to be n. If the dimension of V is infinite, say equal to the cardinal number $n+1$, then again n is called the projective dimension of $\Pi(V)$. However, someone who is familiar with cardinal numbers knows that $n+1 = n$ whenever $n \geq \aleph_0$.

In this section we are interested in the projective 1–dimensional case, i.e. in $\Pi(\mathbb{R}^2)$. In this case we have not yet defined what projective transformations should be. If we carry over to the present situation the definition of projective transformations which we gave in section 5.6.1, we get all bijections of $S(\mathbb{R}^2)$ as such transformations. This seems not to be a good idea. A better idea might be the following: suppose that l is a line of $\Pi(V)$, dim $V \geq 3$, and suppose that

$$L = \{\gamma \in G(V) \mid \gamma(l) = l\} \tag{75}$$

is the stabilizer of l in the projective group $G(V)$ of $\Pi(V)$. For $\gamma_1, \gamma_2 \in L$ define

$$\gamma_1 \equiv \gamma_2 \text{ iff } \forall_{P \in l} \gamma_1(P) = \gamma_2(P).$$

Since $N := \{\gamma \in L \mid \gamma \equiv \text{id}\}$ is a normal subgroup of L, the factor group L/N should be a good candidate for the *projective group* of l.

PROPOSITION 34. *The group L/N does not depend on the real vector space V, dim $V \geq 3$, and it does not depend on $l \in \mathbb{L}(V)$.*

Proof. Let l be the line $\overline{PQ}$ with

$$P = \text{span } \{p\} \text{ and } Q = \text{span } \{q\}$$

and let γ be an element of L of (75). We have that

$$\gamma(\text{span } \{x\}) = \text{span } \{\sigma(x)\}$$

for all $x \neq 0$ in V for a bijective linear mapping σ of V from Theorem 31. There exist real numbers a_{ij}, $i, j \in \{1, 2\}$, with

$$\sigma(p) = a_{11}p + a_{12}q,$$
$$\sigma(q) = a_{21}p + a_{22}q$$

since $\gamma(P), \gamma(Q)$ are on l. Let x_1, x_2 be reals, not both 0. Define

$$\text{span } \{x_1'p + x_2'q\} := \gamma(\text{span } \{x_1p + x_2q\})$$

with $x_1', x_2' \in \mathbb{R}$. Then we get the mapping

$$\gamma^*\left[\mathbb{R}(x_1, x_2)\right] := \mathbb{R}(x_1', x_2') = \mathbb{R}(x_1, x_2) \begin{pmatrix} a_{11} & a_{12} \\ a_{21} & a_{22} \end{pmatrix} \tag{76}$$

with $a_{11}a_{22} - a_{12}a_{21} \neq 0$ since $\sigma(p), \sigma(q)$ are not linearly dependent because $\gamma(P) \neq \gamma(Q)$. For two mappings $\gamma, \gamma_1 \in L$ with $\gamma \equiv \gamma_1$ we get the same image (76) since

$$\gamma(P) = \gamma_1(P), \ \gamma(Q) = \gamma_1(Q)$$

and

$$\gamma(\text{span } \{p+q\}) = \gamma_1(\text{span } \{p+q\}).$$

We would now like to show that every mapping (76) with $a_{11}a_{22} \neq a_{12}a_{21}$ occurs as an image. In fact, extend

$$\{a_{11}p + a_{12}q, \ a_{21}p + a_{22}q\} =: \{p', q'\}$$

to a basis B of V. Then define $\overline{B} = (B\backslash\{p', q'\}) \cup \{p, q\}$ and $\sigma : \overline{B} \to B$ by

$$\sigma(p) = a_{11}p + a_{12}q, \ \sigma(q) = a_{21}p + a_{22}q$$

and $\sigma(b) = b$ for all $b \in \overline{B}\backslash\{p, q\}$. Extend σ to a (bijective) linear mapping σ of V. Hence (76) occurs as image. The group of all mappings of the form (76) is thus isomorphic to L/N. It does not depend on l.   □

We would like to define the projective group $G(\mathbb{R}^2)$ of $\Pi(\mathbb{R}^2)$ to be the group of all mappings (76). If A_1, A_2, A_3 are distinct points in $\Pi(\mathbb{R}^2)$ and if B_1, B_2, B_3 are also distinct points in $\Pi(\mathbb{R}^2)$, then there exists exactly one $f \in G(\mathbb{R}^2)$ with

$$f(A_i) = B_i \text{ for } i = 1, 2, 3.$$

There thus exist only trivial 1–, 2–, 3–point–invariants of the geometry

$$\left(S(\mathbb{R}^2), \ G(\mathbb{R}^2)\right).$$

What about 4–point–invariants? We thus pose the following question.

Let $W \neq \emptyset$ be a set. Determine all

$$f : S \times S \times S \times S \to W$$

such that

$$f(X_1, \ldots, X_4) = f(\gamma(X_1), \ldots, \gamma(X_4)) \tag{77}$$

holds true for all $\gamma \in G(\mathbb{R}^2)$ and all $X_i \in S := S(\mathbb{R}^2)$, $i = 1, \ldots, 4$.

If $\#\{X_1, X_2, X_3, X_4\} < 4$ we obviously must have

$$f(A, A, A, A) = f(P, P, P, P)$$

for $A, P \in S$, and we also must have

$$f(A, A, A, B) = f(P, P, P, Q)$$

for $A \neq B$ and $P \neq Q$. Proceeding this way, we get 14 cases

$$
\begin{array}{cccc}
1111 & 1112 & 1122 & 1123 \\
     & 1121 & 1212 & 1213 \\
     & 1211 & 1221 & 1231 \\
     & 2111 &   & 2113 \\
     &   &   & 2131 \\
     &   &   & 2311
\end{array}
$$

which altogether we denote by $K_0 := \{1111, \ldots, 2311\}$. Put

$$K := K_0 \cup \left[\mathbb{R}\backslash\{0,1\} \right].$$

Define the *cross ratio*

$$\begin{bmatrix} A & B \\ D & C \end{bmatrix}$$

of four distinct points

$$A = \mathbb{R}(a_1, a_2), \ldots, D = \mathbb{R}(d_1, d_2)$$

of $S(\mathbb{R}^2)$ by

$$\begin{bmatrix} A & B \\ D & C \end{bmatrix} = \frac{\begin{vmatrix} a_1 & a_2 \\ c_1 & c_2 \end{vmatrix}}{\begin{vmatrix} a_1 & a_2 \\ d_1 & d_2 \end{vmatrix}} : \frac{\begin{vmatrix} b_1 & b_2 \\ c_1 & c_2 \end{vmatrix}}{\begin{vmatrix} b_1 & b_2 \\ d_1 & d_2 \end{vmatrix}}. \tag{78}$$

Observe that the expression on the right hand side of this equation does not depend on the chosen representatives of the points: if for instance

$$\mathbb{R}(a_1, a_2) = \mathbb{R}(\lambda a_1, \lambda a_2),$$

then obviously λ may be cancelled in this expression.

For the following Theorem 35 see J. Aczél [1], 232 ff, and H. Schwerdtfeger [1], 179:

THEOREM 35. *Let $W \neq \emptyset$ be a set and let $g : K \to W$ be a mapping. Then*

$$f(A, B, C, D) = \begin{cases} g\left(\begin{bmatrix} A & B \\ D & C \end{bmatrix} \right) & \text{for } \#\{A, B, C, D\} \begin{cases} = 4 \\ < 4 \end{cases} \\ g\,(ABCD) \end{cases} \tag{79}$$

is a solution of (77) *for all* $\gamma \in G(\mathbb{R}^2)$, *where AAAA stands for* 1111 *and so on. If on the other hand*

$$f : S^4 \to W$$

is a solution of (77), *then there exists* $g : K \to W$ *such that* (79) *holds true.*

Proof.   Take fixed representatives

$$(a_1, a_2) \text{ of } A, \ldots, (d_1, d_2) \text{ of } D$$

and take $(x_1 x_2)M$,

$$M = \left(\begin{array}{cc} a_{11} & a_{12} \\ a_{21} & a_{22} \end{array} \right),$$

as the representative (x_1', x_2') of the image of $\mathbb{R}(x_1, x_2)$ under the mapping γ of form (76). Then

$$\left| \begin{array}{cc} x_1' & x_2' \\ y_1' & y_2' \end{array} \right| = \left| \begin{array}{cc} x_1 & x_2 \\ y_1 & y_2 \end{array} \right| \cdot |M|$$

and the first part of the theorem is proved. — Now let f be a solution of (77). We define a function $g : K \to W$. If

$$k = 1111,$$

put $g(k) = f(A, A, A, A)$ for a point $A \in S$. For the other elements in K_0 define g correspondingly. If

$$k \in \mathbb{R} \setminus \{0, 1\}$$

put $A_0 = \mathbb{R}(1, 0)$, $B_0 = \mathbb{R}(0, 1)$, $C_0 = \mathbb{R}(1, 1)$, $D_0 = \mathbb{R}(k, 1)$ and

$$g(k) = f(A_0, B_0, C_0, D_0).$$

We finally have to prove that f may be written in the form (79). This is trivial in the case that at most three of A, B, C, D are distinct. In the remaining case take $\gamma \in G(\mathbb{R}^2)$ with

$$\gamma(A) = A_0, \ \gamma(B) = B_0, \ \gamma(C) = C_0$$

and

$$\gamma(D) =: \mathbb{R}(k, 1).$$

Then

$$\begin{aligned} f(A, B, C, D) &= f(A_0, B_0, C_0, D_0) \\ &= g(k) = g\left(\left[\begin{array}{cc} A & B \\ D & C \end{array} \right] \right). \end{aligned}$$

$\square$

REMARK. Concerning the n–point–invariants of the projective line over a field see W. Benz [2], 336 ff.

We now would like to proceed with 1–dimensional projective geometry, however, on a somewhat higher level. Let V be the vector space $\mathbb{R}^n$, n a positive integer, and let

$$\cdot : V \times V \to V$$

be a *multiplication* on V satisfying the following rules:

$$a \cdot b \;=\; b \cdot a$$
$$a \cdot (b \cdot c) \;=\; (a \cdot b) \cdot c$$
$$a \cdot (b + c) \;=\; (a \cdot b) + (a \cdot c)$$
$$\lambda \cdot (a \cdot b) \;=\; (\lambda \cdot a) \cdot b$$

for all $a, b, c \in V$ and all $\lambda \in \mathbb{R}$. We ask moreover for the existence of an element $1 \in V$ with $1 \cdot a = a$ for all $a \in V$. The structure $V(\cdot)$ ist then called an n–dimensional commutative and associative *algebra* over $\mathbb{R}$ with identity element 1. The 2–dimensional examples for $V = \mathbb{R}^2$ are given by the multiplications

(1) $(a_1, a_2) \cdot (b_1, b_2) \;:= (a_1 b_1 - a_2 b_2, a_1 b_2 + a_2 b_1)$,

(2) $(a_1, a_2) \cdot (b_1, b_2) \;:= (a_1 b_1 + a_2 b_2, a_1 b_2 + a_2 b_1)$,

(3) $(a_1, a_2) \cdot (b_1, b_2) \;:= (a_1 b_1, a_1 b_2 + a_2 b_1)$.

Every other such 2–dimensional real algebra (commutative, associative, with identity) must be isomorphic (see 6.2.1) to one of the examples 1,2,3. (Two algebras V_1, V_2 over $\mathbb{R}$ are called isomorphic iff there exists a bijection

$$\varphi : V_1 \to V_2$$

such that the equations

$$\varphi(a + b) \;=\; \varphi(a) + \varphi(b),$$
$$\varphi(a \cdot b) \;=\; \varphi(a) \cdot \varphi(b),$$
$$\varphi(\lambda a) \;=\; \lambda \varphi(a)$$

hold true for all $a, b \in V_1$ and all $\lambda \in \mathbb{R}$.)

Suppose that V is an algebra as defined above. By U we denote the set of all *units* of V, i.e.

$$U = \{ a \in V \mid \exists_{b \in V} \ ab = 1 \}.$$

U is a group with respect to multiplication, the so–called group of units of V. Call

$$U(a_1, a_2) := \{(ua_1, ua_2) \mid u \in U\},$$

$a_1, a_2 \in V$, a *point* iff there exist $\alpha_1, \alpha_2 \in V$ with

$$\alpha_1 a_1 + \alpha_2 a_2 = 1.$$

Observe that then

$$(\alpha_1 u^{-1}) \cdot (ua_1) + (\alpha_2 u^{-1}) \cdot (ua_2) = 1$$

also holds true for all $u \in U$. The set of all these points is called the *projective line* over V. Two points

$$A = U(a_1, a_2) \text{ and } B = U(b_1, b_2)$$

are called *neighbours* iff

$$\begin{vmatrix} a_1 & a_2 \\ b_1 & b_2 \end{vmatrix} := a_1 b_2 - a_2 b_1 \notin U.$$

We shall write $A \oslash B$ whenever

$$\begin{vmatrix} a_1 & a_2 \\ b_1 & b_2 \end{vmatrix} \in U.$$

For points A, B, C, D with $A \oslash D$ and $B \oslash C$ we shall define the *cross ratio*

$$\begin{bmatrix} A & B \\ D & C \end{bmatrix} := \frac{\begin{vmatrix} a_1 & a_2 \\ c_1 & c_2 \end{vmatrix} \begin{vmatrix} b_1 & b_2 \\ d_1 & d_2 \end{vmatrix}}{\begin{vmatrix} a_1 & a_2 \\ d_1 & d_2 \end{vmatrix} \begin{vmatrix} b_1 & b_2 \\ c_1 & c_2 \end{vmatrix}}.$$

The following theorem is called *von Staudt's theorem* (see theorems of H. Schaeffer [1] and B.V. Limaye, N.B. Limaye [1],).

THEOREM 36. *Let V be an algebra as defined above and let S be the set of points of the projective line over V. Suppose that*

$$f : S \to S$$

is a harmonic mapping of S, i.e. a mapping satisfying

$$A' \oslash D', \ B' \oslash C' \text{ and } \begin{bmatrix} A' & B' \\ D' & C' \end{bmatrix} = -1$$

whenever A, B, C, D are points with

$$A \oslash D, \ B \oslash C \text{ and } \begin{bmatrix} A & B \\ D & C \end{bmatrix} = -1,$$

where we put $f(X) =: X'$ for $X \in S$. Then there exist

$$\sigma : V \to V \text{ and } a_{11}, a_{12}, a_{21}, a_{22} \in V$$

such that

$$
\begin{aligned}
\sigma(a+b) &= \sigma(a) + \sigma(b), \\
\sigma(a \cdot b) &= \sigma(a) \cdot \sigma(b), \\
\sigma(\lambda a) &= \lambda \sigma(a), \\
\sigma(1) &= 1, \\
a_{11}a_{22} - a_{12}a_{21} &\in U, \\
f[U(x_1, x_2)] &= U(\sigma(x_1), \sigma(x_2)) \cdot \begin{pmatrix} a_{11} & a_{12} \\ a_{21} & a_{22} \end{pmatrix}
\end{aligned}
$$

hold true for all $a, b \in V$, $\lambda \in \mathbb{R}$, $U(x_1, x_2) \in S$.

Proof. (a) $X \oslash Y$ implies $X' \oslash Y'$ for all $X, Y \in S$: Put

$$X =: U(x_1, x_2), \ Y =: U(y_1, y_2)$$

and

$$P := U(x_1 + y_1, x_2 + y_2), \ Q := U(2x_1 + y_1, 2x_2 + y_2).$$

P, Q are points:

$$\begin{vmatrix} x_1 & x_2 \\ y_1 & y_2 \end{vmatrix} =: u \in U$$

implies that

$$(-x_2 u^{-1})(vx_1 + y_1) + (x_1 u^{-1})(vx_2 + y_2) = 1$$

for all $v \in V$. Now observe that

$$X \oslash Y, \ P \oslash Q \text{ and } \begin{bmatrix} X & P \\ Y & Q \end{bmatrix} = -1.$$

Hence $X' \oslash Y'$, since f is harmonic.

(b) Define $A_0 = U(1, 0)$, $B_0 = U(0, 1)$, $C_0 = U(1, 1)$ and put

$$A_0' =: U(a_1', a_2'), \ldots, C_0' =: U(c_1', c_2').$$

Define

$$p := \begin{vmatrix} a_1' & a_2' \\ b_1' & b_2' \end{vmatrix}, \ldots, r := \begin{vmatrix} c_1' & c_2' \\ a_1' & a_2' \end{vmatrix}$$

and observe that $p, q, r \in U$ from (a). The mapping

$$g\big[U(x_1, x_2)\big] := U(x_1, x_2) \begin{pmatrix} qa_1' & qa_2' \\ rb_1' & rb_2' \end{pmatrix}$$

is a bijection of S with

(i) $g(A_0) = A_0'$, $g(B_0) = B_0'$, $g(C_0) = C_0'$,

(ii) $\forall_{X,Y \in S} \ X \oslash Y \Leftrightarrow g(X) \oslash g(Y)$,

(iii) g and g^{-1} are harmonic.

Statement (iii) is a consequence of the fact that g preserves cross ratios, even in our present, more general context. The mapping

$$f_1 := g^{-1} f$$

thus must be harmonic and it preserves A_0, B_0, C_0.

(c)   If $x \in V$, then $U(x, 1) \oslash U(1, 0)$. Hence

$$f_1\big[U(x, 1)\big] \oslash U(1, 0).$$

We may thus write $f_1\big[U(x, 1)\big] =: U(x', 1)$ with $x' \in V$. If 1_V stands (sometimes) for the identity element of V, then

$$1_V + 1_V = (1 + 1) \cdot 1_V = 2 \cdot 1_V$$

with 1 and 2 in $\mathbb{R}$. Hence

$$\left(\frac{1}{2} 1_V\right) (1_V + 1_V) = 1_V$$

and thus $1_V + 1_V \in U$. We shall mainly write 1 instead of 1_V and 2 instead of $1_V + 1_V$.

(d)   Abbreviate $U(x, 1)$ by x and $U(1, 0)$ by ∞. Note that

$$\frac{x}{2} \oslash 0, \ \infty \oslash x \text{ and } \begin{bmatrix} \dfrac{x}{2} & \infty \\ 0 & x \end{bmatrix} = -1$$

for $x \in U$. Hence

$$\left[\begin{array}{cc} \left(\frac{x}{2}\right)' & \infty \\ 0 & x' \end{array} \right] = -1 = \left[\begin{array}{cc} \frac{x'}{2} & \infty \\ 0 & x' \end{array} \right] \tag{80}$$

by observing that $x \oslash 0$, i.e. $x' \oslash 0$, i.e. $\frac{x'}{2} \oslash 0$. Thus $\left(\frac{x}{2}\right)' = \frac{x'}{2}$ for all $x \in U$ from (80).

(e) $(x+y)' = x' + y'$ holds true for all $x, y \in V$ with

$$x - y \in U \text{ and } x + y \in U :$$

Note (d) and

$$\left[\begin{array}{cc} \frac{x+y}{2} & \infty \\ x & y \end{array} \right] = -1 = \left[\begin{array}{cc} \frac{(x+y)'}{2} & \infty \\ x' & y' \end{array} \right] . \tag{81}$$

Now $x - y \in U$ implies that $x \oslash y$, i.e. $x' \oslash y'$, i.e. $x' - y' \in U$. Hence

$$\left[\begin{array}{cc} \frac{x'+y'}{2} & \infty \\ x' & y' \end{array} \right] = -1, \text{ i.e.}$$

$\frac{x'+y'}{2} = \frac{(x+y)'}{2}$ from (81).

(f) The ring $(\mathbb{R}^n, +, \cdot)$ contains at most n maximal ideals. This implies that for a given finite subset

$$F = \{v_1, \ldots, v_r\} \subset V$$

there exists $v \in V$ such that all $v + v_i$, $i = 1, \ldots, r$, are units: suppose that $v_i \in F$ and suppose that I_j is one of the maximal ideals $I_1, \ldots, I_m$. Then there exists at most one $k \in \mathbb{R}$ with

$$k \cdot 1_V + v_i \in I_j,$$

since otherwise $(k - k_1) \cdot 1_V$ would be an element of I_j for a suitable real $k_1 \neq k$. There hence exist at most $r \cdot m$ real numbers $k_1, k_2, \ldots$ with

$$k_\nu \cdot 1_V + v_i \in I_j.$$

But $\mathbb{R}$ contains more than $r \cdot m$ elements. There hence exists $k \cdot 1_V$ with $k \in \mathbb{R}$ and

$$k \cdot 1_V + v_i \notin I_1 \cup \ldots \cup I_m$$

for all $i = 1, \ldots, r$. Put $v := k \cdot 1_V$. Then all $v + v_i$, $i = 1, \ldots, r$, must be units.

(g) $(x + y)' = x' + y'$ for all $x, y \in V$: Put

$$F = \{x + y, -x - y, x - y, y, -y\}$$

and choose $q \in V$ such that $(-q) + v \in U$ for all $v \in F$. Now (e) implies

$$(x + y)' + q' = (x + y + q)' = x' + (y + q)' = x' + y' + q'.$$

(h) $(x^2)' = (x')^2$ for all $x \in V$ with $x, x + 1, x - 1 \in U$. We have

$$\begin{bmatrix} x^2 & 1 \\ -x & x \end{bmatrix} = \begin{bmatrix} (x')^2 & 1 \\ -x' & x' \end{bmatrix} = -1 = \begin{bmatrix} (x^2)' & 1 \\ -x' & x' \end{bmatrix}$$

by observing that $x + 1 \oslash 0$, i.e.

$$x' + 1 = (x + 1)' \oslash 0,$$

i.e. $(x')^2 \oslash -x'$.

(i) $(xy)' = x'y'$ for all $x, y \in V$ with

$$\{x, x + 1, x - 1, y, y + 1, y - 1, x + y, x + y + 1, x + y - 1\} \subseteq U.$$

Applying (g) and (h), we get

$$(x')^2 + 2(xy)' + (y')^2 = (x^2)' + (2xy)' + (y^2)' = [(x + y)^2]'$$
$$= [(x + y)']^2 = (x')^2 + 2x'y' + (y')^2.$$

(j) $(xy)' = x'y'$ for all $x, y \in V$ with $y, y + 1, y - 1 \in U$. Put

$$F = \{0, 1, -1, -y, 1 - y, -1 - y, -x, 1 - x, -1 - x, -x - y, 1 - x - y, -1 - x - y\}$$

and choose $q \in V$ with $(-q) + v \in U$ for all $v \in F$. Then (g) and (i) imply

$$(xy)' + q'y' = (xy)' + (qy)' = [(x + q)y]' = (x + q)'y' = x'y' + q'y'.$$

(k) $(xy)' = x'y'$ for all $x, y \in V$. Put

$$F = \{0, 1, -1, y, y + 1, y - 1\}.$$

Choose $q \in V$ such that $q + v \in U$ for all $v \in F$. Then (g) and (j) imply

$$(xy)' + x'q' = (xy)' + (xq)' = [x(y + q)]' = x'(y + q)' = x'y' + x'q'.$$

(1) $(\lambda x)' = \lambda x'$ for all $\lambda \in \mathbb{R}$ and $x \in V$. Applying (k) we get

$$(\lambda x)' = \left[(\lambda \cdot 1_V)x\right]' = (\lambda \cdot 1_V)' \cdot x'.$$

The fields $\mathbb{R}$ and $\{k \cdot 1_V \mid k \in \mathbb{R}\}$ are isomorphic. Since for all $\lambda, \mu \in \mathbb{R}$

$$(\lambda \cdot 1_V + \mu \cdot 1_V)' = (\lambda \cdot 1_V)' + (\mu \cdot 1_V)',$$
$$(\lambda 1_V \cdot \mu 1_V)' = (\lambda 1_V)' \cdot (\mu 1_V)',$$
$$(1 \cdot 1_V)' = 1'_V = 1_V = 1 \cdot 1_V$$

hold true in view of (g), (k), $f_1(C_0) = C_0$, we get

$$(\lambda \cdot 1_V)' = \lambda \cdot 1_V \text{ for all } \lambda \in \mathbb{R}, \tag{82}$$

as a consequence of Proposition 3, chapter 1. Hence

$$(\lambda x)' = (\lambda \cdot 1_V)'x' = \lambda 1_V \cdot x' = \lambda x'.$$

(m) Let $U(x_1, x_2)$ be a point. Then there exist real numbers $k \neq l$ such that

$$x_1 - kx_2, \; x_1 - lx_2, \; x_1 - \frac{k+l}{2}x_2 \in U : \tag{83}$$

If I is a maximal ideal of V, then there don't exist distinct real numbers k_1, k_2 with

$$x_1 - k_ix_2 \in I, \; i = 1, 2,$$

since otherwise x_1, x_2 would both be elements of I. Let K be the set of all real numbers such that for every $k_0 \in K$ there exists a maximal ideal of V containing k_0. Since K is finite, there thus exist $k \neq l$ in $\mathbb{R}$ satisfying (83).

(n) $f_1\left[U(x_1, x_2)\right] = U(x'_1, x'_2)$ holds true for all points $U(x_1, x_2)$: Choose real numbers $k \neq l$ with (83) and put

$$a = \frac{\frac{k+l}{2}x_1 - klx_2}{x_1 - \frac{k+l}{2}x_2}.$$

Then

$$U(x_1, x_2) \oslash l, \; a \oslash k \text{ and } \left[\begin{array}{cc} U(x_1, x_2) & a \\ l & k \end{array}\right] = -1.$$

Hence

$$U(y_1, y_2) \oslash l', \; a' \oslash k' \text{ and } \left[\begin{array}{cc} U(y_1, y_2) & a' \\ l' & k' \end{array}\right] = -1,$$

where we put $U(y_1, y_2) := f_1[U(x_1, x_2)]$. Observe furthermore that

$$\frac{y_1 - k'y_2}{y_1 - l'y_2} = \frac{k' - a'}{a' - l'} = \left(\frac{k-a}{a-l}\right)' = \left(\frac{x_1 - kx_2}{x_1 - lx_2}\right)',$$

i.e. $y_1 x_2' = y_2 x_1'$, since $k' = k$ and $l' = l$ in view of (82). There exist $\alpha_1, \alpha_2 \in V$ with

$$\alpha_1 x_1 + \alpha_2 x_2 = 1,$$

since $U(x_1, x_2)$ is a point. Hence

$$y_1 = y_1 \cdot (\alpha_1' x_1' + \alpha_2' x_2') = x_1' \cdot (\alpha_1' y_1 + \alpha_2' y_2),$$
$$y_2 = y_2 \cdot (\alpha_1' x_1' + \alpha_2' x_2') = x_2' \cdot (\alpha_1' y_1 + \alpha_2' y_2).$$

$U(y_1, y_2)$ is also a point, i.e. there exist $\beta_1, \beta_2 \in V$ with

$$1 = \beta_1 y_1 + \beta_2 y_2 = p \cdot (\beta_1 x_1' + \beta_2 x_2')$$

for $p := \alpha_1' y_1 + \alpha_2' y_2$. Thus $p \in U$ and hence $U(y_1, y_2) = U(x_1', x_2')$. Now put $\sigma(v) := v'$ for $v \in V$. $\qquad\square$

REMARK. The proof of Theorem 36 which we presented is due to H. Schaeffer [1]. He proved a more general theorem in the case that the harmonic mappings are assumed to be bijective.

REMARK. Harmonic mappings need not to be bijective: Take example (3), page 229, and define

$$\sigma(a_1, a_2) := a_1 \text{ for } (a_1, a_2) \in \mathbb{R}^2$$

and moreover

$$f[U(x_1, x_2)] := U(\sigma(x_1), \sigma(x_2))$$

for $U(x_1, x_2) \in S$. Then f must be harmonic. — It is easy to verify that

$$f[U(x_1, x_2)] = U(\sigma(x_1), \sigma(x_2)) \cdot \begin{pmatrix} a_{11} & a_{12} \\ a_{21} & a_{22} \end{pmatrix}$$

is harmonic when $\sigma : V \to V$ is a homomorphism with

$$\sigma(1) = 1 \text{ and } \sigma(\lambda a) = \lambda \sigma(a)$$

for all $\lambda \in \mathbb{R}$, $a \in V$, and that $a_{11}a_{22} - a_{12}a_{22} \in U$ holds true. (Observe that $a \in U$ implies $\sigma(a) \in U$ since $ab = 1$ carries over to the images.)

REMARK. All 3–dimensional real algebras (commutative, associative, with identity) are given (up to isomorphism) by

$$x \cdot y = (x_1, x_2, x_3) \cdot (y_1, y_2, y_3)$$

with

$$(\mathbb{R}_1^3)\, x \cdot y = (x_1y_1 - x_2y_2, x_1y_2 + x_2y_1, x_3y_3),$$

$$(\mathbb{R}_2^3)\, x \cdot y = (x_1y_1, x_2y_2, x_3y_3),$$

$$(\mathbb{R}_3^3)\, x \cdot y = (x_1y_1, x_1y_2 + x_2y_1, x_3y_3),$$

$$(\mathbb{R}_4^3)\, x \cdot y = (x_1y_1, x_1y_2 + x_2y_1, x_1y_3 + x_2y_2 + x_3y_1),$$

$$(\mathbb{R}_5^3)\, x \cdot y = (x_1y_1, x_1y_2 + x_2y_1, x_1y_3 + x_3y_1).$$

For all algebras (1), (2), (3) and $(\mathbb{R}_i^3)$, $i = 1, \ldots, 5$, real geometries in $\mathbb{R}^2$ or $\mathbb{R}^3$ may be defined (see W. Benz [2], especially 306 ff, H.J. Samaga [1], and section 6.1.3).

5.6.6 Collineations on triangles

Let $\mathbb{P} \neq \emptyset$ be a set and let $\mathbb{B}$ be a set of non–empty subsets of $\mathbb{P}$. We shall call the elements of $\mathbb{P}$ *points* and the elements of $\mathbb{B}$ *blocks*. Suppose that $(\mathbb{P}, \mathbb{B})$ is such a *block space* (see section 5.2.1 and GT 85 ff). We would like to pose the following general problem:

Let $\mathbb{P}_0 \neq \emptyset$ be a subset of $\mathbb{P}$. Characterize all

$$f : \mathbb{P}_0 \to \mathbb{P}$$

satisfying the following property: To every block b with

$$b \cap \mathbb{P}_0 \neq \emptyset$$

there exists a block b' with $f(b \cap \mathbb{P}_0) \subseteq b'$.

There exist several contributions to this problem for special block spaces. J. Aczél and M.A. Mc Kiernan [1] consider spaces where blocks are circles or lines. We mention also J. Aczél [3], J. Aczél and W. Benz [1], V. Havel [1], J.F. Rigby [1], F. Radó [5], H. Schaeffer (see GT 87 ff) among others. The following theorem was proved by J. Aczél and W. Benz [1] for the case of a general field (which need not be commutative). However, we shall consider only the case of the field of reals.

THEOREM 37. *Let l_1, l_2, l_3 be lines of the projective plane $\Pi(\mathbb{R}^3)$ such that there is no point in $l_1 \cap l_2 \cap l_3$. Define $C := l_1 \cup l_2 \cup l_3$ (i.e. union of points* *in l_1, l_2, l_3) and suppose that*

$$f : C \to S(\mathbb{R}^3)$$

is a mapping satisfying

(i) If $P, Q, R \in C$ are collinear, then also $f(P), f(Q), f(R)$,

(ii) $f(C)$ is not collinear,

(iii) f is injective in $l_1 \cap l_2, l_2 \cap l_3, l_3 \cap l_1$.

(f is said to be injective in $P \in C$ iff $f(P) = f(X)$ implies $P = X$ for all $X \in C$.) Then there exists a non–constant

$$\varphi : \mathbb{R} \to \mathbb{R}$$

with $\varphi(ab) = \varphi(a)\varphi(b)$ for all $a, b \in \mathbb{R}$ such that f has form

$$(x_1, x_2, x_3) \to \big(\varphi(x_1), \varphi(x_2), \varphi(x_3)\big) \tag{84}$$

on $l_1 \cup l_2$, up to suitable projective transformations as factors. f is thus determined on C in view of (i). If $\varphi(-1) = -1$, (84) represents f also on l_3 (up to the factors mentioned).

Proof.   (a) Let $P = \mathbb{R}(p_1, p_2, p_3)$ and Q, R be points not on a common line, and let A, B be points with

$$A \in \overline{PQ}\backslash\{P, Q\}, \; B \in \overline{PR}\backslash\{P, R\}.$$

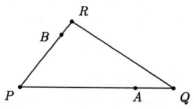

Then there exists a projective transformation τ with

$$\tau(N) = P, \; \tau(X) = Q, \; \tau(Y) = R, \; \tau(E_x) = A, \; \tau(E_y) = B,$$

where we put

$$N = \mathbb{R}(0, 0, 1), \; X = \mathbb{R}(1, 0, 0), \; Y = \mathbb{R}(0, 1, 0)$$

and

$$E_x = \mathbb{R}(1, 0, 1), \; E_y = \mathbb{R}(0, 1, 1).$$

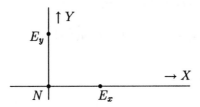

There exist real numbers $\lambda_1, \lambda_2, \mu_1, \mu_2$ with

$$
\begin{aligned}
(a_1, a_2, a_3) &= \lambda_1(p_1, p_2, p_3) + \lambda_2(q_1, q_2, q_3), \\
(b_1, b_2, b_3) &= \mu_1(p_1, p_2, p_3) + \mu_2(r_1, r_2, r_3)
\end{aligned}
$$

and $\lambda_1 \lambda_2 \mu_1 \mu_2 \neq 0$. Define the following bijective linear mapping of $\mathbb{R}^3$:

$$
\sigma(x) = x \cdot \begin{pmatrix} u_1 & u_2 & u_3 \\ v_1 & v_2 & v_3 \\ w_1 & w_2 & w_3 \end{pmatrix}
$$

with $u_i = \lambda_2 \mu_1 q_i$, $v_i = \lambda_1 \mu_2 r_i$, $w_i = \lambda_1 \mu_1 p_i$ for $i = 1, 2, 3$. The mapping

$$
\tau(\text{span } \{x\}) := \text{span } \{\sigma(x)\},
$$

$x \in \mathbb{R}^3 \backslash \{0\}$, has the required properties.

(b)   Let now l_1, l_2, l_3 be lines as described in Theorem 37. Define

$$
P = l_1 \cap l_2, \; Q = l_1 \cap l_3, \; R = l_2 \cap l_3
$$

and take points

$$
A \in \overline{PQ} \backslash \{P, Q\}, \; B \in \overline{PR} \backslash \{P, R\}.
$$

Let τ be a mapping as described in (a). The points $f(P)$, $f(Q)$, $f(R)$ are not collinear, in view of (ii) and (i). Observe that

$$
f(A) \in \overline{f(P)f(Q)} \backslash \{f(P) f(Q)\}
$$

since for instance $f(A) = f(P)$ would imply that $A = P$ in view of (iii). Also

$$
f(B) \in \overline{f(P)f(R)} \backslash \{f(P) f(R)\}.
$$

There hence exists a projective transformation τ_0 satisfying

$$
\tau_0(N) = f(P), \; \tau_0(X) = f(Q), \; \tau_0(Y) = f(R)
$$

and $\tau_0(E_x) = f(A)$, $\tau_0(E_y) = f(B)$. Put

$$
g := \tau_0^{-1} f \tau \tag{85}
$$

and observe that $g : C \to C$ and moreover

$$g(N) = N, \; g(X) = X, \; g(Y) = Y, \; g(E_x) = E_x, \; g(E_y) = E_y.$$

(c)   Put $L_1 := \overline{NX}$, $L_2 := \overline{NY}$, $L_3 := \overline{XY}$ and

$$g : \begin{cases} (x_1, x_2, 1) & \to (\varphi_1(x_1), \varphi_2(x_2), 1) \quad \text{on } (L_1 \cup L_2)\backslash L_3 \\ (1, -z, 0) & \to (1, -\varphi_3(z), 0) \qquad\quad \text{on } L_3\backslash\{Y\} \end{cases}$$

and observe that

$$\varphi_i(0) = 0 \; (i = 1, 2, 3), \; \varphi_1(1) = \varphi_2(1) = 1. \tag{86}$$

The points $\mathbb{R}(0, y_2, 1)$, $\mathbb{R}(y_1, 0, 1)$, $\mathbb{R}(1, -z, 0)$ with $y_1 z \neq 0$ are collinear iff there exist real numbers α, β with

$$(0, y_2, 1) = \alpha(y_1, 0, 1) + \beta(1, -z, 0),$$

i.e. iff $y_2 = y_1 z$ holds true. Since

$$\mathbb{R}(0, \varphi_2(y_2), 1), \; \mathbb{R}(\varphi_1(y_1), 0, 1), \; \mathbb{R}(1, -\varphi_3(z), 0) \tag{87}$$

must also be collinear in view of (i), we get

$$\varphi_2(y_2) = \varphi_1(y_1)\, \varphi_3(z),$$

i.e. $\varphi_2(y_1 z) = \varphi_1(y_1)\, \varphi_3(z)$ (Observe that the points (87) are pairwise distinct in view of (iii) and (ii)!). This equation holds true also when $y_1 z = 0$ from (86). Hence

$$\varphi_2(ab) = \varphi_1(a)\, \varphi_3(b)$$

for $a, b, c \in \mathbb{R}$. Put $a = 1$. Then $\varphi_2(b) = \varphi_3(b)$ with (86). Put $b = 1$. Hence $\varphi_2(a) = \varphi_1(a)$. Thus

$$\varphi_1 = \varphi_2 = \varphi_3 =: \varphi$$

with $\varphi(0) = 0$, $\varphi(1) = 1$. The equation

$$1 = \varphi(1) = \varphi((-1)(-1)) = [\varphi(-1)]^2$$

implies that $\varphi(-1) \in \{-1, +1\}$. Let $\mathbb{R}(x_1, x_2, x_3)$ be a point on $L_1 \cup L_2$, but not on L_3. Then

$$\begin{aligned} g[\mathbb{R}(x_1, x_2, x_3)] &= g[\mathbb{R}(x_3^{-1} x_1, x_3^{-1} x_2, 1)] \\ &= \mathbb{R}(\varphi(x_3^{-1} x_1), \; \varphi(x_3^{-1} x_2), 1). \end{aligned}$$

Note that $\varphi(x_3) \neq 0$ in view of (iii). Since

$$\varphi(x_3) \cdot \varphi(x_3^{-1}x_j) = \varphi(x_j), \quad j = 1, 2,$$

we get

$$g[\mathbb{R}(x_1, x_2, x_3)] = \mathbb{R}(\varphi(x_1), \varphi(x_2), \varphi(x_3)).$$

This formula also holds true for the points X and Y. It thus holds true on $L_1 \cup L_2$.

(d)   Assume that $\varphi(-1) = -1$. Then $\varphi(-z) = -\varphi(z)$ for all $z \in \mathbb{R}$. Let T be a point on L_3 which is not on $L_1 \cup L_2$. Hence

$$T = \mathbb{R}(1, -z, 0) =: \mathbb{R}(x_1, x_2, x_3)$$

with $z \neq 0$. This implies that

$$g(T) = \mathbb{R}(1, -\varphi(z), 0) = \mathbb{R}(1, \varphi(-z), 0)$$

and thus

$$\begin{aligned} g(T) &= g[\mathbb{R}(1, x_1^{-1}x_2, 0)] = \mathbb{R}(1, \varphi(x_1^{-1}x_2), 0) \\ &= \mathbb{R}(\varphi(x_1), \varphi(x_1) \cdot \varphi(x_1^{-1}x_2), 0) \\ &= \mathbb{R}(\varphi(x_1), \varphi(x_2), \varphi(x_3)) \end{aligned}$$

by observing that $\varphi(x_1) \neq 0$ from (iii).

(e)   Assume that $\varphi(-1) = 1$. Then $\varphi(-z) = \varphi(z)$ for all $z \in \mathbb{R}$. Let T be again on L_3, but not on $L_1 \cup L_2$. Then

$$\mathbb{R}(x_1, x_2, x_3) = \mathbb{R}(1, -z, 0) \to \mathbb{R}(1, -\varphi(z), 0) = \mathbb{R}(1, -\varphi(-z), 0)$$

and hence

$$g[\mathbb{R}(x_1, x_2, x_3)] = \mathbb{R}(\varphi(x_1), -\varphi(x_2), \varphi(x_3)).$$

From (85) we finally get

$$f(x) = \tau_0 g \tau^{-1}(x). \square$$

REMARKS. 1) Let $\varphi : \mathbb{R} \to \mathbb{R}$ be a non–constant solution of

$$\varphi(ab) = \varphi(a)\varphi(b) \text{ for all } a, b \in \mathbb{R}. \tag{88}$$

$\varphi(1 \cdot 1) = \varphi(1) \cdot \varphi(1)$ implies that $\varphi(1) = 0$ or $\varphi(1) = 1$. If $\varphi(1) = 0$ we get

$$\varphi(a) = \varphi(a \cdot 1) = \varphi(a) \cdot \varphi(1) = 0$$

and φ would be a constant. Hence $\varphi(1) = 1$. We also get $\varphi(0) = 0$ or $\varphi(0) = 1$. Assume that $\varphi(0)$ is 1. Then

$$1 = \varphi(0) = \varphi(0 \cdot a) = \varphi(0) \cdot \varphi(a) = \varphi(a)$$

and φ is constant, a contradiction. Thus $\varphi(0) = 0$.

We would like to prove that $\varphi(t)$ must be unequal to 0 when $t \neq 0$. Assume otherwise; then we have

$$\varphi(1) = \varphi\left(\frac{1}{t} \cdot t\right) = \varphi\left(\frac{1}{t}\right)\varphi(t) = 0.$$

For $a > 0$ we get $\varphi(a) = \left[\varphi(\sqrt{a})\right]^2 \geq 0$. Hence

$$\varphi(a) > 0 \text{ for all } a > 0.$$

Define for $x \in \mathbb{R}$

$$\psi(x) = \ln\varphi(e^x).$$

Observe that $e^x > 0$ and thus $\varphi(e^x) > 0$. Hence

$$\psi(x + y) = \psi(x) + \psi(y) \tag{89}$$

for all $x, y \in \mathbb{R}$. Since (89) implies

$$\psi(\lambda x) = \lambda\psi(x)$$

for all $\lambda \in \mathbb{Q}$ and $x \in \mathbb{R}$ where $\mathbb{Q}$ denotes the field of rationals, ψ must be a linear mapping of the vector space $\mathbb{R}$ over $\mathbb{Q}$. If B is a basis of the vector space $\mathbb{R}$ over $\mathbb{Q}$, all solutions ψ can be obtained by an arbitrary function

$$\psi_0 : B \to \mathbb{R}$$

as the linear extension of ψ_0 to $\mathbb{R}$. All φ can thus be obtained by

$$\varphi(a) = e^{\psi(\ln a)} \text{ for } a > 0$$

and

$$\varphi(a) = -\varphi(-a) \text{ for all } a < 0$$

or

$$\varphi(a) = \varphi(-a) \text{ for all } a < 0.$$

Every ψ thus leads to two φ's.

2) Now take again the points

$$N = \mathbb{R}(0,0,1), \ X = \mathbb{R}(1,0,0), \ Y = \mathbb{R}(0,1,0)$$

and the lines
$$L_1 = \overline{NX}, \; L_2 = \overline{NY}, \; L_3 = \overline{XY}.$$

For a function φ as above, define

$$f\big[\mathbb{R}(x_1, x_2, x_3)\big] := \mathbb{R}\big(\varphi(x_1), \varphi(x_2), \varphi(x_3)\big) \tag{90}$$

on $L_1 \cup L_2$. If $\varphi(-1) = -1$ define f on L_3 also by (90). If $\varphi(-1) = 1$ define

$$f\big[\mathbb{R}(x_1, x_2, x_3)\big] := \mathbb{R}\big(\varphi(x_1), -\varphi(x_2), \varphi(x_3)\big)$$

on $L_3 \backslash (L_1 \cup L_2)$. Then f satisfies properties (i), (ii), (iii) of Theorem 37. This can easily be verified: in order to prove (iii) we only need to observe that $\varphi(a)$ is unequal to 0 for $a \neq 0$.

If f is monotonic in at least one point of a line L_i with respect to this line, then φ has the following form

$$\varphi(x) = \begin{cases} |x|^\alpha & x \neq 0 \\ & \text{for} \\ 0 & x = 0 \end{cases}$$

or

$$\varphi(x) = \begin{cases} |x|^\alpha \, \mathrm{sgn} x & x \neq 0 \\ & \text{for} \\ 0 & x = 0 \end{cases} ,$$

α a real constant (see loc. cit.).

3) Replacing the triangle of Theorem 37 by a *quadrangle in general position* (no three of the four points involved are collinear), f must already be a restriction of a projective transformation of $\Pi(\mathbb{R}^3)$ on C (see loc. cit. where a more general theorem is proved).

5.7 Non–euclidean geometries

5.7.1 Hyperbolic geometry as a substructure

Let $G = G(\mathbb{R}^{n+1})$ be the group of all projective transformations of the projective geometry
$$\Pi = \Pi(\mathbb{R}^{n+1}), \; n \geq 1.$$

Suppose that S_0 is the set of all points $\mathbb{R}(x_1, \ldots, x_{n+1})$ of $S = S(\mathbb{R}^{n+1})$ with

$$x_1^2 + \ldots + x_n^2 < x_{n+1}^2. \tag{91}$$

This inequality implies that $x_{n+1} \neq 0$ and thus

$$\left(\frac{x_1}{x_{n+1}}\right)^2 + \ldots + \left(\frac{x_n}{x_{n+1}}\right)^2 < 1.$$

In other words: S_0 is the interior I^n of the unit–hypersphere

$$\{y \in \mathbb{R}^n \mid y_1^2 + \ldots + y_n^2 \leq 1\}$$

of $\mathbb{R}^n$. We are interested in the geometry (S_0, G_0) (see section 1.3) with

$$G_0 := \{g \in G \mid g(S_0) = S_0\}.$$

For $(x_1, \ldots, x_{n+1}) \in \mathbb{R}^{n+1}$ satisfying (91), define

$$\omega(x) := \sqrt{x_{n+1}^2 - (x_1^2 + \ldots + x_n^2)} \cdot \operatorname{sgn} x_{n+1}.$$

If $\mathbb{R}(x_1, \ldots, x_{n+1})$ is a point in S_0, then

$$\left(\frac{x_1}{\omega(x)}, \ldots, \frac{x_{n+1}}{\omega(x)}\right)$$

are its Weierstrass coordinates (see section 2.6).

Let

$$L = \begin{pmatrix} l_{11} & \cdots & l_{1,n+1} \\ \vdots & & \\ l_{n+1,1} & \cdots & l_{n+1,n+1} \end{pmatrix} \tag{92}$$

be an arbitrary real matrix with $\det L \neq 0$. Then

$$\mathbb{R}(x) \to \mathbb{R}(y) := \mathbb{R}(xL) \tag{93}$$

is a projective transformation of $\Pi(\mathbb{R}^{n+1})$, and there are no other projective transformations of this geometry (see Theorem 31 for $n \geq 2$, and see section 5.6.5 concerning case $n = 1$).

There exists a real $\alpha \neq 0$ such that αL is a Lorentz matrix for the matrix (92) iff there exists a real $\beta \neq 0$ such that βL is an orthochronous Lorentz matrix. This is trivial since $(-\alpha)L$ must be orthochronous in case that αL is a Lorentz matrix which is not orthochronous (see section 2.6).

THEOREM 38. *The mapping (93) belongs to G_0 if and only if there exists a real $\lambda \neq 0$ such that $\lambda \cdot L$ is an orthochronous Lorentz matrix.*

Proof.   (a) Let $L' = \lambda L$ be an orthochronous Lorentz matrix for a suitable $\lambda \neq 0$. Then (93) may also be written in form

$$\mathbb{R}(y) = \mathbb{R}(x L').$$

For $\mathbb{R}(x) \in S_0$ there thus exists a real $\varrho[\mathbb{R}(x)] \neq 0$ such that

$$\varrho \frac{y}{\omega(y)} = \frac{x}{\omega(x)} L' \tag{94}$$

holds true. Hence (see section 2.6)

$$\varrho^2 \frac{y}{\omega(y)} M \left(\frac{y}{\omega(y)} \right)^T = \frac{x}{\omega(x)} L' M (L')^T \left(\frac{x}{\omega(x)} \right)^T,$$

i.e. $\varrho^2 = 1$. Near the beginning of the proof of Theorem 8 of section 2.6 we showed that, applied to our present situation, the last component of the left–hand side of (94) must be positive. Thus $\varrho = +1$, since $\frac{y_{n+1}}{\omega(y)} > 0$. The mapping (94) is hence a bijection of S_0 from Theorem 8 (section 2.6).

(b)   Let $g \in G$ be a projective transformation with $g(S_0) = S_0$, represented by (93). The image of the point

$$(\xi_1, \ldots, \xi_n) \in I^n \tag{95}$$

under g is thus $(\eta_1, \ldots, \eta_n) \in I^n$ with

$$\eta_i = \frac{\xi_1 l_{1i} + \ldots + \xi_n l_{ni} + l_{n+1,i}}{\xi_1 l_{1,n+1} + \ldots + \xi_n l_{n,n+1} + l_{n+1,n+1}} \tag{96}$$

for $i = 1, \ldots, n$. Observe that the denominator of (96) is unequal to 0 for all points (95), since otherwise there would exist a point such that the last component of

$$\mathbb{R}((\xi_1 \ldots \xi_n 1) L) \tag{97}$$

is equal to 0 which contradicts (91) for the point (97). We would like to show that the denominator of (96) is also unequal to 0 for all

$$(\xi_1, \ldots, \xi_n) \in \mathbb{R}^n$$

with $\xi_1^2 + \ldots + \xi_n^2 = 1$. Assume that there exists $(\bar{\xi}_1, \ldots, \bar{\xi}_n)$ with

$$\bar{\xi}_1 l_{1,n+1} + \ldots + \bar{\xi}_n l_{n,n+1} + l_{n+1,n+1} = 0$$

and $\bar{\xi}_1^2 + \ldots + \bar{\xi}_n^2 = 1$. Then there must exist $i_0 \in \{1, \ldots, n\}$ with

$$\bar{\xi}_1 l_{1 i_0} + \ldots + \bar{\xi}_n l_{n i_0} + l_{n+1, i_0} \neq 0,$$

since otherwise det $L = 0$. For the image $(\eta_1, \ldots, \eta_n)$ of

$$(\xi_1, \ldots, \xi_n) := \alpha \cdot (\bar{\xi}_1, \ldots, \bar{\xi}_n) \in I^n, \ 0 < \alpha < 1,$$

under (96) we hence get $|\eta_{i_0}| > 1$, if $1 - \alpha$ is sufficiently small. But

$$\eta_1^2 + \ldots + \eta_n^2 < 1$$

does not allow $\eta_{i_0}^2 > 1$.

(c) The mapping (96) can thus be extended to $I^n \cup K$ with

$$K := \{(\xi_1, \ldots, \xi_n) \in \mathbb{R}^n \mid \xi_1^2 + \ldots + \xi_n^2 = 1\}.$$

Since the right–hand side of (96) is continous in $I^n \cup K$ for all $i = 1, \ldots, n$, we get

$$g(I^n \cup K) \subseteq I^n \cup K,$$

i.e. $g(K) \subseteq K$ since $g(I^n) = I^n$.

(d) Since $\overset{(n)}{H}$ operates transitively on I^n (see step (a) of the proof of Theorem 9 of section 2.6), we may multiply L with an orthochronous Lorentz matrix L_1 such that $\mathbb{R}(0, \ldots, 0, 1)$ remains invariant under

$$\mathbb{R}(x) \rightarrow \mathbb{R}(xLL_1).$$

Without loss of generality we may thus assume that $\mathbb{R}(0, \ldots, 0, 1)$ remains invariant under g. This implies that

$$l_{n+1,1} = \ldots = l_{n+1,n} = 0. \tag{98}$$

Moreover, without loss of generality, we may put $l_{n+1,n+1} = 1$. For a factor $\varrho \neq 0$ depending on x, y we may write

$$\varrho y = xL$$

instead of $\mathbb{R}(y) := g[\mathbb{R}(x)] = \mathbb{R}(xL)$. Since $g(K) \subseteq K$,

$$x_1^2 + \ldots + x_n^2 - x_{n+1}^2 = 0 \tag{99}$$

implies that $y_1^2 + \ldots + y_n^2 - y_{n+1}^2 = 0$. Hence $xLML^T x^T = 0$ is a consequence of (99). Observe that $A := LML^T$ is symmetric. If we take

$$(\delta_{i1}, \ldots, \delta_{in}, \pm 1), \ i \in \{1, \ldots, n\},$$

for (99), we get

$$a_{ii} \pm 2a_{n+1,i} + a_{n+1,n+1} = 0$$

for $i = 1, \ldots, n$, i.e.

$$a_{n+1,i} = 0 \text{ and } a_{ii} = -a_{n+1,n+1} =: \varepsilon$$

for $i = 1, \ldots, n$. If we take $(\delta_{i1} + \delta_{j1}, \ldots, \delta_{in} + \delta_{jn}, \sqrt{2})$ for (99) for distinct i, j in $\{1, \ldots, n\}$, we get $a_{ij} = 0$. Hence $LML^T = \varepsilon M$. Now (98) together with $l_{n+1,n+1} = 1$ implies that $\varepsilon = 1$, if we figure out the element of the last row and the last column of LML^T. $\square$

In section 2.6 we defined the n–dimensional hyperbolic geometry $(I^n, \overset{(n)}{H})$. A corollary of Theorem 38 (see section 1.4) is

PROPOSITION 39. $(S_0, G_0) \cong (I^n, \overset{(n)}{H})$.

(S_0, G_0) is called the *Cayley–Klein–model* of n–dimensional hyperbolic geometry. In Theorem 9 of section 2.6 we characterized a notion *hyperbolic distance* by natural assumptions. Originally the notion of hyperbolic distance was introduced via cross ratios: define

$$\varphi(x, y) := \left| ln \begin{bmatrix} a & b \\ y & x \end{bmatrix} \right| \tag{100}$$

for points $x \neq y$ of I^n. The points a, b are here the points of intersection of K and the line joining x, y. Moreover define $\varphi(x, x) = 0$ for $x \in I^n$. The cross ratio of four distinct points $A = \mathbb{R}a, \ldots$ on a line l of $\Pi(\mathbb{R}^{n+1})$ is given as follows: take points $\mathbb{R}p \neq \mathbb{R}q$ on l and equations

$$a = a_1 p + a_2 q, \ldots$$

with $a_1, a_2, \ldots \in \mathbb{R}$. Then take the expression (78) which does not depend on the choice of $\mathbb{R}p, \mathbb{R}q$ on l, and which is an invariant of $G(\mathbb{R}^{n+1})$, as it is trivial to prove: if σ is a bijective linear mapping of $\mathbb{R}^{n+1}$, then

$$\sigma(a) = a_1 \sigma(p) + a_2 \sigma(q), \ldots$$

and the right–hand side of (78) thus coincides with

$$\begin{bmatrix} A & B \\ D & C \end{bmatrix} \text{ and } \begin{bmatrix} A' & B' \\ D' & C' \end{bmatrix}$$

with $A' = \mathbb{R}(\sigma(a)), \ldots$. (This simple proof holds true also if we replace $\mathbb{R}^{n+1}$ by an infinite–dimensional vector space V.)

PROPOSITION 40. *There exists a real constant $k > 0$ such that*

$$- \cosh \frac{\varphi(x,y)}{k} = x_1 y_1 + \ldots + x_n y_n - x_{n+1} y_{n+1}$$

holds true in Weierstrass coordinates for all $x, y \in I^n$.

Proof.   This follows from Theorem 9, section 2.6, provided we are able to verify (i), (ii), (iii) of Theorem 9. But (i) is clear, since projective transformations don't change cross ratios. (iii) is trivial. (ii) is also trivial if $\lambda = 0$ or $\lambda = 1$. So take points as described in (ii) with $0 < \lambda < 1$. An immediate consequence of (78) is

$$\begin{bmatrix} a\ b \\ z\ x \end{bmatrix} = \begin{bmatrix} a\ b \\ y\ x \end{bmatrix} \cdot \begin{bmatrix} a\ b \\ z\ y \end{bmatrix}. \tag{101}$$

Here we abbreviated $\mathbb{R}(a_1, \ldots, a_n, 1)$ by $a = (a_1, \ldots, a_n)$ in cartesian coordinates. Assume that a, b are given in such a way that

$$0 = \lambda_a < \lambda_x < \lambda_y < \lambda_z < \lambda_b = 1$$

holds true for $p = a + \lambda_p(b-a) = (1-\lambda_p)a + \lambda_p b$ with $p \in \{a, x, y, z, b\}$. Hence

$$0 < \begin{bmatrix} a\ b \\ y\ x \end{bmatrix} = \frac{\lambda_x}{\lambda_y} \cdot \frac{1 - \lambda_y}{1 - \lambda_x} < 1$$

and

$$0 < \begin{bmatrix} a\ b \\ z\ y \end{bmatrix} = \frac{\lambda_y}{\lambda_z} \cdot \frac{1 - \lambda_z}{1 - \lambda_y} < 1.$$

Thus $\varphi(x,z) = \varphi(x,y) + \varphi(y,z)$ from (101). $\square$

5.7.2   Angles in hyperbolic geometry

Let h' be a half–line of $\mathbb{R}^n$, $n \geq 2$, (see section 5.2.3) with endpoint $p \in I^n$. The intersection $h' \cap I^n$ is then called a half–line h of I^n with endpoint p. Suppose that h_1, h_2 are two half–lines of I^n with the same endpoint $p \in I^n$ such that $h_1 \cup h_2$ is not contained in a line of $\mathbb{R}^n$. To the half–lines $h_i' \supset h_i$, $i = 1, 2$, of $\mathbb{R}^n$ with endpoint p there is associated the angular space A^+ (see section 5.2.3). The object

$$(\{h_1, h_2\}, p, A^+ \cap I^n) =: (h_1, h_2, p)$$

will be called an *angle of hyperbolic geometry.*

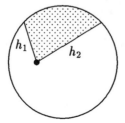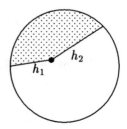

From the euclidean point of view we have thus defined angles to have a
measure in $]0, \pi[$ only. As a matter of fact, we would also like to include case
$h_1 = h_2$ in our definition, and the case that h_1, h_2 are collinear and distinct with
the same endpoint. The last case will be described by $h_1 = -h_2$ or $h_2 = -h_1$.

LEMMA 41. *The set of all angles (h_1, h_2, p) of n–dimensional hyperbolic
geometry is an invariant notion.*

Proof.   Let $(h_1, h_2, p), h_1 \neq \pm h_2$, be an angle with the angular space
$A^+ \cap I^n$ and let γ be an element of $\overset{(n)}{H}$. We have to show that then

$$\left(\gamma(h_1), \gamma(h_2), \gamma(p)\right)$$

is an angle as well. In the first Remark of section 2.6 we proved the following
statement: let

$$x, z \text{ and } y = \lambda x + (1 - \lambda)z \quad (0 \leq \lambda \leq 1)$$

be three points of I^n, given in cartesian coordinates. Then there exists $\mu \in \mathbb{R}$
with

$$\gamma(y) = \mu\gamma(x) + (1 - \mu)\gamma(z) \text{ and } 0 \leq \mu \leq 1,$$

where $\gamma(x), \dots$ are also given in cartesian coordinates. This statement implies
that images of half–lines are half–lines:

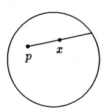

observe that the images of the points of a half–line between p and $x \in h$ must
be on the line through $\gamma(p), \gamma(x)$ between these points. Apply the same idea
now for x, y (s. figure) instead of p, x. □

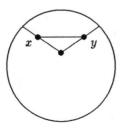

Denote by ANH the set of all angles of $(I^n, \overset{(n)}{H})$, $n \geq 2$. Let $W \neq \emptyset$ be a set and define

$$W_0 = [0, \pi].$$

Then we are interested in all functions $\varphi : ANH \to W$ such that

$$\forall_{\omega \in ANH} \; \forall_{f \in \overset{(n)}{H}} \; \varphi(\omega) = \varphi(f(\omega)) \tag{102}$$

holds true.

THEOREM 42. *Let φ be a solution of (102). Then there exists a function $g : W_0 \to W$ such that*

$$\varphi(h_1, h_2, p) = g(\alpha) \tag{103}$$

with $\alpha \in [0, \pi]$ and

$$\cos \alpha = \frac{\cosh^2 1 - \cosh t}{\sinh^2 1}, \tag{104}$$

where $t = h(x_1, x_2)$ is the hyperbolic distance of points $x_i \in h_i$ with $h(p, x_i) = 1$, $i = 1, 2$. On the other hand, every function φ constructed this way is a solution of (102).

Proof.   (a) Let $p, x_1, x_2 \in I^n$ be the vertices of a non–collinear triangle with

$$h(p, x_1) = 1 = h(p, x_2) \text{ and } h(x_1, x_2) = t.$$

Then $t \leq 2$ because of the triangle inequality (GT 65)

$$h(x_1, x_2) \leq h(x_1, p) + h(p, x_2).$$

Now $0 \leq t \leq 2$ implies that $1 = \cosh 0 \leq \cosh t \leq \cosh 2$, i.e.

$$- \sinh^2 1 \leq \cosh^2 1 - \cosh t \leq \sinh^2 1$$

since $\cosh 2 = \cosh^2 1 + \sinh^2 1$. The right–hand side of (104) is thus in $[-1, +1]$ for $t \in [0, 2]$, and it is strictly monotonic with values 1, -1 at $t = 0$, $t = 2$ respectively. The mapping $t \to \alpha$ of (104) is thus bijective between $[0, 2]$ and $[0, \pi]$. — Let us now consider a function φ of the form (103) which is defined via (104). If f is in $\overset{(n)}{H}$, we get

$$f(x_i) \in f(h_i), \; h(f(p), f(x_i)) = 1, \; i = 1, 2,$$

and $t = h(x_1, x_2) = h\big(f(x_1), f(x_2)\big)$ for half–lines h_1, h_2 with endpoint p and points $x_i \in h_i$ with $h(p, x_i) = 1$ and $t = h(x_1, x_2)$. We hence get the same α for

$$(h_1, h_2, p) \text{ and } \big(f(h_1), f(h_2), f(p)\big),$$

and φ therefore must be a solution of (102).

(b) Assume now, conversely, that $\varphi : ANH \to W$ is a solution of (102). For $\alpha \in [0, \pi]$ take half–lines g_1, g_2 with endpoint 0 such that the angle between g_1, g_2 has euclidean measure α. Then define

$$g(\alpha) := \varphi(g_1, g_2, 0).$$

In order to be sure that g is well–defined, we must show

$$\varphi(g_1, g_2, 0) = \varphi(\bar{g}_1, \bar{g}_2, 0),$$

whenever $\bar{g}_1, \bar{g}_2$ are half–lines with endpoint 0 such that the euclidean measure of the angle between $\bar{g}_1, \bar{g}_2$ is also α: take an orthogonal matrix A of $\mathbb{R}^n$ with $\gamma(g_i) = \bar{g}_i$, $i = 1, 2$,

$$\gamma(\xi_1, \ldots, \xi_n) = (\xi_1, \ldots, \xi_n)A.$$

But this mapping belongs to $\overset{(n)}{H}$,

$$\gamma = (x_1, \ldots, x_{n+1}) \to x \left(\begin{array}{c|c} A & \begin{matrix} 0 \\ \vdots \\ 0 \end{matrix} \\ \hline 0 \ \cdots \ 0 & 1 \end{array} \right),$$

now written in Weierstrass coordinates. Hence (102) implies that

$$\varphi(g_1, g_2, 0) = \varphi\big(\gamma(g_1), \gamma(g_2), \gamma(0)\big) = \varphi(\bar{g}_1, \bar{g}_2, 0).$$

The function $g : [0, \pi] \to W$ is thus well–defined.

(c) We finally have to determine $\varphi(h_1, h_2, p)$ for an arbitrary angle. Take points $x_i \in h_i$ with

$$h(p, x_i) = 1, \ i = 1, 2, \tag{105}$$

and define $t := h(x_1, x_2)$. Since $\overset{(n)}{H}$ operates transitively on I^n, take $\gamma \in \overset{(n)}{H}$ with $\gamma(p) = 0$. As in (b), we may even assume that

$$\gamma(h_1) = \{\lambda e_1 \mid \lambda \geq 0\}, \gamma(h_2) = \{\lambda(\varrho e_1 + \sigma e_2) \mid \lambda \geq 0\}$$

for suitable $\varrho, \sigma \in \mathbb{R}$ with $\varrho^2 + \sigma^2 = 1$, $\sigma \geq 0$, and with

$$e_1 = (1, 0, \ldots, 0), \quad e_2 = (0, 1, 0, \ldots, 0)$$

as elements of $\mathbb{R}^n$. With the first expression ($k = 1$) for hyperbolic distances of Theorem 9 (section 2.6) we get

$$\gamma(x_1) = e_1 \cdot \tanh 1, \quad \gamma(x_2) = (\varrho e_1 + \sigma e_2) \cdot \tanh 1$$

from (105). Furthermore $t = h\bigl(\gamma(x_1), \gamma(x_2)\bigr)$ and hence

$$\cosh t = \frac{1 - \varrho \tanh^2 1}{1 - \tanh^2 1},$$

i.e. $\varrho \cdot \sinh^2 1 = \cosh^2 1 - \cosh t$. If we denote by α the euclidean measure of the angle between $\gamma(h_1), \gamma(h_2)$, we get $\varrho = \cos \alpha$ and thus (104). $\square$

As in section 5.2.5 we may ask for *additive angle measures* for our present geometry $(I^n, \overset{(n)}{H})$, $n \geq 2$. These are all functions

$$h : ANH \to \mathbb{R}_{\geq 0}$$

such that (42) and (*) (see section 5.2.5), carried over to our present situation, hold true. Mutatis mutandis in Theorem 16, we also get here

$$h(h_1, h_2, p) = k\alpha$$

with a constant $k \geq 0$, where α is the value of (103), (104). We shall put $k = 1$, so that

$$\sphericalangle(h_1, h_2, p) = \alpha, \tag{106}$$

where we wrote $\sphericalangle$ instead of h.

It is now easy to prove trigonometric formulas like the cosine theorem for a triangle:

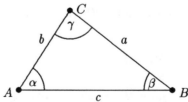

$$\cosh a = \cosh b \cdot \cosh c - \sinh b \cdot \sinh c \cdot \cos \alpha. \tag{107}$$

As in step (c) of the proof of Theorem 42 we may assume that

$$A = 0, \ B = e_1 \cdot \tanh c, \ C = (e_1 \cos \alpha + e_2 \sin \alpha) \cdot \tanh b.$$

Hence

$$\cosh a = \cosh h(B, C) = \frac{1 - \cos \alpha \cdot \tanh c \cdot \tanh b}{\sqrt{1 - \tanh^2 c}\sqrt{1 - \tanh^2 b}},$$

i.e. (107).

The reader might try to prove for himself such classical results (see for instance H. Schwerdtfeger [1], 154 ff) like

(1) *The sum of the angles in every triangle is less than π,*

(2) *If $\alpha, \beta, \gamma \in]0, \pi[$ are three angles satisfying $\alpha + \beta + \gamma < \pi$, then there is a triangle having these angles, and to any two such triangles Δ, Δ' there exists an $f \in \overset{(n)}{H}$ with $f(\Delta) = \Delta'$.*

5.7.3 Volumes in hyperbolic geometry

Let m be a point of I^n and let $r > 0$ be a real number. Then we define

$$S(m, r) := \{x \in I^n \mid h(m, x) \leq r\}.$$

A set $M \subset I^n$ is called h–bounded iff there exists a set $S(m, r)$ containing M. Let $\mathbb{M}$ be the set of all h–bounded and closed subsets M of the metric space (I^n, h) (see GT, 65). Since volumes in geometry may usually be written in terms of integrals, we are interested in a (continuous) function

$$\varphi : I^n \to \mathbb{R}_{>0}$$

such that the Lebesgue integral

$$\mu(M) = \int_M \varphi(\xi) d\xi \tag{108}$$

is a good measure for the volume of $M \in \mathbb{M}$. Of course, we should ask for

$$\mu(M) = \mu\big(\gamma(M)\big) \tag{109}$$

for all $M \in \mathbb{M}$ and all $\gamma \in \overset{(n)}{H}$ with a positive functional determinant. (109) implies

$$\int_M \varphi(\xi) d\xi = \int_{\gamma(M)} \varphi(\xi') d\xi' = \int_M \varphi(\gamma(\xi)) \frac{\partial(\xi'_1, \ldots, \xi'_n)}{\partial(\xi_1, \ldots, \xi_n)} d\xi \qquad (110)$$

with $\gamma(\xi_1, \ldots, \xi_n) =: (\xi'_1, \ldots, \xi'_n)$ in cartesian coordinates. Taking a sequence of closed balls M_ν of $\mathbb{R}^n$, tending to a point $\xi \in I^n$ (110) implies that

$$\varphi(\xi) = \varphi(\gamma(\xi)) \frac{\partial(\xi'_1, \ldots, \xi'_n)}{\partial(\xi_1, \ldots, \xi_n)} \qquad (111)$$

for all $\xi \in I^n$ from a standard mean value theorem. If we apply (111) in the case

$$\gamma(\xi) = \xi A,$$

where A is orthogonal with $\det A = 1$, we get $\varphi(\xi) = \varphi(\gamma(\xi))$, i.e.

$$\xi^2 = \eta^2 \Rightarrow \varphi(\xi) = \varphi(\eta) \qquad (112)$$

for all $\xi, \eta \in I^n$. For $0 \le a < 1$ put

$$\sqrt{1 - a^2} \cdot L := \begin{pmatrix} a_{11} & \cdots & a_{1,n+1} \\ \vdots & & \\ a_{n+1,1} & \cdots & a_{n+1,n+1} \end{pmatrix}$$

with $a_{11} = (-1)^{n+1}$, $a_{1,n+1} = -a$, $a_{n+1,1} = (-1)^n a$,

$$a_{n+1,n+1} = 1, \quad a_{ii} = -\sqrt{1 - a^2}$$

for $i = 2, \ldots, n$, and $a_{ij} = 0$ otherwise. Observe that $L \in \overset{(n)}{H}$. In cartesian coordinates, this mapping reads

$$\xi'_1 = (-1)^n \frac{\xi_1 - a}{a\xi_1 - 1}, \quad \xi'_i = \frac{\xi_i \cdot \sqrt{1 - a^2}}{a\xi_1 - 1}, \qquad (113)$$

$i = 2, \ldots, n$. Hence

$$\frac{\partial(\xi'_1, \ldots, \xi'_n)}{\partial(\xi_1, \ldots, \xi_n)} = \left(\frac{\sqrt{1 - a^2}}{1 - a\xi_1} \right)^{n+1}.$$

(111) and (113) now imply

$$\varphi(a, 0, \ldots, 0) = \varphi(0, \ldots, 0) \left(\frac{1}{\sqrt{1 - a^2}} \right)^{n+1}$$

when $\xi := (a, 0, \ldots, 0)$. If we put

$$k := \varphi(0, \ldots, 0) \in \mathbb{R}_{>0},$$

we get

$$\varphi(a, 0, \ldots, 0) = \frac{k}{(\sqrt{1 - a^2})^{n+1}}$$

and hence

$$\varphi(\xi_1, \ldots, \xi_n) = \varphi(\sqrt{\xi_1^2 + \ldots + \xi_n^2}, 0, \ldots, 0)$$

$$= \frac{k}{\left[\sqrt{1 - (\xi_1^2 + \ldots + \xi_n^2)}\right]^{n+1}}$$

from (112). We will put $k = 1$ and we shall define

$$\mu(M) = \int_M \frac{1}{\left[\sqrt{1 - \xi^2}\right]^{n+1}} d\xi \tag{114}$$

to be the volume of $M \in \mathbb{M}$. Two questions are now important. Does (114) really satisfy (109)? Of course, we got (114) by applying (109) in two special cases. But what about the other cases of (109)? The second question is, how does (114) read in Weierstrass coordinates? We would like to begin with this second question. Observe that (see section 2.6)

$$(x_1, \ldots, x_n) = \sqrt{1 + x_1^2 + \ldots + x_n^2} \cdot (\xi_1, \ldots, \xi_n), \tag{115}$$

where

$$(x_1, \ldots, x_n, \sqrt{1 + x_1^2 + \ldots + x_n^2})$$

are the Weierstrass coordinates, and where $(\xi_1, \ldots, \xi_n)$ are the cartesian coordinates of the same point of I^n. Observe also that

$$x_{n+1} := \sqrt{1 + x_1^2 + \ldots + x_n^2} = \frac{1}{\sqrt{1 - \xi^2}}. \tag{116}$$

We get

$$D := \frac{\partial(\xi_1, \ldots, \xi_n)}{\partial(x_1, \ldots, x_n)} = \begin{vmatrix} \dfrac{\partial \xi_1}{\partial x_1} & \cdots & \dfrac{\partial \xi_1}{\partial x_n} \\ \vdots & & \\ \dfrac{\partial \xi_n}{\partial x_1} & \cdots & \dfrac{\partial \xi_n}{\partial x_n} \end{vmatrix}$$

with

$$x_{n+1}^3 \cdot \frac{\partial \xi_i}{\partial x_j} = \begin{cases} x_{n+1}^2 - x_i^2 & i = j \\ & \text{for} \\ -x_i x_j & i \neq j \end{cases}$$

and hence

$$
x_{n+1}^{3n} \cdot D =
\begin{vmatrix}
x_{n+1}^2 - x_1^2 & -x_1 x_2 & \ldots & -x_1 x_n \\
-x_2 x_1 & x_{n+1}^2 - x_2^2 & \ldots & -x_2 x_n \\
\vdots & & & \\
-x_n x_1 & -x_n x_2 & \ldots & x_{n+1}^2 - x_n^2
\end{vmatrix}
$$

$$
=
\begin{vmatrix}
1 & x_1 & x_2 & \ldots & x_n \\
0 & x_{n+1}^2 - x_1^2 & -x_1 x_2 & \ldots & -x_1 x_n \\
\vdots & \vdots & & & \\
0 & -x_n x_1 & -x_n x_2 & \ldots & x_{n+1}^2 - x_n^2
\end{vmatrix}
$$

$$
=
\begin{vmatrix}
1 & x_1 & x_2 & \ldots & x_n \\
x_1 & x_{n+1}^2 & 0 & \ldots & 0 \\
x_2 & 0 & x_{n+1}^2 & \ldots & 0 \\
\vdots & & & & \\
x_n & 0 & 0 & \ldots & x_{n+1}^2
\end{vmatrix},
$$

i.e.

$$
D = \left(\frac{1}{x_{n+1}} \right)^{n+2}.
$$

This implies that

$$
\mu(M) = \int_M \frac{D}{\left[\sqrt{1 - \xi^2} \right]^{n+1}} dx = \int \frac{1}{x_{n+1}} dx.
$$

The volume of $M \in \mathbb{M}$ is thus given by

$$
\mu(M) = \int_M \frac{dx}{x_{n+1}} \tag{117}
$$

in Weierstrass coordinates.

Now we would like to answer the first question: We will show that (114) satisfies (109). However, we prefer to work with Weierstrass coordinates. Let γ,

$$
(y_1 \ldots y_n \ y_{n+1}) = (x_1 \ldots x_n \ x_{n+1}) L,
$$

be an element of $\overset{(n)}{H}$ with $L =: (l_{ij})$ and

$$\Delta := \frac{\partial(y_1, \ldots, y_n)}{\partial(x_1, \ldots, x_n)} > 0.$$

Observe that

$$y_i = \sum_{\nu=1}^{n} x_\nu \, l_{\nu i} + x_{n+1} \, l_{n+1,i}$$

for $i = 1, \ldots, n$, and hence

$$\frac{\partial y_i}{\partial x_j} = l_{ji} + \frac{\partial x_{n+1}}{\partial x_j} l_{n+1,i} = l_{ji} + \frac{x_j}{x_{n+1}} l_{n+1,i}$$

for $i, j \in \{1, \ldots, n\}$. This implies that

$$\Delta = \begin{vmatrix} l_{11} + \dfrac{x_1}{x_{n+1}} l_{n+1,1} & \cdots & l_{n1} + \dfrac{x_n}{x_{n+1}} l_{n+1,1} \\ \vdots & & \\ l_{1n} + \dfrac{x_1}{x_{n+1}} l_{n+1,n} & \cdots & l_{nn} + \dfrac{x_n}{x_{n+1}} l_{n+1,n} \end{vmatrix}.$$

We add a further column

$$\begin{matrix} l_{n+1,1} \\ \vdots \\ l_{n+1,n} \\ 1 \end{matrix}$$

to this determinant and a further row

$$0 \ldots 0 \, 1.$$

A simple calculation then leads to

$$\Delta = \begin{vmatrix} l_{11} & \cdots & l_{n1} & l_{n+1,1} \\ \vdots & & & \\ l_{1n} & \cdots & l_{nn} & l_{n+1,n} \\ -\dfrac{x_1}{x_{n+1}} & \cdots & -\dfrac{x_n}{x_{n+1}} & 1 \end{vmatrix},$$

i.e. to

$$\Delta = \frac{1}{x_{n+1}} \begin{vmatrix} \cdots & l_{i1} & \cdots & l_{n+1,1} \\ & \vdots & & \vdots \\ & l_{in} & & l_{n+1,n} \\ & -x_i + \sum_{\nu=1}^{n} y_\nu \, l_{i\nu} & & x_{n+1} + \sum_{\nu=1}^{n} y_\nu \, l_{n+1,\nu} \end{vmatrix}.$$

Since $x = yL^{-1}$ and (see section 2.6)

$$
L^{-1} = \begin{pmatrix}
l_{11} & \cdots & l_{n1} & -l_{n+1,1} \\
\vdots & & & \\
l_{1n} & \cdots & l_{nn} & -l_{n+1,n} \\
-l_{1,n+1} & \cdots & -l_{n,n+1} & l_{n+1,n+1}
\end{pmatrix}
$$

we get

$$
x_i = \sum_{\nu=1}^{n} y_\nu \, l_{i\nu} - y_{n+1} \, l_{i,n+1}
$$

for $i = 1, \ldots, n$, and furthermore

$$
x_{n+1} = -\sum_{\nu=1}^{n} y_\nu \, l_{n+1,\nu} + y_{n+1} \, l_{n+1,n+1}.
$$

This implies that

$$
\Delta = \frac{1}{x_{n+1}} \begin{vmatrix}
l_{11} & \cdots & l_{n1} & l_{n+1,1} \\
\vdots & & & \\
l_{1n} & l_{nn} & l_{n+1,n} \\
y_{n+1}l_{1,n+1} & y_{n+1}\,l_{n,n+1} & y_{n+1}\,l_{n+1,n+1}
\end{vmatrix}
$$

and hence

$$
\Delta = \frac{y_{n+1}}{x_{n+1}} \cdot |L|.
$$

A consequence of $\Delta > 0$ is $|L| = 1$, since $|L|$ is ± 1 and since x_{n+1} and y_{n+1} are positive. We finally get

$$
\mu\left(\gamma(M)\right) = \int_{\gamma(M)} \frac{dy}{y_{n+1}} = \int_{M} \frac{1}{y_{n+1}} \Delta dx = \int_{M} \frac{dx}{x_{n+1}}
$$

and hence $\mu\left(\gamma(M)\right) = \mu(M)$ for $M \in \mathbb{M}$.

(114) also leads to $\mu(M_1 \cup M_2) = \mu(M_1) + \mu(M_2)$ if $\mu(M_1 \cap M_2) = 0$ for $M_1, M_2 \in \mathbb{M}$.

5.7.4   A definition of elliptic geometry

Let V be a real vector space with a *scalar product*

$$
\sigma : V \times V \to \mathbb{R}
$$

satisfying

$$xy = yx$$
$$(\lambda x)y = \lambda(xy)$$
$$(x+y)z = xz + yz$$
$$x^2 > 0 \text{ for } x \neq 0$$

for all $x, y, z \in V$ and $\lambda \in \mathbb{R}$, where we write xy instead of $\sigma(x, y)$. The vector space V then is called a *pre–Hilbert space*. Let $S(V)$ be the set of all points of the projective geometry $\Pi(V)$ over a pre–Hilbert space V of dimension at least 2. Define the *elliptic distance*

$$e(\mathbb{R}x, \mathbb{R}y) \in \left[0, \frac{\pi}{2}\right]$$

of points $\mathbb{R}x, \mathbb{R}y \in S(V)$ by

$$\cos e(\mathbb{R}x, \mathbb{R}y) := \frac{|xy|}{\sqrt{x^2}\sqrt{y^2}}.$$

Obviously, this definition does not depend on the chosen representatives x, y of $\mathbb{R}x, \mathbb{R}y$, since

$$\frac{|(\lambda x)(\mu y)|}{\sqrt{(\lambda x)^2}\sqrt{(\lambda \mu)^2}} = \frac{|xy|}{\sqrt{x^2}\sqrt{y^2}}$$

for $\lambda, \mu \in \mathbb{R}\backslash\{0\}$.

The distance space (see section 1.2 and GT, section 2.1)

$$(S(V), \mathbb{R}, e) \tag{118}$$

is now important. The geometry $(S(V), G(e))$ is called the *elliptic geometry* over V. The reader might consult GT, section 2.8, where $G(e)$ is determined in the case $V = \mathbb{R}^n$ ($n \geq 2$) with the euclidean scalar product, and where an easy proof can be found for the fact that

$$(S(\mathbb{R}^n), \mathbb{R}, e), \ n \geq 2,$$

is a metric space.

5.8 A definition of spherical geometry

Let V be again a pre–Hilbert space of dimension at least 2. Define

$$S := \{x \in V \mid x^2 = 1\}$$

and $s(x, y) \in [0, \pi]$ for $x, y \in S$ by means of

$$\cos s(x, y) := xy.$$

$(S, \mathbb{R}, s)$ is a distance space. The geometry

$$(S, G(s)) \tag{119}$$

is called *spherical geometry* over V. In the case of a finite dimensional V, we have already defined spherical geometry in section 1.3 as a suitable substructure of euclidean geometry, and we determined there a defining invariant of

$$(S, \mathbb{R}, s).$$

(See also GT, section 2.9.)

5.9   Lorentz–Minkowski geometry

We already defined this geometry in section 4.1: n–dimensional Lorentz–Minkowski geometry is the geometry $(\mathbb{R}^n, \mathcal{L}^n)$, where $\mathcal{L}^n$ is the Lorentz group of $\mathbb{R}^n$. A 2–point–invariant of $(\mathbb{R}^n, \mathcal{L}^n)$ is given by

$$d(x, y) := (x_1 - y_1)^2 + \ldots + (x_{n-1} - y_{n-1})^2 - (x_n - y_n)^2 \tag{120}$$

for $n \geq 2$ and

$$x = (x_1, \ldots, x_n) \in \mathbb{R}^n \text{ and } y = (y_1, \ldots, y_n) \in \mathbb{R}^n.$$

Instead of Lorentz–Minkowski geometry one also says *pseudo–euclidean geometry*. The following results are fundamental.

THEOREM 43. *Let*

$$f : \mathbb{R}^n \to \mathbb{R}^n \ (n \geq 3)$$

be a bijection satisfying

$$\forall_{x, y} \in \mathbb{R}^n \quad d(x, y) = 0 \Leftrightarrow d(f(x), f(y)) = 0.$$

Then f has the form $f(x) = kxQ + a$ for a positive real number k and for real matrices $a = (a_1, \ldots, a_n)$ and

$$Q = \begin{pmatrix} q_{11} & \cdots & q_{1n} \\ \vdots & & \\ q_{n1} & \cdots & q_{nn} \end{pmatrix}$$

such that $QMQ^T = M$ holds true with

$$M := \begin{pmatrix} 1 & & & 0 \\ & \ddots & & \\ & & 1 & \\ 0 & & & -1 \end{pmatrix}.$$

THEOREM 44. *Let $k \neq 0$ be a fixed real number and let*

$$f : \mathbb{R}^n \to \mathbb{R}^n \ (n \geq 2)$$

be a mapping satisfying

$$\forall_{x,y \in \mathbb{R}^n} \quad d(x,y) = k \Rightarrow d\big(f(x), f(y)\big) = k.$$

Then $f \in \mathcal{L}^n$.

Theorem 43 was proved by A.D. Alexandrov [1], [2], [3]. Theorem 44 was proved in the case $n > 2$ and $k > 0$ by June Lester [3], and in the cases

(a) $n = 2$,

(b) $n > 2$ and $k < 0$

by W. Benz [11] (case (a)), [10] (case (b)). Proofs for theorems 43 and 44 are also in our book [1], section 6.6 and sections 6.13, 6.14, 6.15.

Chapter 6

HIGHER GEOMETRIES

6.1 Cremona geometries

6.1.1 Birational transformations

Let F be a commutative field. For an integer $n \geq 1$ we will consider the quotient field $F(X_1, \ldots, X_n)$ of the ring $F[X_1, \ldots, X_n]$ of polynomials in n indeterminates $X_1, \ldots, X_n$ over F. Obviously,

$$F \subset F[X_1, \ldots, X_n] \subset F(X_1, \ldots, X_n).$$

Every automorphism α of $F(X_1, \ldots, X_n)$ is called a *birational transformation* of F^n provided that it leaves invariant every $k \in F$. If we define $\alpha \cdot \beta$ for the birational transformations α, β of F^n by means of

$$\forall t \in F(X_1, \ldots, X_n) \quad [\alpha\beta](t) := \alpha[\beta(t)],$$

we get a group, the group B_F^n of all birational transformations of F^n. To every $\alpha \in B_F^n$ we will assign a mapping

$$(\alpha) : M \to F^n$$

with $M \subseteq F^n$. Define

$$\alpha(X_i) =: \frac{f_i(X_1, \ldots, X_n)}{g_i(X_1, \ldots, X_n)}$$

for $i = 1, \ldots, n$ with $f_i, g_i \in F[X_1, \ldots, X_n]$ such that there are no common non–trivial divisors of f_i and g_i, $i \in \{1, \ldots, n\}$. Put

$$M := D(\alpha) := \left\{ a = (a_1, \ldots, a_n) \in F^n \mid \prod_{i=1}^{n} g_i(a_1, \ldots, a_n) \neq 0 \right\}$$

and

$$(\alpha)(a) := \left(\frac{f_1(a)}{g_1(a)}, \ldots, \frac{f_n(a)}{g_n(a)}\right) \tag{1}$$

for $a \in D(\alpha)$. The mapping (α) is defined on $D(\alpha)$. The points in

$$\Phi(\alpha) := F^n \backslash D(\alpha) \tag{2}$$

are called the *singular points* of α. Let β, γ be birational transformations of F^n and let $a \in F^n$ be an element with

$$a \in D(\beta) \text{ and } (\beta)(a) \in D(\gamma).$$

Then

$$(\beta\gamma)(a) = (\gamma)[(\beta)(a)] \tag{3}$$

holds true (see GT 152 f).

We would like to consider some examples of birational transformations of F^n.

A) Let the entries $p_{ij} \in F$ of

$$P = \begin{pmatrix} p_{11} & \cdots & p_{1n} \\ \vdots & & \\ p_{n1} & \cdots & p_{nn} \end{pmatrix}$$

be integers such that $(\det P)^2 = 1$. The entries q_{ij} of $Q := P^{-1}$ are then also integers. For such a matrix P define

$$\alpha(X_i) := X_1^{p_{i1}} X_2^{p_{i2}} \ldots X_n^{p_{in}} \tag{4}$$

for $i = 1, 2, \ldots, n$ and furthermore

$$\alpha[f(X_1, \ldots, X_n)] := f(\alpha(X_1), \ldots, \alpha(X_n)) \tag{5}$$

for all $f \in F[X_1, \ldots, X_n]$. It is trivial to check that

$$\alpha : F[X_1, \ldots, X_n] \to F(X_1, \ldots, X_n)$$

is a homomorphism. We also define

$$\alpha\left[\frac{f(X_1, \ldots, X_n)}{h(X_1, \ldots, X_n)}\right] := \frac{\alpha[f(X_1, \ldots, X_n)]}{\alpha[h(X_1, \ldots X_n)]} \tag{6}$$

for all $f, h \in F[X_1, \ldots, X_n]$ with $\alpha(h) \neq 0$. It is easy to prove that

$$\alpha\left(\frac{f}{h} + \frac{\varphi}{\psi}\right) = \alpha\left(\frac{f}{h}\right) + \alpha\left(\frac{\varphi}{\psi}\right),$$

$$\alpha\left(\frac{f}{h} \cdot \frac{\varphi}{\psi}\right) = \alpha\left(\frac{f}{h}\right) \cdot \alpha\left(\frac{\varphi}{\psi}\right)$$

hold true for all $f, h, \varphi, \psi \in F[X_1, \ldots, X_n]$ satisfying $\alpha(h) \neq 0$ and $\alpha(\psi) \neq 0$. Observe that

$$[\alpha(X_1)]^{q_{i1}} \ldots [\alpha(X_n)]^{q_{in}} = \Pi X_\mu^{p_{1\mu} q_{i1}} \ldots \Pi X_\mu^{p_{n\mu} q_{in}}$$
$$= X_1^{p_{11} q_{i1} + \cdots + p_{n1} q_{in}} \ldots X_n^{p_{1n} q_{i1} + \cdots + p_{nn} q_{in}}$$
$$= X_i$$

in view of (4) and $Q = P^{-1}$. This implies that

$$X_i = \alpha(X_1^{q_{i1}} \ldots X_n^{q_{in}}) \tag{7}$$

for $i = 1, 2, \ldots, n$. We would like to show that

$$0 \neq g \in F[X_1, \ldots, X_n]$$

implies that $0 \neq \alpha(g) \in F(X_1, \ldots, X_n)$. Put

$$g = a_0 + \sum_{i=1}^{t}\left[\sum_{\nu_1, \ldots, \nu_i=1}^{n} a_{\nu_1 \nu_2 \ldots \nu_i} X_{\nu_1} X_{\nu_2} \ldots X_{\nu_i}\right]$$

with $a_0, a_{\nu_1 \ldots \nu_i} \in F$. Assume that $g \neq 0$ and that

$$g(\alpha(X_1), \ldots, \alpha(X_n)) = 0 \tag{8}$$

hold true. Taking into account that some of the exponents in (4) may be negative, $g(\alpha(X_1), \ldots (X_n))$ can be written as quotient $\frac{\varphi}{\psi}$ of two polynomials $\varphi, \psi \in F[X_1, \ldots, X_n]$. Equation (8) then implies that φ must be 0. Replacing X_i in (8) by

$$X_1^{q_{i1}} \ldots X_n^{q_{in}},$$

we hence get

$$g(\alpha(X_1^{q_{11}} \ldots X_n^{q_{1n}}), \ldots) = 0,$$

i.e. $g(X_1, \ldots, X_n) = 0$ from (7). This is a contradiction. We thus have equation (6) for all $f, h \in F[X_1, \ldots, X_n]$ with $h \neq 0$. The mapping

$$\alpha : F(X_1, \ldots, X_n) \to F(X_1, \ldots, X_n)$$

is a birational transformation of F^n. We certainly have $\alpha(k) = k$ for $k \in F$, and we certainly have that α is an endomorphism of $F(X_1, \ldots, X_n)$. The mapping α is surjective since

$$H\big(\alpha^{-1}(X_1), \ldots, \alpha^{-1}(X_n)\big)$$

is an inverse image of $H(X_1, \ldots, X_n)$, and it is injective since $\alpha(H) = 0$ together with $H \neq 0$ would lead to

$$\alpha(X_1) = \alpha\left(\frac{X_1}{H}\right) \cdot \alpha(H) = 0.$$

A prominent example of a birational transformation of type (4) is the so–called *standard quadratic transformation*

$$\alpha(X_i) = X_i^{-1} \tag{9}$$

for $i = 1, \ldots, n$. The set of singular points of this transformation is given by

$$\Phi(\alpha) = \{a \in F^n \mid a_1 \ldots a_n = 0\}.$$

REMARK. If we extend the standard quadratic transformation $(x_1, x_2) \rightarrow (x_1^{-1}, x_2^{-2})$ of $\mathbb{R}^2$ to the real projective plane $\Pi(\mathbb{R}^3)$ by means of

$$(*) \quad \mathbb{R}(x_1, x_2, x_3) \rightarrow \mathbb{R}(x_2 x_3, x_3 x_1, x_1 x_2),$$

we obtain a mapping from $\Pi(\mathbb{R}^3) \backslash \Xi$ into $\Pi(\mathbb{R}^3)$ where Ξ is determined by all points $\mathbb{R}(x_1, x_2, x_3)$ of $\Pi(\mathbb{R}^3)$ such that

$$x_2 x_3 = x_3 x_1 = x_1 x_2 = 0.$$

Hence $\Xi = \big\{\mathbb{R}(1, 0, 0), \ \mathbb{R}(0, 1, 0), \ \mathbb{R}(0, 0, 1)\big\}$. The points of Ξ are called the *fundamental* points of $(*)$. A similar procedure is possible in other cases.

B) Let

$$P = \begin{pmatrix} p_{11} & \cdots & p_{1,n+1} \\ \vdots & & \\ p_{n+1,1} & \cdots & p_{n+1,n+1} \end{pmatrix}$$

be a matrix with $p_{ij} \in F$ and $\det P \neq 0$. Put

$$Q = \begin{pmatrix} q_{11} & \cdots & q_{1,n+1} \\ \vdots & & \\ q_{n+1,1} & \cdots & q_{n+1,n+1} \end{pmatrix} := P^{-1}$$

and define

$$\alpha(X_i) := \frac{p_{1i}X_1 + \ldots + p_{ni}X_n + p_{n+1,i}}{p_{1,n+1}X_1 + \ldots + p_{n,n+1}X_n + p_{n+1,n+1}} \tag{10}$$

for $i = 1, 2, \ldots, n$, and define furthermore $\alpha[f(X_1, \ldots, X_n)]$ by means of (5) for all $f \in F[X_1, \ldots, X_n]$. Then

$$\alpha : F[X_1, \ldots, X_n] \to F(X_1, \ldots, X_n)$$

is a homomorphism. Put

$$L := p_{1,n+1}X_1 + \ldots + p_{n,n+1}X_n + p_{n+1,n+1}.$$

Then (10) implies that

$$L \cdot \left(\alpha(X_1) \ldots \alpha(X_n)1\right) = (X_1 \ldots X_n 1) \cdot P \tag{11}$$

holds true. Hence

$$\frac{1}{L}(X_1 \ldots X_n 1) = \left(\alpha(X_1) \ldots \alpha(X_n)1\right)Q,$$

and thus

$$\frac{1}{L} \cdot 1 = q_{1,n+1}\alpha(X_1) + \ldots + q_{n,n+1}\alpha(X_n) + q_{n+1,n+1}.$$

This implies that

$$(X_1 \ldots X_n 1) = \frac{(X_1' \ldots X_n' \, 1) \, Q}{q_{1,n+1}X_1' + \ldots + q_{n,n+1}X_n' + q_{n+1,n+1}} \tag{12}$$

holds true for $X_i' := \alpha(X_i)$ for $i = 1, \ldots, n$. We would like to show that also in our present situation

$$0 \neq g \in F[X_1, \ldots, X_n]$$

implies that $0 \neq \alpha(g) \in F(X_1, \ldots, X_n)$. Assume that $g \neq 0$ and that

$$g\left(\alpha(X_1), \ldots, \alpha(X_n)\right) = 0$$

hold true. Replace here X_i by

$$Y_i := \frac{q_{1i}X_1 + \ldots + q_{ni}X_n + q_{n+1,i}}{q_{1,n+1}X_1 + \ldots + q_{n,n+1}X_n + q_{n+1,n+1}}$$

(before that, adopt also definition (6) for $f, h \in F[X_1, \ldots, X_n]$ with $\alpha(h) \neq 0$). Hence

$$g\left(\alpha(Y_1), \ldots, \alpha(Y_n)\right) = 0.$$

But $\alpha(Y_i)$ is equal to X_i, in view of (12). This is a contradiction. We hence have equation (6) for all $f, h \in F[X_1, \ldots, X_n]$ with $h \neq 0$. The mapping α is thus a birational transformation of F^n.

If $F = \mathbb{R}$ and if

$$p_{1,n+1} = \ldots = p_{n,n+1} = 0, \tag{13}$$

then (α) is an affine mapping of $\mathbb{R}^n$. Every affine mapping of $\mathbb{R}^n$ can be obtained this way. In the case that (13) does not hold true, (α) is the restriction of a projective mapping onto $\mathbb{R}^n$. Affine groups and projective groups in the finite dimensional real cases are hence isomorphic to suitable groups of birational transformations.

C) Let $V(\cdot)$ be an n–dimensional commutative and associative algebra over $\mathbb{R}$ with identity element 1 (see section 5.6.5). The number n is assumed to be a positive integer. Put $V = \mathbb{R}^n$ and

$$E_1 = (1, 0, \ldots, 0), \ldots, E_n = (0, \ldots, 0, 1).$$

Define real numbers e_i and $\Gamma_{ij,k}$ for $i, j, k \in \{1, \ldots, n\}$ by

$$(e_1, \ldots, e_n) \quad = 1 \in V,$$

$$E_i E_j \quad = \sum_{\nu=1}^{n} \Gamma_{ij,\nu} E_\nu.$$

Observe that $\Gamma_{ij,\nu} = \Gamma_{ji,\nu}$ holds true for all $i, j, \nu \in \{1, 2, \ldots, n\}$.

LEMMA 1. *Suppose that $x = (x_1, \ldots, x_n)$ is an element of $\mathbb{R}^n(\cdot)$. Then there exists $y \in \mathbb{R}^n(\cdot)$ with $xy = 1$ if and only if*

$$\Delta(x) := \begin{vmatrix} \sum_{\nu=1}^{n} \Gamma_{\nu 1,1} x_\nu & \cdots & \sum_{\nu=1}^{n} \Gamma_{\nu n,1} x_\nu \\ \vdots & & \\ \sum_{\nu=1}^{n} \Gamma_{\nu 1,n} x_\nu & \cdots & \sum_{\nu=1}^{n} \Gamma_{\nu n,n} x_\nu \end{vmatrix} \neq 0.$$

Proof. $xy = 1$ is equivalent to

$$\left(\sum_{\nu=1}^{n} \Gamma_{\nu 1,\varrho} x_\nu \right) \cdot y_1 + \ldots + \left(\sum_{\nu=1}^{n} \Gamma_{\nu n,\varrho} x_\nu \right) \cdot y_n = e_\varrho \tag{14}$$

for $\varrho = 1, \ldots, n$. If $\Delta(x) \neq 0$, then there exists a solution y of this equation. Assume now that $\Delta(x) = 0$ and that there is an element $y \in \mathbb{R}^n(\cdot)$ with $xy = 1$. Since $\Delta(x) = 0$, there exists $\eta \in \mathbb{R}^n(\cdot)$ with $\eta \neq 0$ and such that

$$\left(\sum \Gamma_{\nu 1, \varrho} x_\nu\right) \cdot \eta_1 + \ldots + \left(\sum \Gamma_{\nu n, \varrho} x_\nu\right) \cdot \eta_n = 0$$

holds true. Hence $xy = 1 = x(y + \eta)$, i.e.

$$y = y[x(y + \eta)] = y + \eta,$$

i.e. $\eta = 0$. $\qquad\qquad\square$

Replacing the i-th column of $\Delta(x)$ by

$$\begin{pmatrix} e_1 \\ \vdots \\ e_n \end{pmatrix},$$

we get a new determinant which we shall denote by $\Delta_i(x)$.

PROPOSITION 2. *Suppose that x is an element of $\mathbb{R}^n(\cdot)$ with $\Delta(x) \neq 0$. Then*

$$x \cdot (y_1, \ldots, y_n) = 1$$

holds true if and only if

$$y_i = \frac{\Delta_i(x)}{\Delta(x)} \qquad\qquad (15)$$

for $i = 1, \ldots, n$.

Proof. Since $\Delta(x) \neq 0$, the only solution of (14) is (15). $\qquad\square$

Replacing the x_i in $\Delta(x)$ by indeterminates X_i, we shall write $\Delta(X)$. Define

$$\alpha(X_i) := \frac{\Delta_i(X)}{\Delta(X)} \qquad\qquad (16)$$

for $i = 1, \ldots, n$ and define furthermore $\alpha[f(X_1, \ldots, X_n)]$ by means of (5) for all $f \in \mathbb{R}[X_1, \ldots, X_n]$. Adopt also (6) for $f, h \in \mathbb{R}[X_1, \ldots, X_n]$ with $\alpha(h) \neq 0$. Observe that

$$(X_1, \ldots, X_n) \cdot (\alpha(X_1), \ldots, \alpha(X_n)) = 1$$

holds true and hence also

$$(\alpha(X_1), \ldots, \alpha(X_n)) \cdot (X_1, \ldots, X_n) = 1.$$

As underlying structure for the last two formulas choose the vector space

$$K^n, \; K := \mathbb{R}(X_1, \ldots, X_n),$$

with the multiplication

$$(f_1, \ldots, f_n) \cdot (g_1, \ldots, g_n) := \sum_{\nu,\mu,\varrho} f_\nu g_\mu \Gamma_{\nu\mu,\varrho} E_\varrho. \tag{17}$$

Then

$$X_i = \frac{\Delta_i\big(\alpha(X)\big)}{\Delta\big(\alpha(X)\big)} = \alpha\left(\frac{\Delta_i(X)}{\Delta(X)}\right)$$

for $i = 1, \ldots, n$. Also in the present situation, $0 \neq g \in F[X_1, \ldots, X_n]$ together with

$$g\big(\alpha(X_1), \ldots, \alpha(X_n)\big) = 0$$

is impossible: otherwise replace here X_i by

$$\frac{\Delta_i(X)}{\Delta(X)}$$

which leads to the contradiction $g(X_1, \ldots, X_n) = 0$. The mapping α is hence a birational transformation of $\mathbb{R}^n$.

The reader might verify that the mapping α of (16) is given in the case of $\mathbb{R}_2^3$ (see the end of section 5.6.5) by

$$\alpha(X_i) = \frac{1}{X_i}$$

for $i = 1, 2, 3$. In the case of $\mathbb{R}_4^3$ we get

$$\alpha(X_1) = \frac{1}{X_1}, \; \alpha(X_2) = -\frac{X_2}{X_1^2}, \; \alpha(X_3) = \frac{X_2^2}{X_1^3} - \frac{X_3}{X_1^2}.$$

6.1.2   Cremona groups

A subgroup Γ of the group B_F^n of all birational transformations of F^n is said to be a *Cremona group* of F^n if and only if there exist a $\gamma \in \Gamma$ and three distinct and collinear points

$$a, b, c \in D(\gamma)$$

such that $(\gamma)(a)$, $(\gamma)(b)$, $(\gamma)(c)$ are not on a common line of F^n. We are now in the position to define the notion of a *Cremona geometry*.

Definition. *Let* Γ *be a Cremona group of* F^n *and let* S *be a set containing* F^n *such that every*

$$(\gamma) : D(\gamma) \to F^n \text{ with } \gamma \in \Gamma$$

can be extended to a bijection of S, *also written in the form* (γ), *satisfying*

$$(\alpha\beta)(s) = (\beta)[(\alpha)(s)] \tag{18}$$

for all $\alpha, \beta \in \Gamma$ *and all* $s \in S$. *The geometry* (S, Γ^*) *is then called a Cremona geometry of* F^n, *where the group* Γ^* *is defined as the set*

$$\{(\alpha) \mid \alpha \in \Gamma\} \tag{19}$$

with the multiplication $(\alpha) \cdot (\beta) := (\beta\alpha)$ *for all* $\alpha, \beta \in \Gamma$. *The mapping* (α) *in (19) denotes the chosen extension* $(\alpha) : S \to S$ *of* $(\alpha) : D(\gamma) \to F^n$.

REMARK. Notice that (18) is not a new assumption in all cases $s \in F^n$ satisfying $s \in D(\alpha)$ and $(\alpha)(s) \in D(\beta)$ (see (3)).

6.1.3 Real chain geometries

Let $V = V(\cdot) = \mathbb{R}^n(\cdot)$ be an n–dimensional commutative and associative algebra over $\mathbb{R}$ with identity element 1 (see section 5.6.5). Sometimes we shall write again 1_V instead of 1 in order to emphasize that the identity element of V is meant. The integer n is supposed to be greater or equal to 2. We would like to embed $\mathbb{R}$ into V. This will be done by identifying $k \in \mathbb{R}$ with

$$k \cdot 1_V \in V.$$

In this connection observe that the following rules hold true.

a) *If* k, l *are distinct real numbers, then* $k \cdot 1_V \neq l \cdot 1_V$,

b) $\forall_{k,l \in \mathbb{R}} (k + l) \cdot 1_V = k \cdot 1_V + l \cdot 1_V$,

c) $\forall_{k,l \in \mathbb{R}} (kl) \cdot 1_V = (k \cdot 1_V) \cdot (l \cdot 1_V)$.

Proof.   Notice that V is a vector space with $1_V \in V$. This implies that

$$k \neq l \text{ and } k \cdot 1_V = l \cdot 1_V$$

lead to $(k - l) \cdot 1_V = 0$ and hence to

$$1_V = 1 \cdot 1_V = [(k-l)^{-1}(k-l)] \cdot 1_V = (k-l)^{-1} \cdot 0 = 0.$$

As far as statement c) is concerned, observe that

$$(kl) \cdot 1_V = k(l \cdot 1_V) = k\big(1_V \cdot [l \cdot 1_V]\big)$$

holds true. One of the rules the algebra V has to satisfy, is

$$\lambda \cdot (a \cdot b) = (\lambda \cdot a) \cdot b$$

(see section 5.6.5) for all $a, b \in V$ and $\lambda \in \mathbb{R}$. This implies that

$$k\big(1_V \cdot [l \cdot 1_V]\big) = (k \cdot 1_V) \cdot (l \cdot 1_V)$$

holds true.   □

As a consequence of these considerations, we do not longer distinguish between $k \in \mathbb{R}$ and $k \cdot 1_V$, and we shall write $\mathbb{R} \subset V$. (Observe that $\mathbb{R} \neq V$, since $\dim V \geq 2$.) As in section 5.6.5, U denotes the group of units of V. We will call the ordered pair

$$\frac{x}{y}$$

of elements x, y of V a *quotient* of V provided that there exist elements α, β in V with $\alpha x + \beta y = 1$. We shall write

$$\frac{x}{y} = \frac{x'}{y'} \tag{20}$$

for two quotients iff $xy' = x'y$ holds true.

LEMMA 3. *The equation* (20) *holds true iff there exists* $u \in U$ *with* $x' = ux$, $y' = uy$.

Proof.   Assume that (20) holds true. Since there exist real numbers $\alpha, \alpha', \beta, \beta'$ with

$$\alpha x + \beta y = 1 \text{ and } \alpha' x' + \beta' y' = 1,$$

we get

$$\begin{aligned}
y' &= \alpha x y' + \beta y y' &= (\alpha x' + \beta y')y, \\
x' &= x'(\alpha x + \beta y) &= (\alpha x' + \beta y')x, \\
1 &= \alpha' x' + \beta' y' &= (\alpha x' + \beta y')(\alpha' x + \beta' y),
\end{aligned}$$

i.e. $u := \alpha x' + \beta y' \in U$. — Conversely, assume that x/y is a quotient and that u is a unit of V. If we then put $x' := ux$, $y' = uy$, we get another quotient x'/y' satisfying equation (20). This is a consequence of

$$xy' = xuy = x'y. \,\square$$

Let x_i/y_i, $i = 1, 2, 3$, be quotients. Then the following rules hold true.

$$x_1/y_1 = x_1/y_1,$$

$$x_1/y_1 = x_2/y_2 \text{ implies that } x_2/y_2 = x_1/y_1,$$

$$x_1/y_1 = x_2/y_2 \text{ and } x_2/y_2 = x_3/y_3 \text{ imply that } x_1/y_1 = x_3/y_3.$$

The proof follows immediately from Lemma 3. Denote by S the set of all equivalence classes of quotients. In the sequel we do not distinguish between a quotient q and the equivalence class containing q. We shall embed $\mathbb{R}^n$ into S: identify $a \in V = \mathbb{R}^n$ with the quotient

$$\frac{a}{1}.$$

We would like to say a word about the connection of *old* quotients, so to speak, and *new* quotients. By an old quotient a/u we mean the solution $x \in V$ of the equation $ux = a$ with $u \in U$. Observe that two old quotients a_i/u_i, $i = 1, 2$, are equal iff $a_1 u_2 = a_2 u_1$, so that the equality definition for quotients generalizes this situation. Observe that the equality of two quotients a/u and x/y with $u \in U \not\ni y$ is not possible, in view of Lemma 3. Since

$$\frac{a}{u} = \frac{au^{-1}}{1}$$

for $u \in U$, we may say that the old quotients are the points of $\mathbb{R}^n$, and that the quotients x/y with $y \notin U$ represent the *points* of S which are not in $\mathbb{R}^n$.

If $a_{11}, a_{12}, a_{21}, a_{22}$ are elements of V with

$$a := \begin{vmatrix} a_{11} & a_{12} \\ a_{21} & a_{22} \end{vmatrix} \in U,$$

then

$$\frac{x}{y} \rightarrow \frac{xa_{11} + ya_{12}}{xa_{21} + ya_{22}} \tag{21}$$

is a bijection of S. First of all we have to prove that the right–hand side of (21) is a quotient whenever x/y is a quotient. Assume that

$$\alpha x + \beta y = 1$$

holds true with elements $\alpha, \beta \in V$. This implies that

$$\gamma(xa_{11} + ya_{12}) + \delta(xa_{21} + ya_{22}) = 1$$

holds true for

$$a\gamma := \alpha a_{22} - \beta a_{21} \text{ and } a\delta := \beta a_{11} - \alpha a_{12}.$$

Changing the representative of the quotient x/y into ux/uy with $u \in U$, we get a quotient on the right–hand side of (21) which is equal to

$$\frac{xa_{11} + ya_{12}}{xa_{21} + ya_{22}}.$$

It remains to show that (21) is a bijective mapping. Let p/q be an arbitrary quotient. The problem we would like to pose then is to solve

$$\frac{xa_{11} + ya_{12}}{xa_{21} + ya_{22}} = \frac{p}{q} \tag{22}$$

with respect to quotients x/y. Equation (22) may be written in the form

$$xa_{11} + ya_{12} = up$$
$$xa_{21} + ya_{22} = uq$$

with $u = u(x, y) \in U$, in view of Lemma 3. We get

$$upa_{22} \quad -uqa_{12} = ax$$
$$-upa_{21} \quad +uqa_{11} = ay$$

with $a = a_{11}a_{22} - a_{12}a_{21}$, and hence

$$\frac{x}{y} = \frac{pa_{22} - qa_{12}}{-pa_{21} + qa_{11}}$$

with

$$\begin{vmatrix} a_{22} & -a_{12} \\ -a_{21} & a_{11} \end{vmatrix} = a \in U.$$

The mapping (21) is thus bijective.

REMARK. If we identify the quotient a_1/a_2 with the point $U(a_1, a_2)$ of section 5.6.5, we get that S is the projective line over V. This has the consequence that the notion of cross ratio for points of S is at our disposal.

Denoting the mapping (21) by

$$\sigma(a_{ij}) = \sigma \begin{pmatrix} a_{11} & a_{12} \\ a_{21} & a_{22} \end{pmatrix},$$

we get the following rule:

$$\sigma(a_{ij})\sigma(b_{ij}) \left(\frac{x}{y} \right) = \sigma(AB) \left(\frac{x}{y} \right) \tag{23}$$

where we put $A := (a_{ij})$ and $B := (b_{ij})$.

We are now interested in the mapping (21) insofar as it maps points of $\mathbb{R}^n \subset S$ into points of $\mathbb{R}^n$. A point of $\mathbb{R}^n$ is given in the form $x = x/1$. This means that we are interested in all $x \in \mathbb{R}^n$ such that

$$x a_{21} + 1 \cdot a_{22}$$

is in U. If we put

$$D := \{x \in \mathbb{R}^n \mid x a_{21} + a_{22} \in U\}, \qquad (24)$$

we may define $\tau : D \to \mathbb{R}^n$ by means of

$$\tau(x) = \frac{x a_{11} + a_{12}}{x a_{21} + a_{22}}. \qquad (25)$$

This is the mapping we obtain if we restrict (21) on $\mathbb{R}^n$ in such a way that images are also in $\mathbb{R}^n$.

We shall define a birational transformation

$$\alpha : \mathbb{R}(X_1, \dots, X_n) \to \mathbb{R}(X_1, \dots, X_n) \qquad (26)$$

such that (α) is equal to τ. In section 6.1.1 (see examples C) we considered the special case

$$\begin{pmatrix} a_{11} & a_{12} \\ a_{21} & a_{22} \end{pmatrix} = \begin{pmatrix} 0 & 1 \\ 1 & 0 \end{pmatrix}$$

which comes from the mapping

$$\frac{x}{y} \to \frac{y}{x},$$

written in the form (21).

A ring R with identity element 1 is said to be of *stable rank* 2 iff the following property holds true:

(∗) *The equation* $\alpha x + \beta y = 1$ *for elements* $\alpha, x, \beta, y \in R$ *implies the existence of elements* $\gamma, \delta \in R$ *with* $\gamma x + \gamma \delta y = 1$.

PROPOSITION 4. *The ring* $\mathbb{R}^n(\cdot)$ *has stable rank* 2.

Proof.   If $\alpha x + \beta y = 1$ holds true for $\alpha, x, \beta, y \in \mathbb{R}^n(\cdot)$, then $U(x, y)$ must be a point in the sense of section 5.6.5. Step (m) of the proof of Theorem 36 of section 5.6.5 shows the existence of a real number k with

$$p := x - ky \in U.$$

But this implies that $p^{-1}x + p^{-1}(-k)y = 1$.   □

LEMMA 5. *Let $a_{11}, a_{12}, a_{21}, a_{22}$ be elements of $\mathbb{R}^n(\cdot)$ such that*

$$a := a_{11}a_{22} - a_{12}a_{21} \in U.$$

Then there exists an element $k \in \mathbb{R}^n(\cdot)$ with

$$u := a_{11} - ka_{21} \in U,$$

and the following equation holds true

$$\begin{pmatrix} a_{11} & a_{12} \\ a_{21} & a_{22} \end{pmatrix} = T(k) \cdot I \cdot T\left(\frac{a_{21}}{u}\right) \cdot P \cdot I \cdot T\left(\frac{a_{12} - ka_{22}}{u}\right) \tag{27}$$

with

$$T(p) = \begin{pmatrix} 1 & p \\ 0 & 1 \end{pmatrix}, I = \begin{pmatrix} 0 & 1 \\ 1 & 0 \end{pmatrix}, P = \begin{pmatrix} v & 0 \\ 0 & u \end{pmatrix}$$

where $u \cdot v := a$.

Proof. $\mathbb{R}^n(\cdot)$ has stable rank 2. Observe that

$$(a_{22}) \cdot a_{11} + (-a_{12}) \cdot a_{21} = a \in U.$$

There hence exists $\gamma, \delta \in \mathbb{R}^n(\cdot)$ with

$$\gamma a_{11} + \gamma \delta a_{21} = 1.$$

Put $k := -\delta$. Then

$$u := a_{11} - ka_{21} \in U$$

holds true.   □

REMARK. If a_{ij} are elements of a commutative field with

$$a := a_{11}a_{22} - a_{12}a_{21} \neq 0,$$

we get an easier decomposition than that of (27) for the matrix (a_{ij}). The reason is that in the case described, a_{21} must either be 0 or a unit. In the general case it occurs that both elements a_{21}, a_{22} are non–units despite the fact that a is an element of U.

Three types of mappings are involved in the decomposition (27) of (a_{ij}), namely the *translation*

$$T(p)\begin{pmatrix} x \\ y \end{pmatrix} = \frac{x + yp}{y},$$

the *dilatation*

$$P\left(\frac{x}{y}\right) = \frac{x \cdot \frac{v}{u}}{y} =: \frac{xq}{y} \text{ with } q \in U,$$

and the mapping

$$I\left(\frac{x}{y}\right) = \frac{y}{x}.$$

If we restrict $T(p)$ or P on $\mathbb{R}^n$, we obtain bijections, namely affine mappings. This is trivial for $T(p)$, since $T(p) \mid \mathbb{R}^n$ is also a translation of $\mathbb{R}^n$. The restriction of P on $\mathbb{R}^n$,

$$x \to xq,$$

can be written in the form

$$(x_1, \ldots, x_n) \to (x'_1, \ldots, x'_n)$$

with

$$x'_i = x_1 \cdot \sum_{\mu=1}^{n} q_\mu \Gamma_{1\mu,i} + \ldots + x_n \cdot \sum_{\mu=1}^{n} q_\mu \Gamma_{n\mu,i}. \tag{28}$$

Since q is in U, Lemma 1 yields

$$0 \neq \Delta(q) = \left| \left(\sum_{\mu=1}^{n} \Gamma_{\mu j,i} \, q_\mu \right) \right| = \left| \left(\sum_{\mu=1}^{n} \Gamma_{j\mu,i} \, q_\mu \right) \right|,$$

so that (28) is a bijective affine mapping of $\mathbb{R}^n$.

All factors $T(p), P, I$ of the decomposition (27) are induced by birational transformations, because of examples B and C of section 6.1.1. The geometry of the present section which we based on a ring $\mathbb{R}^n(\cdot)$ is thus a Cremona geometry (S, Γ^*) (see also Lemma 6).

Let Γ be the group of birational transformations of $\mathbb{R}^n$ which is generated by all automorphisms of $\mathbb{R}(X_1, \ldots, X_n)$ determined by any element of one of the following classes,

(I) $\quad (\alpha(X_1), \ldots, \alpha(X_n)) := (X_1 + p_1, \ldots, X_n + p_n),$

(II) $\quad \alpha(X_i) := \sum_{\nu=1}^{n} \left[X_\nu \sum_{\mu=1}^{n} q_\mu \Gamma_{\nu\mu,i} \right], i = 1, \ldots, n,$

(III) $\quad$ example C for $\mathbb{R}^n(\cdot)$

with $(p_1, \ldots, p_n) \in \mathbb{R}^n$ and $(q_1, \ldots, q_n) \in U$.

The group Γ^* which consists of all bijections (21) of S can be written in the form

$$GL(2, V)/\text{center of } GL(2, V),$$

if we define $GL(2, V)$ as the group of all matrices

$$A = \left(\begin{array}{cc} a_{11} & a_{12} \\ a_{21} & a_{22} \end{array} \right)$$

with $\det A \in U$. It is trivial to check that the center of this group is given by all matrices

$$B = \left(\begin{array}{cc} u & 0 \\ 0 & u \end{array} \right)$$

with $u \in U$.

LEMMA 6. *There exist a $\gamma \in \Gamma$ and distinct and collinear points*

$$a, b, c \in D(\gamma)$$

such that $(\gamma)(a)$, $(\gamma)(b)$, $(\gamma)(c)$ are not collinear.

Proof.   Since $n \geq 2$, there exists $r \in \mathbb{R}^n \backslash \mathbb{R}$. Since $U(r, 1)$ is a point in the sense of section 5.6.5, there exist real numbers $k \neq l$ such that

$$r - k, \ r - l, \ r - \frac{k + l}{2}$$

are elements of U, in view of step (m) of the proof of Theorem 36. Put

$$p := \frac{2r - (k + l)}{l - k}$$

and observe that $p \notin \mathbb{R}$ and that p, $p + 1$, $p - 1 \in U$ hold true. The points

$$p, 1, \frac{1}{2}(p + 1)$$

of $\mathbb{R}^n$ are collinear, since

$$\frac{1}{2}(p + 1) = \frac{1}{2} \cdot p + \left(1 - \frac{1}{2} \right) \cdot 1$$

is satisfied. For γ take the birational transformation introduced in examples C of section 6.1.1 in connection with $\mathbb{R}^n(\cdot)$. Hence

$$(\gamma)(x) = \frac{1}{x}.$$

for $x \in D(\gamma) := \{x \in \mathbb{R}^n \mid x \in U\}$. Observe that

$$p, 1, \frac{1}{2}(p+1) \in D(\gamma)$$

are distinct points. The points

$$\frac{1}{p}, 1, \frac{2}{p+1} \in \mathbb{R}^n$$

are not collinear: if there existed $\lambda \in \mathbb{R}$ with

$$\lambda \cdot \frac{1}{p} + (1 - \lambda) \cdot 1 = \frac{2}{p+1},$$

we would get $p \in \mathbb{R}$ from $p - 1 \in U$. $\qquad\qquad\qquad\qquad\qquad$ $\square$

Let $\overline{\mathbb{R}}$ be the subset $\mathbb{R} \cup \{\frac{1}{0}\}$ of S. Every set $\gamma(\overline{\mathbb{R}})$ of points with $\gamma \in \Gamma^*$ is called a *chain* of (S, Γ^*). The set of all chains of (S, Γ^*) is an invariant notion of (S, Γ^*). The distinct points $P = p_1/p_2$ and $Q = q_1/q_2$ are called *parallel*, written in form $P \parallel Q$, if and only if there is no chain c through P and Q. We also put $P \parallel P$ for every $P \in S$.

LEMMA 7. *The points P, Q are parallel iff they are neighbours in the sense of section 5.6.5.*

Proof.   We shall prove $P \nparallel Q$ iff

$$\begin{vmatrix} p_1 & p_2 \\ q_1 & q_2 \end{vmatrix} \in U. \qquad\qquad\qquad (29)$$

If (29) holds true, the chain

$$\left\{ \frac{r_1 p_1 + r_2 q_1}{r_1 p_2 + r_2 q_2} \,\middle|\, \frac{r_1}{r_2} \in \overline{\mathbb{R}} \right\}$$

contains P and Q by observing that $\frac{1}{0}, \frac{0}{1}$ are elements of $\overline{\mathbb{R}}$. Conversely, if P, Q are distinct points on the chain

$$\left\{ \frac{r_1 a_{11} + r_2 a_{12}}{r_1 a_{21} + r_2 a_{22}} \,\middle|\, \frac{r_1}{r_2} \in \overline{\mathbb{R}} \right\},$$

then

$$\frac{p_1}{p_2} = \frac{r_1 a_{11} + r_2 a_{12}}{r_1 a_{21} + r_2 a_{22}} \quad \text{and} \quad \frac{q_1}{q_2} = \frac{s_1 a_{11} + s_2 a_{12}}{s_1 a_{21} + s_2 a_{22}}$$

hold true for distinct elements $r_1/r_2, s_1/s_2$ of $\overline{\mathbb{R}}$. But this implies that there exist units $u, v \in U$ with

$$up_i = r_1 a_{i1} + r_2 a_{i2} \text{ and } vq_i = s_1 a_{i1} + s_2 a_{i2}$$

for $i = 1, 2$, in view of Lemma 3. Hence

$$\begin{pmatrix} u & 0 \\ 0 & v \end{pmatrix} \begin{pmatrix} p_1 & p_2 \\ q_1 & q_2 \end{pmatrix} = \begin{pmatrix} r_1 & r_2 \\ s_1 & s_2 \end{pmatrix} \begin{pmatrix} a_{11} & a_{21} \\ a_{12} & a_{22} \end{pmatrix},$$

and thus $p_1 q_2 - p_2 q_1 \in U$.   □

It is important to know that two distinct points of a chain satisfy (29).

PROPOSITION 8. *Let A, B, C be pairwise non–parallel points. Then there exists exactly one chain through A, B, C which we will denote by $(A\,B\,C)$.*

Proof.   Put $A = a_1/a_2$ etc. The elements u, v satisfying

$$c_i = ua_i + vb_i, \quad i = 1, 2,   \tag{30}$$

must be units, since A, B, C are pairwise non–parallel. Then the chain

$$\xi := \left\{ \frac{r_1 u a_1 + r_2 v b_1}{r_1 u a_2 + r_2 v b_2} \,\middle|\, \frac{r_1}{r_2} \in \overline{\mathbb{R}} \right\}   \tag{31}$$

contains A, B, C by observing that $1/0$, $0/1$ and $1/1$ are elements of $\overline{\mathbb{R}}$. — Let now

$$\eta := \left\{ \frac{k_1 p_{11} + k_2 p_{12}}{k_1 p_{21} + k_2 p_{22}} \,\middle|\, \frac{k_1}{k_2} \in \overline{\mathbb{R}} \right\}   \tag{32}$$

be an arbitrary chain containing A, B, C. This implies that there exist units u, v, w and elements r_1/r_2, s_1/s_2, t_1/t_2 in $\overline{\mathbb{R}}$ with

$$
\begin{aligned}
(ua_1, ua_2) &= (r_1, r_2)\, P, \\
(vb_1, vb_2) &= (s_1, s_2)\, P, \\
(wc_1, wc_2) &= (t_1, t_2)\, P, \\
P &:= \begin{pmatrix} p_{11} & p_{21} \\ p_{12} & p_{22} \end{pmatrix}.
\end{aligned}
$$

Without loss of generality we may assume that all numbers r_i, s_i, t_i are real. The points

$$\mathbb{R}(r_1, r_2), \ \mathbb{R}(s_1, s_2), \ \mathbb{R}(t_1, t_2)$$

of the real projective line are pairwise distinct. In the case

$$\mathbb{R}(r_1, r_2) = \mathbb{R}(s_1, s_2)$$

for instance, we would get $A = B$, in view of our equations above. There hence exists a real and regular (2,2)–matrix B satisfying

$$\alpha(r_1, r_2) = (1, 0)B, \ \beta(s_1, s_2) = (0, 1)B, \ \gamma(t_1, t_2) = (1, 1)B$$

with real numbers α, β, γ, all unequal to 0. Thus

$$\begin{aligned}
(u'a_1, u'a_2) &= (1, 0)BP, \\
(v'b_1, v'b_2) &= (0, 1)BP, \\
(w'c_1, w'c_2) &= (1, 1)BP,
\end{aligned}$$

where we put $u' = \alpha u$ etc. This leads to

$$BP = \begin{pmatrix} u'a_1 & u'a_2 \\ v'b_1 & v'b_2 \end{pmatrix}$$

and to $w'c_i = u'a_i + v'b_i$ for $i = 1, 2$. Since (30) determines u, v uniquely, we get $u' = w'u$ and $v' = w'v$. Hence

$$BP = w' \cdot \begin{pmatrix} ua_1 & ua_2 \\ vb_1 & vb_2 \end{pmatrix}$$

and thus $\eta = \xi$: the arbitrary point $(k_1, k_2)P$ of η is in ξ since

$$(k_1, k_2)P = (l_1, l_2)BP$$

holds true with $(l_1, l_2) := (k_1, k_2)B^{-1}$; the arbitrary point

$$(k_1, k_2)BP$$

of ξ is in η since it has the form $\big[(k_1, k_2)B\big]P$.   □

PROPOSITION 9. *Let A, B, C, D be pairwise non–parallel points. There exists a chain through A, B, C, D if and only if*

$$\begin{bmatrix} A & B \\ D & C \end{bmatrix} \in \mathbb{R}.$$

Proof.   Let ξ of (31) be the chain through A, B, C such that (30) holds true. The elements p, q satisfying

$$d_i = p \cdot ua_i + q \cdot vb_i, \ i = 1, 2, \tag{33}$$

must be units, since A, B, D are pairwise non–parallel. Hence

$$\begin{bmatrix} A & B \\ D & C \end{bmatrix} = \frac{p}{q} \in U$$

since

$$\begin{vmatrix} a_1 & a_2 \\ ua_1 + vb_1 & ua_2 + vb_2 \end{vmatrix} = v \cdot (a_1 b_2 - a_2 b_1),$$

$$\begin{vmatrix} a_1 & a_2 \\ pua_1 + qvb_1 & pua_2 + qvb_2 \end{vmatrix} = qv \cdot (a_1 b_2 - a_2 b_1)$$

etc. If now $D \in \xi$ holds true, then $\frac{p}{q}$ of (33) must be in $\mathbb{R}$ $\left(\text{see } (31)\right)$. Conversely, if $\frac{p}{q} \in \mathbb{R}$, then $\frac{d_1}{d_2}$ must be an element of ξ because of equation (33). $\square$

Let a, b be chains through the point P. If $a = b$ we shall say that a *is in contact with* b in P. If $a \neq b$ we shall say that a is in contact with b in P if and only if the following properties hold true:

(i) $a \cap b = \{P\}$,

(ii) There exist chains c, d and pairwise distinct points P, A, A', B, B', Q with $a = (P A A')$, $b = (P B B')$ such that P, A, B, Q are on c and P, A', B', Q are on d.

Whenever a is in contact with b in P, we shall write $a P b$. Observe that $b P a$ is a consequence of $a P b$. Let Ψ be the group of all bijections ψ of S such that $\psi(c)$ and $\psi^{-1}(c)$ are chains for every chain c. According to the definition of chains, Γ^* must be a subgroup of Ψ. We are also interested in the geometry (S, Ψ), since we would like to determine Ψ. From the definition of the contact relation it follows immediately that

$$\{(a, b, P) \mid a P b\}$$

is an invariant notion of (S, Ψ), taking into account that

$$\{(M, N) \in S^2 \mid M \nparallel N\}$$

is an invariant notion of (S, Ψ).

THEOREM 10. *Let a, b be distinct chains through P and let $\gamma \in \Gamma^*$ be a mapping with $\gamma(P) = 1/0$. Then $a P b$ holds true if and only if*

$$\gamma(a) \backslash \left\{ \frac{1}{0} \right\}, \; \gamma(b) \backslash \left\{ \frac{1}{0} \right\}$$

are parallel lines of $\mathbb{R}^n$.

Proof.   (a) If η is a chain through $1/0$, then $\eta\backslash\{1/0\}$ must be a line of $\mathbb{R}^n$: if η has form (32), we may assume, without loss of generality, that $(k_1, k_2) = (1, 0)$ in (32) leads to the point $1/0$ (otherwise we would work with a matrix B as in the proof of Proposition 8, changing P into BP in (32)). But then $p_{21} = 0$ holds true and $p_{22} \in U$, since $\det P \in U$. Hence

$$\eta\backslash\left\{\frac{1}{0}\right\} = \left\{\lambda \cdot \frac{p_{11}}{p_{22}} + \frac{p_{12}}{p_{22}} \,\Big|\, \lambda \in \mathbb{R}\right\}$$

is a line of $\mathbb{R}^n$ (observe that $p_{11} \in U$).

(b) Since γ is also in Ψ, $\gamma(a)$, $\gamma(b)$ are chains through $1/0$. Assume now that $a\,P\,b$ holds true. We would like to denote $\gamma(F)$ by F_0 for the point F. If g is a chain through P, we shall write $g_0 := \gamma(g)\backslash\{1/0\}$. Because of (i) and (ii) we know the following facts:

(i) $a_0 \cap b_0 = \emptyset$,

(ii) There exist lines c_0, d_0 and distinct points $A_0, A_0', B_0, B_0', Q_0$ of $\mathbb{R}^n$ with

$$a_0 \ni A_0, A_0', \qquad b_0 \ni B_0, B_0'$$
$$c_0 \ni A_0, B_0, Q_0, \quad d_0 \ni A_0', B_0', Q_0.$$

Q_0 is not on a_0, since otherwise $a_0 = c_0$, i.e. $B_0 \in a_0 \cap b_0$. The points A_0, A_0', Q_0 hence determine a 2–dimensional plane π of $\mathbb{R}^n$ with

$$\pi \ni A_0, A_0', Q_0.$$

Thus $\pi \supset c_0 \cup d_0$, i.e. $\pi \ni A_0, A_0', B_0, B_0', Q_0$. Since now a_0, b_0 are lines in π with (i), we get that a_0, b_0 are parallel.

(c) Assume that a_0, b_0 are parallel lines of $\mathbb{R}^n$. We have to show that $a\,P\,b$. Since $a \neq b$, we get $a_0 \neq b_0$, i.e. $a_0 \cap b_0 = \emptyset$, i.e. $a \cap b = \{P\}$. Take distinct points A_0, A_0' on a_0. Since then A, A' are distinct points on the chain a, we have $A \nparallel A'$ and hence $A_0 \nparallel A_0'$. Thus

$$x_2 := A_0' - A_0 \in U.$$

Take a point on b_0 which we will denote by $x_1 + A_0$. Since $U(x_1, x_2)$ is a point in the sense of section 5.6.5, there exist real numbers $k \neq l$ with

$$x_1 - kx_2, \; x_2 - lx_2 \in U$$

in view of step (m) of the proof of Theorem 36 in section 5.6.5. Assume that $k > l$ and put

$$
\begin{aligned}
B_0' &:= x_1 + A_0 + (1 - l)x_2, \\
B_0 &:= x_1 + A_0 - kx_2, \\
Q_0 &:= A_0 + (l - k)^{-1} \cdot (x_1 - kx_2).
\end{aligned}
$$

(Observe that $k > l$ implies that $l - k \neq 1$.)

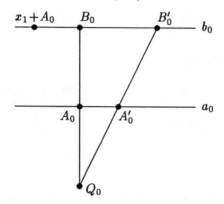

The points A_0, B_0, Q_0 are pairwise non–parallel. This follows from the fact that

$$
B_0 - A_0 = x_1 - kx_2, \quad Q_0 - A_0 = \frac{x_1 - kx_2}{l - k}, \quad Q_0 - B_0 = \lambda \cdot (x_1 - kx_2)
$$

with $(l - k)\lambda := 1 - l + k$ are units. Also the points A_0', B_0', Q_0 are pairwise non–parallel. Put $c = (P\,A\,B)$ and $d = (P\,A'\,B')$. Since c_0 is the line through A_0, B_0, we have $Q_0 \in c_0$ and hence $Q \in c$. Similarly, $Q \in d$. Since now conditions (i) and (ii) are satisfied, we get $a\,P\,b$.

The following Theorem 11 determines the group Ψ, since harmonic mappings are characterized by Theorem 36 of section 5.6.5.

THEOREM 11. *The bijection $\psi : S \to S$ is in Ψ if and only if it is a harmonic mapping of S.*

Proof.   (a) Let ψ be a harmonic bijection of S. Then

$$
\psi\left(\frac{x_1}{x_2}\right) = \frac{\sigma(x_1)a_{11} + \sigma(x_2)a_{21}}{\sigma(x_1)a_{12} + \sigma(x_2)a_{22}}, \tag{34}
$$

in view of Theorem 36, loc. cit. Observe that

$$
1 = \alpha x_1 + \beta x_2,
$$

$\alpha, \beta \in V$, implies that

$$1 = \sigma(1) = \sigma(\alpha)\sigma(x_1) + \sigma(\beta)\sigma(x_2)$$

holds true, and hence that $\sigma(x_1)/\sigma(x_2)$ must be a quotient whenever x_1/x_2 is a quotient. It is now trivial to verify that $\psi(c)$ is a chain whenever c is a chain. Since ψ^{-1} is also of the form (34) with suitable σ and a_{ij}, ψ indeed must be an element of Ψ.

(b) The more interesting part of the proof is to show that a $\psi \in \Psi$ must be harmonic. Let $A, B, C, D \in S$ be points with

$$A \nparallel D, \ B \nparallel C \text{ and } \begin{bmatrix} A & B \\ D & C \end{bmatrix} = -1. \tag{35}$$

The equation

$$\frac{\begin{vmatrix} a_1 & a_2 \\ c_1 & c_2 \end{vmatrix} \cdot \begin{vmatrix} b_1 & b_2 \\ d_1 & d_2 \end{vmatrix}}{\begin{vmatrix} a_1 & a_2 \\ d_1 & d_2 \end{vmatrix} \cdot \begin{vmatrix} b_1 & b_2 \\ c_1 & c_2 \end{vmatrix}} = -1$$

shows that also $A \nparallel C$ and $B \nparallel D$ hold true. Since (35) implies that

$$\begin{bmatrix} A & C \\ D & B \end{bmatrix} = 1 - \begin{bmatrix} A & B \\ D & C \end{bmatrix} = 2$$

is satisfied, we get $A \nparallel B$ and $C \nparallel D$. The points A, B, C, D are hence pairwise non–parallel and there exists a chain containing them, in view of Proposition 9.

(c) *Let A, B, C, D be distinct points on a chain c. Then the following two statements are equivalent:*

1. $\begin{bmatrix} A & B \\ D & C \end{bmatrix} = -1.$

2. *There exist points F, G, H such that*

a) *$C \nparallel H$ and A, B, D, F, G, H are pairwise non–parallel,*

b) *$(DAB) \cap (DFG) = \{D\}$,*

c) *$H \in (DAF) \cap (DBG)$,*

d) *$(AGD)D(CHD)$ and $(CHD)D(BFD)$.*

In order to prove statement (c), we would like to begin with the following observations. We know that the contact relation is an invariant notion of (S, Ψ). This implies especially that $p \, R \, q$ holds true iff $p' R' q'$ is satisfied for all $\gamma \in \Gamma^*$ where we put $p' := \gamma(p)$ etc. It is trivial to verify that

$$\begin{bmatrix} K & L \\ N & M \end{bmatrix} = \begin{bmatrix} K' & L' \\ N' & M' \end{bmatrix}$$

holds true for pairwise non–parallel points K, L, M, N and for $\gamma \in \Gamma^*$, where we put again $K' = \gamma(K)$ etc. So also the value -1 of a cross ratio is preserved under $\gamma \in \Gamma^*$. These observations enable us to restrict the proof of (c) on the special situation

$$D = \frac{1}{0}, \; C = \frac{0}{1}, \; B = \frac{1}{1}, \tag{36}$$

since there exists a $\gamma \in \Gamma^*$ with

$$\gamma\left(\frac{1}{0}\right) = D, \; \gamma\left(\frac{0}{1}\right) = C, \; \gamma\left(\frac{1}{1}\right) = B,$$

namely

$$\gamma\left(\frac{x_1}{x_2}\right) = \frac{x_1 u d_1 + x_2 v c_1}{x_1 u d_2 + x_2 v c_2}$$

with $b_i =: u d_i + v c_i$, $i = 1, 2$. (Observe that u, v are in U since B, C, D are pairwise non–parallel.)

Now we assume that (36) holds true and moreover that

$$\begin{bmatrix} A & B \\ D & C \end{bmatrix} = -1$$

is satisfied. Hence $A = -1$. Take an element $p \in \mathbb{R}^n \backslash \mathbb{R}$ such that $p, p+1, \; p-1$ are in U. (At the beginning of the proof of Lemma 6 we constructed such an element p.) Define

$$F := 2p + 1, \; G := 2p - 1, \; H := p.$$

Then it is trivial to verify conditions 2a, b, c, d, in view of Theorem 10. — We finally assume that (36) holds true and that F, G, H are points satisfying a, b, c, d. We then have to show that A is the point -1. Since D is not parallel to A, F, G, H, these points must be elements of $\mathbb{R}^n$. Put

$$A = \frac{\alpha}{1}, \; F = \frac{f}{1}, \; G = \frac{g}{1}, \; H = \frac{l}{1}$$

for $\alpha, f, g, l \in V = \mathbb{R}^n$. We observe that $\alpha \in \mathbb{R}$, since $A \in (D\, C\, B)$. The points A, B are distinct. Hence $\alpha \neq 1$. We observe $H \notin (D\, C\, B)$, since otherwise $G \in (B\, H\, D) = (D\, C\, B)$ would imply

$$G \in (D\, A\, B) \cap (D\, F\, G) = \{D\}.$$

Hence $l \in \mathbb{R}^n \backslash \mathbb{R}$. We also get $f, g \in \mathbb{R}^n \backslash \mathbb{R}$ since $F, G \notin (D\, B\, C)$. Now 2 c) implies that

$$f = \varrho \cdot l + (1 - \varrho) \cdot \alpha \qquad (37)$$

$$g = \sigma \cdot l + (1 - \sigma) \cdot 1 \qquad (38)$$

with $\varrho, \sigma \in \mathbb{R}$ holds true. 2 b) implies that the lines A, B and F, G are parallel, in view of Theorem 10. Hence

$$g - f = \xi \cdot (1 - \alpha)$$

with a real $\xi \neq 0$. Property 2 d) yields

$$g - \alpha = \eta \cdot (l - 0) \qquad (39)$$

$$l - 0 = \xi \cdot (f - 1) \qquad (40)$$

with reals η, ξ, both unequal to 0. Hence

$$\xi(1 - \alpha) = g - f = (\sigma - \varrho)l + (1 - \sigma) - (1 - \varrho)\alpha. \qquad (41)$$

This implies that $\sigma - \varrho = 0$, since otherwise l would be in $\mathbb{R}$, in view of (41). Now $\varrho = \sigma$ and (41) and $\alpha \neq 1$ yield $\xi = 1 - \varrho$. Equations (37), (38), (39), (40) lead to

$$\sigma l + 1 - \sigma - \alpha = g - \alpha = \eta l,$$

$$l = \xi(f - 1) = \xi(\varrho l + \alpha - \varrho \alpha - 1).$$

The first of these equations leads to $\sigma = \eta$, since otherwise l would be in $\mathbb{R}$. Hence

$$\sigma = \eta \text{ and thus } \alpha = 1 - \varrho.$$

The other equation leads to

$$1 = \zeta \varrho \text{ and } (1 - \varrho)\alpha = 1.$$

Hence $\alpha^2 = 1$, i.e. $\alpha = -1$, since $\alpha \neq 1$.

(d) We are now in the position to prove that every $\psi \in \Psi$ must be harmonic. Let $A, B, C, D \in S$ be points satisfying (35). Then (b) implies that A, B, C, D are pairwise non–parallel points on a circle c. Now (c) implies the existence of points F, G, H satisfying 2 a, b, c, d. Replacing the points A, B, C, D, F, G, H by their images under ψ, we get points $\psi(A), \dots, \psi(H)$ which also satisfy 2 a, b, c, d in the form

a) $\psi(C) \nparallel \psi(H)$ and $\psi(A), \dots$ are pairwise non parallel,

$\vdots$

d) $\big(\psi(A)\psi(G)\psi(D)\big)\psi(D)\big(\psi(C), \psi(H), \psi(D)\big) \dots$

Then according to (c),

$$\left[\begin{array}{cc} \psi(A) & \psi(B) \\ \psi(D) & \psi(C) \end{array} \right] = -1$$

holds true.   □

REMARK. Chain geometry may be developed over an arbitrary field and even in a more general context (Havlicek [1], [3], Herzer [1], [2], [3], Hotje [1], [2], [3], Samaga [1], [2], Schaeffer [4], Seier [1], Werner [1], [2], [3]).

6.2   Circle geometries

6.2.1   2–dimensional chain geometries

The 2–dimensional real chain geometries are called (real) *circle geometries*. Let V be a commutative ring with identity element 1 such that $\mathbb{R}$ is a subring of V and such that there exists an element $p \in V \backslash \mathbb{R}$ with

$$\{\alpha + \beta p \mid \alpha, \beta \in \mathbb{R}\} = V.$$

Since p^2 is an element of V, an equation

$$p^2 = \nu + \mu p$$

with $\nu, \mu \in \mathbb{R}$ must hold true. Put $q := p - \dfrac{\mu}{2}$. Then

$$V = \{\alpha + \beta q \mid \alpha, \beta \in \mathbb{R}\}, \ q^2 = \tau$$

with $q \in V \backslash \mathbb{R}$ and $4\tau := \mu^2 + 4\nu$ holds true. Put $r \cdot \sqrt{|\tau|} := q$ whenever $\tau \neq 0$. We get

$$V = \{\alpha + \beta r \mid \alpha, \beta \in \mathbb{R}\}, \ r^2 = t \tag{42}$$

with $r \in V \backslash \mathbb{R}$ and $t \in \{-1, 0, +1\}$.

Let R_t be the set of all matrices

$$\begin{pmatrix} \alpha & \beta \\ t\beta & \alpha \end{pmatrix}$$

for real α, β and with fixed $t \in \{-1, 0, +1\}$. With the usual addition and multiplication, R_t must be a commutative ring with identity element

$$E := \begin{pmatrix} 1 & 0 \\ 0 & 1 \end{pmatrix}.$$

R_t contains $\mathbb{R}$ in form $\mathbb{R} \cdot E$. Put

$$r := \begin{pmatrix} 0 & 1 \\ t & 0 \end{pmatrix}.$$

Then

$$R_t = \{\alpha E + \beta r \mid \alpha, \beta \in \mathbb{R}\}, \quad r^2 = tE$$

holds true with $r \in R_t \backslash \mathbb{R} \cdot E$. Therefore V exists in all three cases $t \in \{-1, 0, +1\}$. We would like to show that the three rings R_{-1}, R_0, R_{+1} are pairwise non–isomorphic. R_{-1} is the field $\mathbb{C}$ of complex numbers. It therefore contains no zero–divisor $\neq 0$. But both rings R_0, R_{+1} contain zero–divisors $\neq 0$: in the case $t = 0$ we have

$$\begin{pmatrix} 0 & 1 \\ 0 & 0 \end{pmatrix} \cdot \begin{pmatrix} 0 & 1 \\ 0 & 0 \end{pmatrix} = 0$$

and for $t = +1$ we obtain

$$\begin{pmatrix} 1 & 1 \\ 1 & 1 \end{pmatrix} \cdot \begin{pmatrix} 1 & -1 \\ -1 & 1 \end{pmatrix} = 0.$$

Also the rings R_0, R_{+1} are not isomorphic, since there exists an element $\neq 0$ in R_0, namely r, the square of which is 0. But there is no element $a \neq 0$ in R_{+1} with $a^2 = 0$. The ring R_0 is the ring $\mathbb{D}$ of dual numbers. The usual notation is

$$\mathbb{D} = \{\alpha + \beta\varepsilon \mid \alpha, \beta \in \mathbb{R}\}, \quad \varepsilon^2 = 0,$$

with $\varepsilon \in \mathbb{D}\backslash\mathbb{R}$. The *real part* of $z \in \mathbb{D}$, written $Re\, z$, is α if $z = \alpha + \beta\varepsilon$ for $\alpha, \beta \in \mathbb{R}$; β is called the *dual part* of z, written $Du\, z$. The ring R_1 is the ring $\mathbb{A}$ of *double numbers* (see section 4.11). The usual notation here is

$$\mathbb{A} = \{\alpha + \beta j \mid \alpha, \beta \in \mathbb{R}\}, \quad j^2 = 1,$$

with $j \in \mathbb{A}\backslash\mathbb{R}$. Sometimes the ring $\mathbb{A}$ is called the ring of *abnormal complex numbers*. Double numbers are very often written in form (a_1, a_2), $a_1, a_2 \in \mathbb{R}$, with operations defined by

$$(a_1, a_2) + (b_1, b_2) \quad := \quad (a_1 + b_1, a_2 + b_2),$$
$$(a_1, a_2) \cdot (b_1, b_2) \quad := \quad (a_1 b_1, a_2 b_2).$$

In fact, this new ring R is isomorphic to $\mathbb{A}$ by putting

$$\sigma(\alpha + \beta j) := (\alpha + \beta, \ \alpha - \beta)$$

for $\alpha, \beta \in \mathbb{R}$: the mapping $\sigma : \mathbb{A} \to R$ is a bijection satisfying

$$\begin{aligned} \sigma(x + y) &= \sigma(x) + \sigma(y), \\ \sigma(x \cdot y) &= \sigma(x) \cdot \sigma(y) \end{aligned}$$

for all $x, y \in \mathbb{A}$.

Before looking to the single circle geometries $\mathbb{D}, \mathbb{C}, \mathbb{A}$, we would like to prove Miquel's theorem. In this connection the following notation might be useful. If A, B, C, D are four pairwise non–parallel points with $A \in (B\,C\,D)$, then we shall write $(A\,B\,C\,D)$.

THEOREM 12. *Let $\Sigma(V)$ be an arbitrary real chain geometry as defined in section 6.1.3, and let A, B, C, D, E, F, G, H be eight pairwise non–parallel points of $\Sigma(V)$ such that*

$$(A\,B\,C\,D), \ (A\,E\,H\,D), \ (F\,B\,C\,G), \ (A\,F\,C\,H), \ (E\,B\,G\,D)$$

hold true. Then also $(E\,F\,G\,H)$ is satisfied.

Proof.   It is trivial to verify that

$$\begin{bmatrix} A & B \\ D & C \end{bmatrix} \cdot \begin{bmatrix} E & F \\ H & G \end{bmatrix} = \begin{bmatrix} A & E \\ D & H \end{bmatrix} \cdot \begin{bmatrix} F & B \\ G & C \end{bmatrix} \cdot \begin{bmatrix} A & F \\ H & C \end{bmatrix} \cdot \begin{bmatrix} E & B \\ D & G \end{bmatrix}$$

holds true. Five of these cross ratios are in $\mathbb{R}$, in view of Proposition 9. All the cross ratios are units, since all the points are pairwise non–parallel. This implies

$$\begin{bmatrix} A & B \\ D & C \end{bmatrix} \in \mathbb{R},$$

i.e. $(A\,B\,C\,D)$, in view of Proposition 9. $\square$

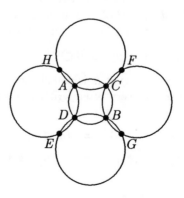

6.2.2 The real Laguerre plane

In section 3.11 we introduced the notion of spear coordinates (a_0, a_1, a_2, a_3). We are now interested in the mapping

$$\delta(a_0, a_1, a_2, a_3) = \begin{cases} a_2 + a_0\varepsilon/a_1 - a_3 & a_1 \neq a_3 \\ & \text{for} \\ 2a_3/a_0\varepsilon & a_1 = a_3 \end{cases}$$

which assigns to every spear of $\mathbb{R}^2$ a quotient of $\mathbb{D}$. We know from section 3.11 that (a_0, a_1, a_2, a_3) is a spear iff $a_1^2 + a_2^2 = a_3^2 \neq 0$. This implies that also $2a_3/a_0\varepsilon$ is a quotient. Let now p/q be a quotient of $\mathbb{D}$. How many spears T of $\mathbb{R}^2$ do exist with $\delta(T) = p/q$? If q is in

$$U = \{\alpha + \beta\varepsilon \mid \alpha, \beta \in \mathbb{R} \text{ with } \alpha \neq 0\},$$

then p/q may be written in form $\xi + \eta\varepsilon/1$. In this case we have to solve

$$\frac{a_2 + a_0\varepsilon}{a_1 - a_3} = \xi + \eta\varepsilon \text{ with } a_1 - a_3 \neq 0$$

in a_i. This is an equation (20) and we hence get

$$a_2 = (a_1 - a_3)\,\xi \text{ and } a_0 = (a_1 - a_3)\,\eta.$$

Thus T has coordinates $\left(\eta, \frac{a_1}{a_1-a_3}, \xi, \frac{a_3}{a_1-a_3}\right)$. Together with

$$\left(\frac{a_1}{a_1 - a_3}\right)^2 + \xi^2 = \left(\frac{a_3}{a_1 - a_3}\right)^2 \neq 0$$

we get that T has coordinates $\left(\eta, \dfrac{1-\xi^2}{2}, \xi, -\dfrac{1+\xi^2}{2}\right)$. If there exists an inverse image of $\xi + \eta\varepsilon/1$, it hence must be this T. On the other hand, T is an inverse image.

The other case is that q is not in U. The special structure of $\mathbb{D}$ then requires that p is in U, since p/q is a quotient: $p, q \in \mathbb{R} \cdot \varepsilon$ would imply $w_1 p + w_2 q \in \mathbb{R} \cdot \varepsilon$ for all $w_1, w_2 \in \mathbb{D}$, and hence the contradiction $1 \in \mathbb{R}\varepsilon$. So we may write

$$\frac{p}{q} = \frac{1}{p^{-1}q} =: \frac{1}{\alpha\varepsilon}$$

with $\alpha \in \mathbb{R}$, and we have to solve

$$\frac{2a_3}{a_0\varepsilon} = \frac{1}{\alpha\varepsilon}$$

in a_i with $a_1 = a_3$ and $a_1^2 + a_2^2 = a_3^2 \neq 0$. Hence

$$a_1 = a_3 \neq 0, \ a_2 = 0, \ 2a_3\alpha = a_0$$

and T has thus coordinates

$$(2\alpha, 1, 0, 1). \tag{43}$$

The mapping δ is hence a bijection between the set Σ^2 of all spears of $\mathbb{R}^2$ and the set $S(\mathbb{D})$ of all points of the chain geometry over $\mathbb{D}$. We would like to draw a picture of the spear with coordinates (43). The equation of the underlying line of T is

$$2\alpha + 1 \cdot x_1 + 0 \cdot x_2 = 0.$$

Then we have $(a_1, a_2) = (1, 0)$, $a_3 = 1$ and

$$1 = a_3 = \sqrt{a_1^2 + a_2^2} \cdot \operatorname{sgn} \begin{vmatrix} a_1 & a_2 \\ v_1 & v_2 \end{vmatrix} = \operatorname{sgn} v_2,$$

in view of (28) of section 3.11. Now $a_1v_1 + a_2v_2 = 0$ leads to $v_1 = 0$. We put $(v_1, v_2) = (0, 1)$.

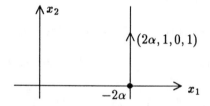

In section 3.11 we defined *parallelity* of two spears

$$A = \big(l, (v_1, v_2)\big), \ B = \big(m, (w_1, w_2)\big)$$

by means of

$$l \parallel m \text{ and } (v_1, v_2) = \lambda(w_1, w_2) \text{ with } \lambda > 0,$$

and we characterized it there by

$$\left(\frac{a_1}{a_3}, \frac{a_2}{a_3} \right) = \left(\frac{b_1}{b_3}, \frac{b_2}{b_3} \right), \tag{44}$$

where A, B have coordinates $(a_i), (b_i)$ respectively.

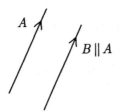

We would like to prove *that two spears A, B are parallel iff the points $\delta(A)$, $\delta(B)$ of $S(\mathbb{D})$ are parallel*. If A, B are parallel spears, then $a_1 = a_3$ holds true iff $b_1 = b_3$ is satisfied, in view of (44). Now observe that in the case $a_1 \neq a_3$

$$\text{Re} \begin{vmatrix} a_2 + a_0\varepsilon & a_1 - a_3 \\ b_2 + b_0\varepsilon & b_1 - b_3 \end{vmatrix} = a_3 b_3 \left[\frac{a_2}{a_3}\left(\frac{b_1}{b_3} - 1\right) - \frac{b_2}{b_3}\left(\frac{a_1}{a_3} - 1\right) \right] = 0 \quad (45)$$

is a consequence of (44); also

$$\begin{vmatrix} 2a_3 & a_0\varepsilon \\ 2b_3 & b_0\varepsilon \end{vmatrix} \notin U$$

holds true. If $\delta(A)$, $\delta(B)$ are parallel points, then

$$\delta(A) = a_2 + a_0\varepsilon/a_1 - a_3$$

$(a_1 \neq a_3)$ and $\delta(B) = 2b_3/b_0\varepsilon$ $(b_1 = b_3)$ is not possible at the same time, since

$$\begin{vmatrix} a_2 + a_0\varepsilon & a_1 - a_3 \\ 2b_3 & b_0\varepsilon \end{vmatrix} \in U.$$

Two cases are left:

1) $\delta(A) = \dfrac{a_2 + a_0\varepsilon}{a_1 - a_3}$, $\delta(B) = \dfrac{b_2 + b_0\varepsilon}{b_1 - b_3}$

with $a_1 \neq a_3$, $b_1 \neq b_3$ and

2) $\delta(A) = \dfrac{2a_3}{a_0\varepsilon}$, $\delta(B) = \dfrac{2b_3}{b_0\varepsilon}$

with $a_1 = a_3$, $b_1 = b_3$.

In the case 2) we have $A \parallel B$. In the case 1) we get

$$a_2(b_1 - 1) = b_2(a_1 - 1)$$

from (45) by putting $a_3 = b_3 = 1$, without loss of generality. Squaring this equation and observing that

$$a_1^2 + a_2^2 = 1 = b_1^2 + b_2^2$$

holds true, we obtain

$$(1 - a_1^2)(b_1 - 1)^2 = (1 - b_1^2)(a_1 - 1)^2,$$

i.e. $(1 + a_1)(b_1 - 1) = (1 + b_1)(a_1 - 1)$, since $a_1 \neq a_3 = 1$ etc. Hence $a_1 = b_1$ and thus $a_2 = b_2$. Now (44) yields $A \parallel B$. $\qquad\qquad\qquad\qquad\qquad\qquad\square$

Another fundamental notion of the real Laguerre plane is the notion of a *Laguerre cycle*. Such a cycle z is a point of $\mathbb{R}^2$ or an oriented circle of $\mathbb{R}^2$. Let A be a spear and let z be a cycle. If z is a point of $\mathbb{R}^2$, we say that *A is in contact with z* if and only if the underlying line l of A contains z. If z is an oriented circle with underlying circle c, we say that *A is in contact with z* if and only if l is a tangent of c and the orientations of z and A coincide in the point of contact. Instead of A is in contact with z we also say that z is in contact with A. In the situation of contact we shall write

$$A - z \text{ or } z - A.$$

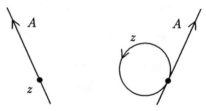

If z is the point $(m_1, m_2) \in \mathbb{R}^2$, then

$$(z_0, z_1, z_2, z_3)$$

are called the *cycle coordinates* of z where we put

$$z_0 = 1, \; z_1 = m_1, \; z_2 = m_2, \; z_3 = 0.$$

If z is an oriented circle with center (m_1, m_2), then we are interested in the uniquely determined spear

$$T(z) - z \text{ with coordinates } (a, 1, 0, 1).$$

Then

$$(1, m_1, m_2, -a - m_1)$$

are called the *cycle coordinates* of z. Observe that $|a + m_1|$ is the radius of the underlying circle c of z.

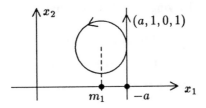

PROPOSITION 13. *Let $A(a_0, a_1, a_2, a_3)$ be a spear and let $z(z_0, z_1, z_2, z_3)$ be a cycle. Then $A - z$ holds true iff*

$$a_0 z_0 + a_1 z_1 + a_2 z_2 + a_3 z_3 = 0 \tag{46}$$

is satisfied.

Proof.   If z is a point, then $z_3 = 0$. In this case we have $z \in l$ iff

$$a_0 + a_1 z_1 + a_2 z_2 = 0,$$

where l denotes the underlying line of A. Assume now that $z_3 \neq 0$ holds true. Put $z_i =: m_i$ for $i = 1, 2$ and let $T(z) - z$ be the spear with coordinates $(a, 1, 0, 1)$ for a suitable real a. By $\varrho > 0$ we denote the radius of the underlying circle c of z.

Case 1: $-a > m_1$. Hence $\varrho = -a - m_1 = z_3$. We assume that $a_3 = 1$, without loss of generality.

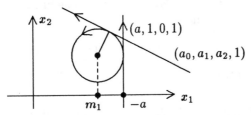

If $A(a_0, a_1, a_2, 1)$ is in contact with z, then $(m_1, m_2) + \varrho \cdot (a_1, a_2) \in l$ with $l : a_0 + a_1 x_1 + a_2 x_2 = 0$. Hence

$$0 = a_0 + a_1(m_1 + \varrho a_1) + a_2(m_2 + \varrho a_2) = a_0 + a_1 m_1 + a_2 m_2 + \varrho.$$

Conversely, let $A(a_0, a_1, a_2, 1)$ be a spear satisfying

$$a_0 + a_1 m_1 + a_2 m_2 + (-a - m_1) = 0. \tag{47}$$

Then
$$(m_1, m_2) + \varrho \cdot (a_1, a_2) \in l,$$
where l denotes the underlying line of A. The line l is hence tangent of c: if we now had $A \not\!\!\sim z$, then
$$A'(a_0, a_1, a_2, -1) - z$$
would lead to $a_0 + a_1 m_1 + a_2 m_2 + (-1)(-a - m_1) = 0$ which contradicts (47).

Case 2: $-a < m_1$. Then $\varrho = m_1 + a = -z_3$.

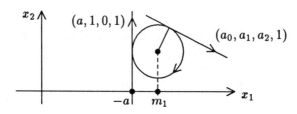

If $A(a_0, a_1, a_2, 1)$ is in contact with z, then
$$(m_1, m_2) + \varrho \cdot (-a_1, -a_2) \in l$$
with $l : a_0 + a_1 x_1 + a_2 x_2 = 0$. Hence
$$0 = a_0 + a_1(m_1 - \varrho a_1) + a_2(m_2 - \varrho a_2) = a_0 + a_1 m_1 + a_2 m_2 - \varrho.$$
Conversely, if $A(a_0, a_1, a_2, 1)$ satisfies (47), then
$$(m_1, m_2) + \varrho \cdot (-a_1, -a_2) \in l$$
holds true, where l is the underlying line of A. The line l is therefore a tangent of c. Also here $A \not\!\!\sim z$ would lead to
$$A'(a_0, a_1, a_2, -1) - z$$
which contradicts (47).   □

PROPOSITION 14. *If z is a Laguerre cycle, then*
$$\delta(\{Q \in \Sigma^2 \mid Q - z\}) \tag{48}$$
is a chain. If c is a chain of the chain geometry over $\mathbb{D}$, then there exists exactly one cycle z such that c is given by (48).

Proof.   Let z be the cycle with coordinates $(1, z_1, z_2, z_3)$. Then
$$A(-z_1 - z_3, 1, 0, 1), \ B(-z_2 - z_3, 0, 1, 1), \ C(z_2 - z_3, 0, -1, 1)$$

are pairwise non–parallel spears, all in contact with z, in view of Proposition 13. Put $\delta(X) =: X'$ for $X \in \Sigma^2$. Let X be an arbitrary spear in Σ^2 which is not parallel to A, B or C. Then the following equation

$$2(x_1 - x_3) \cdot \begin{bmatrix} A' & B' \\ X' & C' \end{bmatrix} = (x_1 + x_2 - x_3) + \varepsilon \cdot \sum_{i=0}^{3} x_i z_i \qquad (49)$$

holds true where (x_i) are coordinates of X. Put $L := \{Q \in \Sigma^2 \mid Q - z\}$. We would like to show that

$$\delta(L) = (A'B'C').$$

If $X \neq A, B, C$ belongs to L, then $X \nparallel A$, i.e, $x_1 \neq x_3$. Moreover,

$$\sum_{i=0}^{3} x_i z_i = 0.$$

This together with (49) leads to $X' \in (A'B'C')$, in view of Proposition 9. If Y' belongs to $(A'B'C')\backslash\{A', B', C'\}$, then

$$\begin{bmatrix} A' & B' \\ Y' & C' \end{bmatrix} \in \mathbb{R} \qquad (50)$$

holds true by applying again Proposition 9. $Y' \nparallel A'$ implies that Y, A are non–parallel. Hence $y_1 \neq y_3$. Then (50) and

$$2(y_1 - y_3) \begin{bmatrix} A' & B' \\ Y' & C' \end{bmatrix} = (y_1 + y_2 - y_3) + \varepsilon \cdot \sum_{i=0}^{3} y_i z_i$$

lead to $Y \in L$.

Let now $c = (P'Q'R')$ be an arbitrary chain of the chain geometry over $\mathbb{D}$. Put $P = \delta^{-1}(P')$ etc. Then P, Q, R are pairwise non–parallel spears of Σ^2. There is exactly one cycle z which is in contact with P, Q and R. Now take A, B, C as at the beginning of the proof of Proposition 14, provided that (z_i) are coordinates of z. Hence

$$\delta(\{Q \in \Sigma^2 \mid Q - z\}) = c$$

and thus $\{Q \in \Sigma^2 \mid Q - z\} = \delta^{-1}(c)$. The left–hand side determines z unique–ly. $\qquad \square$

It is worth while looking again to Theorem 12 in the case $V := \mathbb{D}$. The consequence of this Theorem 12 there is the following Theorem of Emil Müller.

Let A, B, C, D, E, F, G, H be eight pairwise non–parallel spears of $\mathbb{R}^2$ such that

$$(A\,B\,C\,D),\ (A\,E\,H\,D),\ (F\,B\,C\,G),\ (A\,F\,C\,H),\ (E\,B\,G\,D)$$

hold true. Then also $(E\,F\,G\,H)$ is satisfied. By $(P_1 P_2 P_3 P_4)$ we mean that there exists a cycle z which is in contact with P_i for all $i = 1,2,3,4$.

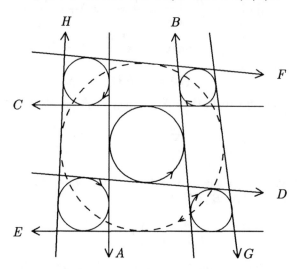

The Theorem of Miquel–Müller is a so–called $(8_3, 6_4)$–configuration. There are 8 spears and 6 cycles involved. Every spear is in contact with 3 cycles and every cycle with 4 spears.

REMARKS. 1. Let k, l be cycles with $k \cap l = \{A, B\}; A \neq B$. In this notation we identify a cycle z with the set of spears which are in contact with z.

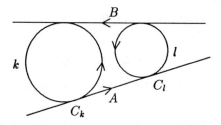

Denote by C_k, C_l the points of contact of A with k, l, respectively. Let K, L be spears with

$$K \in k\backslash\{A, B\} \text{ and } L \in l\backslash\{A, B\}$$

and put

$$\begin{bmatrix} A & B \\ L & K \end{bmatrix} =: u + v\varepsilon \text{ with } u, v \in \mathbb{R}.$$

The euclidean distance between C_k, C_l is then given by $\left|\dfrac{v}{u}\right|$. This distance is called the *tangential distance* between k and l.

2. There is another $(8_3, 6_4)$–configuration in chain geometry, the so–called bundle theorem. *Let $A, A', B, B', C, C', D, D'$ be eight pairwise non–parallel points with*

$$B' \in (A\,A'\,B), \ C' \in (A\,A'\,C), \ D' \in (A\,A'\,D), \ C' \in (B\,B'\,C), \ D' \in (B\,B'\,B)$$

and such that

$$(A\,A'\,B), \ (A\,A'\,C), \ (A\,A'\,D), \ (B\,B'\,C), \ (B\,B'\,D)$$

are at least four distinct chains, then $D' \in (C\,C'\,D)$ holds true.

Not every real chain geometry satisfies the bundle theorem. Let Q be the set of all units u of V (see section 6.1.3) which are in $\mathbb{R}$ or which are quadratic over $\mathbb{R}$, i.e. which satisfy an equation

$$u^2 + \alpha u + \beta = 0$$

with $\alpha, \beta \in \mathbb{R}$. Then the following Theorem (W. Benz [5]) holds true: *The real chain geometry over V satisfies the bundle theorem if and only if*

$$\forall_{p,q} \in Q \ \ p \cdot q \in Q.$$

This property is satisfied for every 2–dimensional real chain geometry. It is not true in the case

$$V = \{x_1 + x_2 i + x_3 j + x_4 ij \mid x_\nu \in \mathbb{R}\}, \ i, j \notin \mathbb{R},$$

with $i^2 = -1$ and $j^2 = 1$. The elements $1 + i$ and j are here in Q since

$$(1+i) \cdot \frac{1-i}{2} = 1 = j \cdot j \text{ and } (1+i)^2 - 2(1+i) + 2 = 0$$

hold true. If there existed an equation

$$[(1+i)j]^2 + \alpha(1+i)j + \beta = 0$$

with $\alpha, \beta \in \mathbb{R}$, we would obtain

$$\alpha(1+i)j = -\beta - 2i$$

with $\alpha \neq 0$, since $i \notin \mathbb{R}$. We hence would get $j \in \mathbb{C}$.

The bundle theorem is for $V = \mathbb{D}$ a theorem of K. Ogura. The bundle theorem holds true in the chain geometry over $\mathbb{R}_i^3$ (see section 5.6.5) iff $i \in \{1, 4, 5\}$.

Theorem 11 and Theorem 36 (section 5.6.5) allow us to determine the so-called *Laguerre group*: it consists of all bijections ψ of the set Σ^2 of spears of $\mathbb{R}^2$ such that $\psi(c), \psi^{-1}(c)$ are cycles whenever c is a cycle. Here again we identify a cycle with the set of all spears which are in contact with it. First of all we have to determine all bijective mappings $\sigma : V \to V$ as desribed in Theorem 36 (loc. cit.) for $V := \mathbb{D}$. Put

$$\sigma(\varepsilon) =: \alpha + \beta \varepsilon.$$

Then $0 = \sigma(0) = \sigma(\varepsilon \cdot \varepsilon) = \sigma(\varepsilon) \cdot \sigma(\varepsilon) = \alpha^2 + 2\alpha\beta\varepsilon$ implies that $\alpha = 0$. Hence

$$\sigma(\gamma + \delta\varepsilon) = \sigma(\gamma) + \sigma(\delta) \cdot \beta\varepsilon$$

for $\gamma, \delta \in \mathbb{R}$. Moreover, $\sigma(\gamma) = \sigma(\gamma \cdot 1) = \gamma\sigma(1) = \gamma$. Thus

$$\sigma(\gamma + \delta\varepsilon) = \gamma + \delta \cdot \beta\varepsilon. \tag{51}$$

Whenever $\beta \neq 0$, this mapping is a bijection of $\mathbb{D}$ and it satisfies

$$\sigma(a + b) = \sigma(a) + \sigma(b), \quad \sigma(a \cdot b) = \sigma(a) \cdot \sigma(b),$$
$$\sigma(\gamma a) = \gamma\sigma(a), \quad \sigma(1) = 1$$

for all $a, b \in \mathbb{D}$ and $\gamma \in \mathbb{R}$. *The elements of the Laguerre group are now given exactly by the mappings*

$$\frac{x_1}{x_2} \to \frac{\sigma(x_1)\, a_{11} + \sigma(x_2)\, a_{21}}{\sigma(x_1)\, a_{12} + \sigma(x_2)\, a_{22}} \tag{52}$$

where a_{ij} are elements of $\mathbb{D}$ with

$$a_{11}a_{22} - a_{12}a_{21} \in U$$

and where σ is a mapping (51) with a fixed $\beta \in \mathbb{R} \backslash \{0\}$.

Two geometries are of interest in connection with Laguerre geometry. These geometries are

$$(\Sigma^2, L_6) \text{ and } (\Sigma^2, L_7).$$

L_7 denotes the group of all mappings (52), and L_6 is the subgroup of those mappings in L_7 with $\sigma =$ id, i.e. with $\beta = 1$ in (51). The group L_6 depends on six real parameters and L_7 on seven.

The set

$$N := \{\{k, l\} \mid k, l \text{ cycles with } |k \cap l| = 2\},$$

is an invariant notion of the geometry (Σ^2, L_6). Tangential distance is an invariant

$$h : N \to \mathbb{R}_{>0} \tag{53}$$

of (Σ^2, L_6). It can be characterized as an invariant of type (53) which is additive, of course up to a constant positive factor. The set of chains is an invariant notion of (Σ^2, L_6), but it is not a defining notion of this geometry, since its group is L_7. The cross ratio is an invariant of (Σ^2, L_6), but it is not an invariant of (Σ^2, L_7).

REMARK. More material about Laguerre geometry may be found in W. Benz [1], [2], and W. Blaschke [1], [2].

6.2.3   The other two geometries

The chain geometry over $\mathbb{C}$ is called 2-dimensional *Möbius geometry*. Since the group U of units is given by $\mathbb{C}\backslash\{0\}$ in the case $V = \mathbb{C}$, there is only one quotient a/b, up to equality, with $b \notin U$, namely $1/0$. This quotient is usually denoted by ∞. The set S of points is given here by $\mathbb{R}^2 \cup \{\infty\}$. Two points are parallel iff they coincide. In fact,

$$\begin{vmatrix} x_1 & x_2 \\ y_1 & y_2 \end{vmatrix} = 0$$

leads to $x_1/x_2 = y_1/y_2$. This is the reason that one does not talk about parallelity of points in Möbius geometry. Let

$$\xi = \left\{ \frac{r_1 a_{11} + r_2 a_{12}}{r_1 a_{21} + r_2 a_{22}} \,\middle|\, \frac{r_1}{r_2} \in \overline{\mathbb{R}} \right\}$$

be a chain. Assume that ∞ is on ξ. Step (a) of the proof of Theorem 10 implies then that $\xi\backslash\{\infty\}$ is a line of $\mathbb{R}^2$. If $\infty \notin \xi$, then

$$r_1 a_{21} + r_2 a_{22} \neq 0$$

for all $r_1/r_2 \in \overline{\mathbb{R}}$. Hence $a_{21} \neq 0$, since $1/0 \in \overline{\mathbb{R}}$. We shall assume that $a_{21} = 1$, without loss of generality. Then

$$\xi\backslash\{a_{11}\} = \left\{ \frac{r a_{11} + a_{12}}{r + a_{22}} \,\middle|\, r \in \mathbb{R} \right\} \tag{54}$$

with $a_{11}a_{22} \neq a_{12}$ and $a_{22} \notin \mathbb{R}$. Put

$$\frac{ra_{11} + a_{12}}{r + a_{22}} = x. \tag{55}$$

Hence $r \cdot (a_{11} - x) = a_{22}x - a_{12}$. Here we have $a_{11} \neq x$, since otherwise

$$0 = a_{22}a_{11} - a_{12}.$$

Thus

$$\mathrm{Im}\,\frac{a_{22}x - a_{12}}{a_{11} - x} = 0, \tag{56}$$

i.e.

$$\begin{aligned} a_2(x_1^2 + x_2^2) \quad &+ (a_1c_2 - a_2c_1 - b_2)x_1 \\ &- (a_1c_1 + a_2c_2 - b_1)x_2 = b_1c_2 - b_2c_1 \end{aligned} \tag{57}$$

where we put

$$a_{22} = a_1 + ia_2, \; a_{12} = b_1 + ib_2, \; a_{11} = c_1 + ic_2$$

with $a_1, a_2, b_1, b_2, c_1, c_2 \in \mathbb{R}$, and where we have $a_2 \neq 0$ because $a_{22} \notin \mathbb{R}$ holds true. Also a_{11}, i.e. $(x_1, x_2) = (c_1, c_2)$, satisfies (57). If

$$(x_1, x_2) \neq (c_1, c_2)$$

satisfies (57), then (56) holds true and

$$r := \frac{a_{22}x - a_{12}}{a_{11} - x} \in \mathbb{R}$$

with $x := x_1 + ix_2$. Hence

$$x = \frac{ra_{11} + a_{12}}{r + a_{22}} \in \xi \setminus \{a_{11}\}.$$

Chains $\xi \not\ni \infty$ are thus euclidean circles of $\mathbb{R}^2$. — We now would like to verify that $l \cup \{\infty\}$ is a chain whenever l is a line of $\mathbb{R}^2$, and that every euclidean circle c is also a chain of the chain geometry over $\mathbb{C}$. In fact, take three distinct points of l or of c and look to the chain ξ through those three points. Obviously,

$$\xi = l \cup \{\infty\} \text{ or } \xi = c.$$

By a *circle* in Möbius geometry is meant a euclidean circle of $\mathbb{R}^2$ or a point set $l \cup \{\infty\}$ where l is a line of $\mathbb{R}^2$.

Theorem 11 allows us to determine the so–called *Möbius group*: it consists of all bijections ψ of $\mathbb{R}^2 \cup \{\infty\}$ such that $\psi(c)$, $\psi^{-1}(c)$ are circles whenever c is a circle. All those bijections are given by (52) with complex numbers $a_{11}, a_{12}, a_{21}, a_{22}$ with

$$a_{11}a_{22} - a_{12}a_{21} \neq 0$$

and with the two automorphisms

$$\sigma(z) = z \text{ for all } z \in \mathbb{C}$$

or

$$\sigma(z) = \bar{z} \text{ for all } z \in \mathbb{C}.$$

The chain geometry over $\mathbb{A}$ is called 2–dimensional *Minkowski geometry*. It already occured in sections 4.10 and 4.11. In section 4.11, formula (82), we represented *Minkowski circles* by equations

$$(z_1\, z_2)M(\bar{z}_1\bar{z}_2)^T = 0 \tag{58}$$

with $M = \overline{M}^T$ and $\det M \neq 0$. We would like to show now that those circles are exactly the chains of the chain geometry over $\mathbb{A}$. In formula (83), loc. cit., we represented M in (58) by

$$M = \begin{pmatrix} a & b+cj \\ b-cj & d \end{pmatrix} \tag{59}$$

with $a, b, c, d \in \mathbb{R}$ such that $0 \neq \det M = ad - b^2 + c^2$ holds true.

PROPOSITION 15. *The set of all quotients x_1/x_2 of $\mathbb{A}$ satisfying*

$$(x_1 x_2)M(\bar{x}_1\bar{x}_2)^T = 0$$

where M is the matrix (59) with $a, b, c, d \in \mathbb{R}$ and $\det M \neq 0$, is a chain. Conversely, every chain has such a representation.

Proof. (a) The chain $\overline{\mathbb{R}}$ has equation

$$(x_1 x_2) \begin{pmatrix} 0 & j \\ -j & 0 \end{pmatrix} \begin{pmatrix} \bar{x}_1 \\ \bar{x}_2 \end{pmatrix} = 0.$$

If we consider the mapping γ,

$$U(x_1' x_2') = U(x_1 x_2) \cdot A,$$

where A is a $(2,2)$–matrix over $\mathbb{A}$ with det $A \in U$, then $\gamma(\overline{\mathbb{R}})$ is the general chain. This chain has equation

$$(x_1' x_2') M (\overline{x'}_1 \overline{x'}_2)^T = 0$$

with det $M \neq 0$ and $M = \overline{M}^T$ for

$$M := B \cdot \begin{pmatrix} 0 & j \\ -j & 0 \end{pmatrix} \overline{B}^T, \quad B := A^{-1}.$$

The arbitrary chain has therefore a representation (58).

(b) Suppose that M is a matrix (59) with det $M \neq 0$.

Case 1. $a = 0$. This implies that $b^2 \neq c^2$, since det $M \neq 0$. Let

$$(\xi_1, \eta_1), \ (\xi_2, \eta_2) \in \mathbb{R}^2$$

be distinct points of the line of equation $2bx + 2cy + d = 0$. Put

$$A := \begin{pmatrix} (\xi_2 - \xi_1) + (\eta_2 - \eta_1)j & 0 \\ \xi_1 + \eta_1 j & 1 \end{pmatrix}.$$

Then

$$A M \overline{A}^T = [c(\xi_1 - \xi_2) + b(\eta_1 - \eta_2)] \cdot \begin{pmatrix} 0 & j \\ -j & 0 \end{pmatrix}. \tag{60}$$

Observe that $c(\xi_1 - \xi_2) + b(\eta_1 - \eta_2) \neq 0$, since otherwise $b^2 = c^2$, because $b(\xi_1 - \xi_2) + c(\eta_1 - \eta_2) = 0$ holds true. Going over to determinants in the equation (60) yields that det $A \in U$. We hence get that the set of quotients y_1/y_2 of $\mathbb{A}$ satisfying $(y_1 y_2) M (\overline{y}_1 \overline{y}_2)^T = 0$ is the chain $\gamma(\overline{\mathbb{R}})$ with

$$U(y_1 y_2) = U(x_1 x_2) \cdot A.$$

Case 2. $a \neq 0$. We are interested in the set of all quotients z_1/z_2 satisfying

$$(z_1 z_2) M (\overline{z}_1 \overline{z}_2)^T = 0 \tag{61}$$

where M has the form (59) with $a \neq 0$ and det $M \neq 0$. Put

$$P := \begin{pmatrix} t(1 + j) + (1 - j) & 1 + j \\ 1 & 1 - j \end{pmatrix}$$

with $at := c - b$. Observe that det $P \in U$. Observe moreover that

$$P M \overline{P}^T = \begin{pmatrix} 0 & \cdot \\ \cdot & \cdot \end{pmatrix} =: N$$

holds true with $N = \overline{N}^T$ and det $N \neq 0$. Define the mapping δ,

$$U(z_1 z_2) = U(y_1 y_2) \cdot P.$$

By means of (61) we then get

$$(y_1 y_2) N (\overline{y}_1 \overline{y}_2)^T = 0.$$

This can be written in the form $\gamma(\overline{\mathbb{R}})$, in view of the considerations of case 1. (61) hence can be written as $\delta \gamma(\overline{\mathbb{R}})$ and must thus be a chain. □

Theorem 11 allows us to determine the so–called *Minkowski group*: it consists of all bijections ψ of the set of points of the Minkowski plane Π (see section 4.10) such that $\psi(c), \psi^{-1}(c)$ are (Minkowski) circles whenever c is such a circle. All those bijections are given by (52) with double numbers $a_{11}, a_{12}, a_{21}, a_{22}$ with

$$a_{11} a_{22} - a_{12} a_{21} \neq 0$$

and with the two automorphisms

$$\sigma(z) = z \text{ for all } z \in \mathbb{A}$$

or

$$\sigma(z) = \overline{z} \text{ for all } z \in \mathbb{A}.$$

REMARKS. 1. Since the (Minkowski) circles are exactly the chains of the chain geometry over $\mathbb{A}$ (see Proposition 15), we may apply Proposition 8: through three pairwise non parallel points there is exactly one circle of Π.

2. Let $\mathbb{P}$ be a set and let $\mathbb{B}$ be a set of subsets of $\mathbb{P}$. We will call the elements of $\mathbb{P}$ *points* and the elements of $\mathbb{B}$ *circles*. If $P \in \mathbb{P}$ is a point and $c \in \mathbb{B}$ a circle such that $P \in c$ holds true, we shall say that P is on c or that c goes through P. In this case we also shall say that P is incident with c or that c is incident with P. The structure $\Sigma = (\mathbb{P}, \mathbb{B})$ is said to be an *inversive plane* if and only if the following properties (M1), (M2), (M3) hold true.

(M1) *If P, Q, R are distinct elements of $\mathbb{P}$, then there exists exactly one element c in $\mathbb{B}$ with $P, Q, R \in c$.*

(M2) *If c is a circle and if $P \in c$ and $Q \notin c$ are points, then there exists exactly one circle c' through P, Q with $c \cap c' = \{P\}$.*

(M3) *There exist four distinct points not on a common circle, and every circle contains at least one point.*

An inversive plane $(\mathbb{P}, \mathbb{B})$ is called *miquelian* if and only if the following property (M) holds true.

(M) *Let A, B, C, D, E, F, G, H be eight pairwise distinct points such that $(A\,B\,C\,D)$, $(A\,E\,H\,D)$, $(F\,B\,C\,G)$, $(A\,F\,C\,H)$, $(E\,B\,G\,D)$ is satisfied. Then also $(E\,F\,G\,H)$ holds true.*

As in Theorem 12, $(A\,B\,C\,D)$ (etc.) represents the fact that A, B, C, D are on a common circle. Let Δ be a commutative field and let Γ be a subfield of Δ with $[\Delta : \Gamma] = 2$. The pair Γ, Δ then determines a miquelian inversive plane $\Sigma = (\mathbb{P}, \mathbb{B})$. Let $\mathbb{P}$ be the projective line over Δ and let the circles be the sets of points $\delta(\Gamma')$ where Γ' is the projective line over Γ (considered as a subset of $\mathbb{P}$) and where δ is any projective transformation of $\mathbb{P}$. A theorem of B.L. van der Waerden, L.J. Smid, and Yi Chen states that all miquelian inversive planes are given (up to isomorphism) by pairs Γ, Δ of fields as described above. (For a proof of this theorem see our book [2]).

3.   Let Π be one of the algebras $\mathbb{D}, \mathbb{C}, \mathbb{A}$. In the case $z \in \Pi$ we shall write

$$z = a + b\tau$$

with $a, b \in \mathbb{R} \not\ni \tau$ and

$$\tau^2 = \left\{ \begin{array}{c} 0 \\ -1 \\ 1 \end{array} \right. \text{ for } \Pi = \left\{ \begin{array}{c} \mathbb{D} \\ \mathbb{C} \\ \mathbb{A} \end{array} \right. .$$

The *Mandelbrot set* M_Π is defined as the set of all $z_0 \in \Pi$ such that the sequences

$$(a_n), (b_n) \quad (n = 0, 1, 2, 3, \ldots) \tag{62}$$

are bounded where we put

$$z_{n+1} = z_n^2 + z_0 \quad (n = 0, 1, 2, 3, \ldots),$$

$$z_n =: a_n + b_n \tau \quad \text{with } a_n, b_n \in \mathbb{R}.$$

The *Julia set* $J_\Pi(w)$ depending on

$$w = c + d\tau \in \Pi \text{ with } c, d \in \mathbb{R}$$

is defined as the set of all $z_0 \in \Pi$ such that the sequences (62) are bounded where we put

$$z_{n+1} = z_n^2 + w \quad (n = 0, 1, 2, 3, \ldots),$$

$$z_n =: a_n + b_n \tau \quad \text{with } a_n, b_n \in \mathbb{R}.$$

Concerning sets $M_\mathbb{A}, M_\mathbb{D}, J_\mathbb{A}(w), J_\mathbb{D}(w)$ see R. Artzy [3], H.J. Samaga [4]. Generalizations to algebras $\Pi = \mathbb{R}_i^3$ (see the end of section 5.6.5) are due to H.J. Samaga [4].

6.3 Sphere geometries

6.3.1 The group of automorphisms

Let $n > 1$ be an integer and let $\varepsilon_1, \ldots, \varepsilon_n$ be real numbers with $\varepsilon_1 = 1$ and $\varepsilon_i^2 = 1$ for $i = 2, \ldots, n$. If

$$a = (a_1, \ldots, a_n) \text{ and } b = (b_1, \ldots, b_n)$$

are elements of $\mathbb{R}^n$, we shall write

$$ab := \sum_{\nu=1}^{n} \varepsilon_\nu a_\nu b_\nu. \tag{63}$$

$a \in \mathbb{R}^n$ is said to be *isotropic* iff $a^2 := aa = 0$. In this section 6.3 we shall call the elements of $\mathbb{R}^n$ *proper points*. The symbol ∞ is said to be an improper point. Also every point set

$$K(v, \beta) := \{x \in \mathbb{R}^n \mid vx = \beta\} \tag{64}$$

will be called an improper point provided that $\beta \in \mathbb{R}$ and that $v \neq 0$ is an isotropic element of $\mathbb{R}^n$. In the case $n = 2$ and $\varepsilon_2 = -1$ the sets (64) are exactly the lines of $\mathbb{R}^2$ of slope $+1$ or -1 (see the beginning of section 4.10).

We would now like to define the *spheres* of the *sphere geometry of signature* $(\varepsilon_1, \ldots, \varepsilon_n)$. The set of points of this geometry consists of the set $\overline{\mathbb{R}^n}$ of all proper and improper points as introduced above.

I. If α is in $\mathbb{R}$ and if $a \in \mathbb{R}^n$ is non–isotropic, then the *sphere* $S_I(a, \alpha)$ consists of ∞, of all $x \in \mathbb{R}^n$ with $ax = \alpha$, and of all improper points $K(v, \beta)$ with $av = 0$.

II. If $\alpha \neq 0$ is in $\mathbb{R}$ and if m is in $\mathbb{R}^n$, then $S_{II}(m, \alpha)$ consists of all $x \in \mathbb{R}^n$ with $(x - m)^2 = \alpha$ and of all improper points $K(v, \beta)$ with $vm = \beta$. If $S_{II}(m, \alpha) \neq \emptyset$, then $S_{II}(m, \alpha)$ is also called a *sphere*.

In GT, 126 f, we prove that the improper points of $S_{II}(m, \alpha) \neq \emptyset$ are exactly the asymptotes of

$$\{x \in \mathbb{R}^n \mid (x - m)^2 = r\}.$$

The sphere geometry of signature $(1, 1, \ldots, 1)$ is called *sphere geometry of Möbius*. In the case

$$\varepsilon_1 = \ldots = \varepsilon_{n-1} = -\varepsilon_n$$

we speak of the *sphere geometry of Minkowski*. If $n =: 2k$ is even and if

$$\varepsilon_1 = \ldots = \varepsilon_k = -\varepsilon_{k+1} = \ldots = -\varepsilon_{2k}$$

holds true, then our sphere geometry is called *sphere geometry of Plücker*.

In the case of the sphere geometry of Möbius there do not exist improper points $K(v, \beta)$, since

$$v_1^2 + \ldots + v_n^2 = 0$$

implies $v = 0$. Here we have $\overline{\mathbb{R}^n} = \mathbb{R}^n \cup \{\infty\}$ and the spheres are given by

$$S_\mathrm{I}(a, \alpha) = \{x \in \mathbb{R}^n \mid ax = \alpha\} \cup \{\infty\}$$

for $a \neq 0$, and by

$$S_\mathrm{II}(m, \alpha) = \{x \in \mathbb{R}^n \mid (x - m)^2 = \alpha\}$$

with $\alpha > 0$. (Observe that $\alpha \neq 0$ and that $\alpha < 0$ would lead to $S_\mathrm{II} = \emptyset$.)

If we denote the sphere geometry of signature $(\varepsilon_1, \ldots, \varepsilon_n)$ by $\Sigma_{\varepsilon_1, \ldots, \varepsilon_n}$, we may say that $\Sigma_{1,1}$ and $\Sigma_{1,-1}$ are the two geometries of section 6.2.3.

A bijection of the set of points of $\Sigma = \Sigma_{\varepsilon_1, \ldots, \varepsilon_n}$ is called an *automorphism* of Σ iff images and inverse images of spheres are spheres. By $\Gamma = \Gamma_{\varepsilon_1, \ldots, \varepsilon_n}$ we denote the group of automorphisms of Σ. The geometry $(\overline{\mathbb{R}^n}, \Gamma_{\varepsilon_1, \ldots, \varepsilon_n})$ in the sense of chapter 1 then defines precisely the sphere geometry of signature $(\varepsilon_1, \ldots, \varepsilon_n)$.

Examples of automorphisms of $\Sigma = \Sigma_{\varepsilon_1, \ldots, \varepsilon_n}$:

a) Take $\varepsilon, t \in \mathbb{R}$ with $\varepsilon^2 = 1$ and $t \neq 0$. Define

$$\gamma(x_1 \ldots x_n) = t \cdot (x_1 \ldots x_n) \begin{pmatrix} a_{11} & \cdots & a_{1n} \\ \vdots & & \vdots \\ a_{n1} & \cdots & a_{nn} \end{pmatrix} + (a_1 \ldots a_n) \qquad (65)$$

for $x \in \mathbb{R}^n$ and fixed $a_{ij}, a_k \in \mathbb{R}$ with

$$\sum_{\nu=1}^{n} \varepsilon_\nu a_{i\nu} a_{j\nu} = \begin{cases} \varepsilon \varepsilon_i & i = j \\ & \text{for} \\ 0 & i \neq j \end{cases}.$$

Define moreover $\gamma(\infty) = \infty$ and $\gamma[K(v, \beta)]$ as the image under γ of the hyperplane of equation $vx = \beta$.

(For the proof that these mappings γ are automorphisms see GT 129 f.) In the case $t = 1$ and $a_{ij} = \delta_{ij}$, the mapping γ is called a *translation*.

b) The set $S_{\text{II}}(0,1)$ contains for instance the point $(1,0,\ldots,0) \in \mathbb{R}^n$. This set $S_{\text{II}}(0,1)$ is called the *unit–sphere* of $\Sigma_{\varepsilon_1,\ldots,\varepsilon_n}$. We shall now define the *inversion* ι with respect to the unit–sphere:

$$\iota(x) \quad := \frac{x}{x^2} \text{ for } x \in K^n \text{ with } x^2 \neq 0,$$

$$\iota(x) \quad := K\left(x, \frac{1}{2}\right) \text{ for } x \in K^n \backslash \{0\} \text{ with } x^2 = 0,$$

$$\iota(0) \quad := \infty \text{ and } \iota(\infty) := 0,$$

$$\iota[K(v,\beta)] \quad := \begin{cases} \dfrac{v}{2\beta} & \beta \neq 0 \\ & \text{for} \quad . \\ K(v,\beta) & \beta = 0 \end{cases}$$

(For the proof that ι is an automorphism see GT 128.) The mapping ι satisfies $\iota^2 = \text{id} \neq \iota$. The points of $\overline{\mathbb{R}^n}$ which remain fixed under ι are exactly the points of the unit–sphere.

THEOREM 16. *Let π be an automorphism of the sphere geometry of signature $(\varepsilon_1,\ldots,\varepsilon_n)$. Then there exist translations τ_1,τ_2, mappings $\chi_1,\chi_2 \in \{\iota, \text{id}\}$ and a mapping γ of the form (65) such that*

$$\pi = \tau_1 \, \chi_1 \, \tau_2 \, \chi_2 \, \gamma$$

holds true. In the case of signature $(1,\ldots,1)$ the mappings τ_2 and χ_2 may be chosen as the mapping id.
(For the proof of this theorem see GT 137 f.) The mapping ι stems from a birational transformation of $\mathbb{R}^n$, and $\Sigma_{\varepsilon_1,\ldots,\varepsilon_n}$ may be considered as a Cremona geometry (GT 154 f).

6.3.2 Lie geometry

Lie geometry (GT, chapter 4) and sphere geometry of Minkowski may be considered as the same structure (GT, section 4.10). Let $\overline{\mathbb{R}^n}$ be again the set of points of $\Sigma_{\varepsilon_1,\ldots,\varepsilon_n}$. Two distinct elements A, B of $\overline{\mathbb{R}^n}$ are called *parallel*, written $A \parallel B$, iff there exists $C \in \overline{\mathbb{R}^n} \backslash \{A, B\}$ such that every sphere through A, B contains also C. Moreover put $A \parallel A$ for every $A \in \overline{\mathbb{R}^n}$. Observe that $A \parallel B$ implies $B \parallel A$ for all $A, B \in \overline{\mathbb{R}^n}$. Also the following statement holds true (GT 134):

LEMMA 17. $\infty \parallel A \in \overline{\mathbb{R}^n}$ *holds true iff A is improper.* $\mathbb{R}^n \ni x \parallel K(v,\beta)$ *iff $vx = \beta$. The points $x, y \in \mathbb{R}^n$ are parallel iff $(x-y)^2 = 0$.*

In order now to define n–*dimensional Lie geometry* in terms of $(n+1)$–dimensional sphere geometry of Minkowski,

$$\Sigma_{\varepsilon_1,\ldots,\varepsilon_{n+1}},$$

$\varepsilon_1 = \ldots = \varepsilon_n = -\varepsilon_{n+1}$, we proceed as follows: call the points of $\overline{\mathbb{R}^{n+1}}$ *Lie cycles*. The set of all these Lie cycles denote by L^n. For $A, B \in L^n$ write $A - B$ iff $A \parallel B$. The statement $A - B$ is read in Lie geometry as *A is in contact with B*. A *Lie transformation* of L^n is a bijection λ of L^n satisfying

$$A - B \Leftrightarrow \lambda(A) - \lambda(B)$$

for all $A, B \in L^n$. The automorphisms of the sphere geometry $\Sigma_{\varepsilon_1,\ldots,\varepsilon_{n+1}}$ are exactly the Lie transformations (Theorem A.10.1 in GT, 197 f). Call the improper points $\neq \infty$ of $\overline{\mathbb{R}^{n+1}}$ *spears* and the proper points *Laguerre cycles*. If S is a spear and if x is a Laguerre cycle, then define

$$S \text{ is on } x, \quad \text{written } S \in x,$$

iff $S - x$ holds true for the Lie cycles S and x. Bijections of the set of spears such that images and inverse images of Laguerre cycles x (considered as sets

$$\{S \mid S \in x\}$$

of spears) are Laguerre cycles, are called *Laguerre transformations*. The group of all these Laguerre transformations is exactly the stabilizer of ∞ of the group of all automorphisms of $\Sigma_{\varepsilon_1,\ldots,\varepsilon_{n+1}}$ (A.10.1 in GT, 197 f).

6.3.3   Theorem of Liouville for arbitrary signature

A famous theorem in geometry is a theorem of Liouville on angle preserving mappings in $\mathbb{R}^3$. Let G be a region of $\mathbb{R}^3$, i.e. a nonempty open connected subset of $\mathbb{R}^3$, and suppose that

$$x = (x_1, x_2, x_3) \to y = y\,(x_1, x_2, x_3) = (y_1, y_2, y_3)$$

is a mapping from G into $\mathbb{R}^3$ such that all

$$\frac{\partial\, y_i}{\partial\, x_j}\,(i, j \in \{1, 2, 3\})$$

exist in G and are continuous there, and such that the Jacobian

$$\frac{\partial\,(y_1, y_2, y_3)}{\partial\,(x_1, x_2, x_3)}$$

is $\neq 0$ in G. Let $x(t)$ be continuously differentiable in

$$I =]\, t_0 - \varepsilon, t_0 + \varepsilon\,[, \; \varepsilon > 0,$$

with $\dot{x} := \frac{dx}{dt} \neq 0$ in I and $x(t) \in G$ for all $t \in I$. Observe that

$$\dot{y}(x(t)) = (\dot{x}_1 \; \dot{x}_2 \; \dot{x}_3) \begin{pmatrix} \dfrac{\partial y_1}{\partial x_1} & \dfrac{\partial y_2}{\partial x_1} & \dfrac{\partial y_3}{\partial x_1} \\[2mm] \dfrac{\partial y_1}{\partial x_2} & \dfrac{\partial y_2}{\partial x_2} & \dfrac{\partial y_3}{\partial x_2} \\[2mm] \dfrac{\partial y_1}{\partial x_3} & \dfrac{\partial y_2}{\partial x_3} & \dfrac{\partial y_3}{\partial x_3} \end{pmatrix}$$

holds true, and that $\dot{y}(x(t)) \neq 0$ in I, since the Jacobian is $\neq 0$ in G. As indicated in a drawing, it now makes sense to ask for mappings $x \to y$ which preserve angles, and a theorem of Liouville characterizes those mappings under

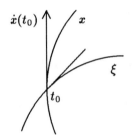 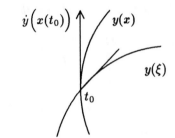

suitable differentiability assumptions as restrictions (on G) of automorphisms of the sphere geometry of signature $(1, 1, 1)$. We will present a theorem here which asks only for the preservance of certain right angles and which holds true for all signatures $(\varepsilon_1, \ldots, \varepsilon_n)$, $n \geq 3$. If a, b are elements of $\mathbb{R}^n$, we shall write $a \perp b$ iff

$$a \cdot b = \sum_{\nu=1}^{n} \varepsilon_\nu \, a_\nu \, b_\nu = 0.$$

Let G be a region of $\mathbb{R}^n$ and let

$$f : G \to \mathbb{R}$$

be a function. $f \in C^3(G)$ denotes the fact that all partial derivatives of f exist up to the third order and are continuous in G. By Y_ν, $\nu = 1, \ldots, n$, we denote

$$Y_\nu := \left(\frac{\partial y_1}{\partial x_\nu}, \ldots, \frac{\partial y_n}{\partial x_\nu} \right)$$

in the case that

$$(x_1, \ldots, x_n) \to (y_1(x_1, \ldots, x_n), \ldots, y_n(x_1, \ldots, x_n)) \tag{66}$$

is a mapping from a region G of $\mathbb{R}^n$ into $\mathbb{R}^n$ with $y_1, \ldots, y_n \in C^1(G)$.

THEOREM 18. *Let G be a region of $\mathbb{R}^n$, $n \geq 3$, and let $\sigma : G \to \mathbb{R}^n$ be a mapping (66) with $y_1, \ldots, y_n \in C^3(G)$. If then*

(i) $Y_1^2 \neq 0$,

(ii) $a, b \in \mathbb{R}^n$ *with* $a^2 \neq 0 \neq b^2$ *and* $a \perp b$ *implies*

$$\sum_{\nu=1}^{n} a_\nu Y_\nu \perp \sum_{\nu=1}^{n} b_\nu Y_\nu,$$

holds true for every $(x_1, \ldots, x_n) \in G$, *there exists an automorphism π of the sphere geometry of signature $(\varepsilon_1, \ldots, \varepsilon_n)$ such that σ is the restriction of π on G. In the case $G = \mathbb{R}^n$, σ must be a mapping γ of the form (65). Moreover, it is sufficient to ask* (ii) *only for the following pairs*

$$\alpha) \quad a = E_i, \qquad b = E_j \text{ for } i \neq j,$$
$$\beta) \quad a = E_1 + 2E_i, \quad b = 2E_1 - \varepsilon_i E_i \text{ for } i \geq 2,$$

where we put

$$E_i := (\delta_{i1}, \delta_{i2}, \ldots, \delta_{in}),$$

$i = 1, \ldots, n$.
(For the proof of this theorem see GT, section 3.6.)

6.4 Line geometries

6.4.1 Introduction

Every geometry Δ in which *lines* are defined, leads to a *line geometry*. The set M of lines of a geometry Δ is of interest and many problems arise in connection with those sets M. If M is for instance the set of lines of 3–dimensional real projective space, we may ask for all bijections λ of M such that two lines have a point in common iff the image lines intersect in a point. This is a classical question in line geometry (Plücker geometry, see GT, chapter 5). This question may be posed in many other similar situations, say in the case of affine geometry, of hyperbolic geometry, of Einstein's cylinder universe, of de Sitter's world, and so on. Of course, it is worth while answering even more general questions than that before. For instance: determine all mappings λ of the set M^n of lines of

$\mathbb{R}^n$, $n \geq 3$, into itself such that $\lambda(l_1)$, $\lambda(l_2)$ intersect in a point whenever the lines l_1, l_2 have a point in common. June Lester [2] proved the following

THEOREM 19. *If λ is a bijection of M^3 such that distance 1 between lines is preserved in both directions λ and λ^{-1}, then λ is induced by an isometry of $\mathbb{R}^3$.*
(For a proof see GT, section 5.2.)

In connection with line geometry see also theorems A.3.1, A.6.1, A.6.2 of chapter 5 in GT.

6.4.2 A theorem of Wen–ling Huang

In this section the following theorem of Wen–ling Huang will be proved.

THEOREM 20: *Let $\pi : M^n \to M^n$ be a mapping of the set M^n of lines of $\mathbb{R}^n$, $n \geq 2$, into itself such that the following holds true:*

Whenever $a, b, c \in M^n$ are lines which are sides of a triangle of area 1, then also $\pi(a)$, $\pi(b)$, $\pi(c)$ are sides of a triangle of area 1.

Then π is induced by a congruent mapping (isometry) of $\mathbb{R}^n$ for $n \geq 3$, and it is induced by an equiaffine mapping in the case $n = 2$.

REMARK. In the case that π is bijective, Theorem 20 reduces to a result of June Lester [6]. The problem seems to be much more difficult without bijectivity assumption.

We follow the proof of Theorem 20 as given by Wen–ling Huang in [1]. We shall call $\{a, b, c\} \subset M^n$ a triangle abc iff

(i) a, b, c are in a common plane

and

(ii) $\#a \cap b = \#b \cap c = \#c \cap a = 1$

hold true. The area of abc will be denoted by $\Delta(a, b, c) \geq 0$. We put $\Delta(a, b, c) = 0$ in the case that a, b, c are concurrent lines.

1. Let a, b, c be distinct elements of M^2. Define

$$H_{abc} := \{h \in M^2 \mid \Delta(h, a, b) = 1 = \Delta(h, a, c)\}$$

and observe that the following statements hold true.

(α) $a \parallel b$ or $a \parallel c \Rightarrow H_{abc} = \emptyset$.

(β)   If a, b, c are concurrent lines, then H_{abc} consists of exactly two lines h_1, h_2 with $h_1 \parallel h_2$.

(γ) $a \not\parallel b \parallel c$ implies that H_{abc} consists exactly of two lines h_1, h_2. The lines a, h_1, h_2 are moreover concurrent.

Suppose that $\Delta(a, b, c) =: x > 0$. Define

$$A := b \cap c, \ B := c \cap a, \ C := a \cap b.$$

If $h \in M^2$ is a line with $\Delta(h, a, b) > 0$ and $\Delta(h, a, c) > 0$, then there exist reals α, β with $\alpha \cdot \beta \neq 0$, $\alpha \neq \beta$, and

$$h = \{(1 - \lambda)\alpha(B - C) + \lambda\beta(A - C) + C \mid \lambda \in \mathbb{R}\}.$$

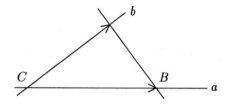

We would like to show that $\Delta(h, a, b) = 1 = \Delta(h, a, c)$ implies that

$$|\alpha\beta| = \frac{1}{x} = (\alpha - 1)^2 \cdot \left| \frac{\beta}{\alpha - \beta} \right| \tag{67}$$

holds true. The vertices of hab are

$$C, \ C + \alpha(B - C), \ C + \beta(A - C).$$

Since

$$\begin{vmatrix} c_1 & c_2 & 1 \\ c_1 + \alpha(b_1 - c_1) & c_2 + \alpha(b_2 - c_2) & 1 \\ c_1 + \beta(a_1 - c_1) & c_2 + \beta(a_2 - c_2) & 1 \end{vmatrix} = \alpha\beta \cdot \begin{vmatrix} c_1 & c_2 & 1 \\ b_1 & b_2 & 1 \\ a_1 & a_2 & 1 \end{vmatrix}$$

by putting $A =: (a_1, a_2)$ etc, we obtain $|\alpha\beta x| = 1$. The vertices of hac are

$$B, \ C + \alpha(B - C), \ B + \beta\frac{\alpha - 1}{\alpha - \beta}(A - B).$$

These points are not on a common line, since $\Delta(h, a, c) = 1$. Hence $\alpha - 1 \neq 0$ and

$$1 = \Delta(h, a, c) = \left| (\alpha - 1) \cdot \beta\frac{\alpha - 1}{\alpha - \beta} \right| \cdot x.$$

Analysing (67), we get the following cases.

(a) $\alpha\beta = \dfrac{1}{x} = (\alpha-1)^2 \cdot \dfrac{\beta}{\alpha-\beta}$. Here we obtain

$$(\alpha,\beta) = \left(\frac{x+1}{2x}, \frac{2}{x+1}\right), 1 \neq x > 0.$$

(Observe that $x = 1$ would lead to $\alpha = \beta$.)

(b) $-\alpha\beta = \dfrac{1}{x} = (\alpha-1)^2 \cdot \dfrac{\beta}{\alpha-\beta}$.

This would imply $\alpha < 0$ and $\alpha > \beta$ for $\beta > 0$, and $\alpha > 0$ and $\alpha < \beta$ for $\beta < 0$. So (b) does not occur.

(c) $\alpha\beta = \dfrac{1}{x} = -(\alpha-1)^2 \cdot \dfrac{\beta}{\alpha-\beta}$. This leads to

$$(\alpha,\beta) \in \left\{ \left(\frac{x+\varepsilon\varphi(x)}{2x}, \frac{2}{x+\varepsilon\varphi(x)}\right) \middle| \varepsilon \in \{1,-1\} \right\}$$

with $x \in (0,2]\backslash\{1\} =: W$ and $\varphi(x) := \sqrt{x(2-x)} \geq 0$.

(d) $\alpha\beta = -\dfrac{1}{x} = (\alpha-1)^2 \cdot \dfrac{\beta}{\alpha-\beta}$. Here we get

$$(\alpha,\beta) = \left(\frac{x-1}{2x}, \frac{2}{1-x}\right)$$

with $x \in V := \{r \in \mathbb{R} \mid 1 \neq r > 0\}$.

2. We remain in the framework of section 1. Put

$$\alpha_1(x) := \frac{x+1}{2x} \quad \text{and} \quad \beta_1(x) := \frac{2}{x+1} \quad \text{for } x \in V,$$

$$\alpha_2(x) := \frac{x-1}{2x} \quad \text{and} \quad \beta_2(x) := \frac{2}{1-x} \quad \text{for } x \in V,$$

$$\alpha_3(x) := \frac{x+\varphi(x)}{2x} \quad \text{and} \quad \beta_3(x) := \frac{2}{x+\varphi(x)} \quad \text{for } x \in W,$$

$$\alpha_4(x) := \frac{x-\varphi(x)}{2x} \quad \text{and} \quad \beta_4(x) := \frac{2}{x-\varphi(x)} \quad \text{for } x \in W.$$

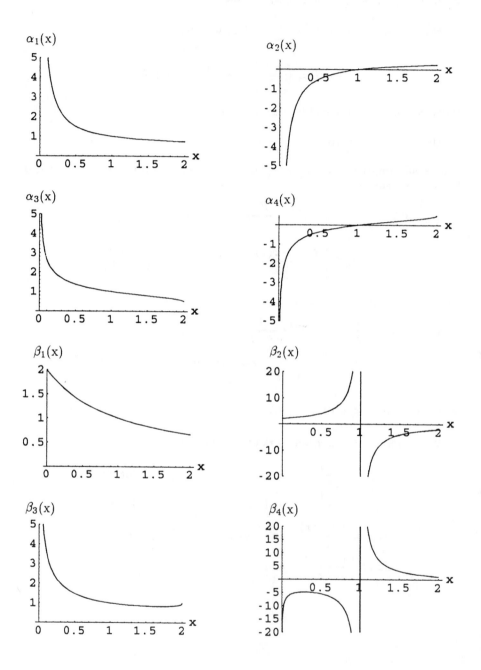

Define $h_1 = h_1^{a,b,c}$ and $h_2 = h_2^{a,b,c}$ by means of

$$h_1 \cap a := \alpha_1(x)(B - C) + C, \quad h_1 \cap b := \beta_1(x)(A - C) + C$$

and

$$h_2 \cap a := \alpha_2(x)(B - C) + C, \quad h_2 \cap b := \beta_2(x)(A - C) + C$$

whenever $\Delta(a, b, c) = x \in V$. Observe that

$$h_1^{a,b,c} = h_2^{a,c,b} \quad \text{and} \quad h_2^{a,b,c} = h_1^{a,c,b}$$

hold true.

For $x = 2$ define $h_i = h_i^{a,b,c}$, $i = 3, 4$, by means of

$$h_3 \cap a := \alpha_3(x)(B - C) + C \;=\; \alpha_4(x)(B - C) + C =: h_4 \cap a,$$
$$h_3 \cap b := \beta_3(x)(A - C) + C \;=\; \beta_4(x)(A - C) + C =: h_4 \cap b.$$

We get $h_3^{a,b,c} = h_4^{a,b,c} = h_3^{a,c,b} = h_4^{a,c,b}$ and moreover that all the lines h_1, h_2, h_3 contain the point

$$C + \frac{2}{5}(A - C) + \frac{3}{10}(B - C).$$

In the case $1 \neq x \in (0, 2)$ the lines $h_3 = h_3^{a,b,c}$ and $h_4 = h_4^{a,b,c}$ are defined by means of

$$h_3 \cap a := \alpha_3(x)(B - C) + C, \quad h_3 \cap b := \beta_3(x)(A - C) + C,$$

and

$$h_4 \cap a := \alpha_4(x)(B - C) + C, \quad h_4 \cap b := \beta_4(x)(A - C) + C.$$

The equations $h_3^{a,b,c} = h_4^{a,c,b}$ and $h_4^{a,b,c} = h_3^{a,c,b}$ are satisfied.

In the case $x > 2$, $H_{abc} = \{h_1, h_2\}$ holds true, and H_{abc} is equal to $\{h_1, h_2, h_3, h_4\}$ whenever $x \in (0, 2)\backslash\{1\}$. Hence

$$(*) \qquad \#H_{abc} = \begin{cases} 0 & x = 1 \\ 2 & x > 2 \\ 3 & \text{for} \quad x = 2 \\ 4 & x \in (0, 2)\backslash\{1\} \end{cases}$$

is satisfied, since

$$\alpha_1(x) \neq \alpha_2(x) \quad \text{for all } x \in V$$

and

$$\alpha_2(x) < \alpha_4(x) < \alpha_3(x) < \alpha_1(x) \quad \text{for all } 1 \neq x \in (0, 2)$$

hold true.

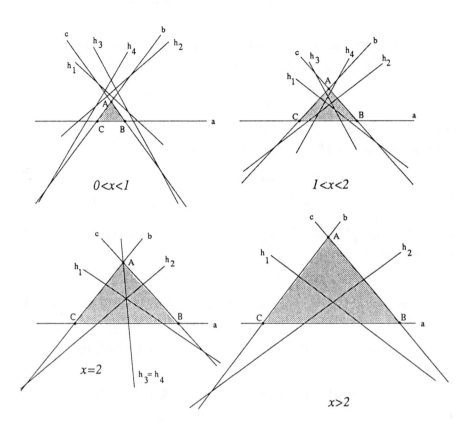

Let abc be a triangle with $\Delta(a,b,c) =: x \in V$. Suppose that h_1, h_2 (and eventually h_3, h_4) are defined as above. If h_i, h_j are lines in H_{abc} with $i \neq j$, then a, h_i, h_j are pairwise distinct. The definition of H_{abc} implies that

$$1 = \Delta(b, a, h_i) = \Delta(b, a, h_j) = \Delta(c, a, h_i) = \Delta(c, a, h_j)$$

holds true. Then $b, c \in H_{ah_i h_j}$. The lines h_i, h_j are not parallel, since otherwise (γ) of section 1 would imply that a, b, c contain a common point, in contradiction to $\Delta(a, b, c) > 0$. Two distinct lines of

$$M := \{a, b, c\} \cup H_{abc}$$

therefore meet in exactly one point. If l_1, l_2, l_3 are distinct lines in M, then $l_1 l_2 l_3$ must be a triangle. Define the following classes (a), (b), (c), (f) of functions:

$$a_1(x) := \Delta(a, h_1, h_2) \quad = \frac{2}{1+x^2} \qquad \text{for } x \in V,$$

$$a_2(x) := \Delta(a, h_1, h_3) \quad = \frac{1 - \varphi(x)}{1 + 2x + \varphi(x)} \qquad \text{for } x \in W,$$

$$a_3(x) := \Delta(a, h_1, h_4) \quad = \frac{1 + \varphi(x)}{1 + 2x - \varphi(x)} \qquad \text{for } x \in W,$$

$$a_4(x) := \Delta(a, h_2, h_3) \quad = a_3(x) \qquad \text{for } x \in W,$$

$$a_5(x) := \Delta(a, h_2, h_4) \quad = a_2(x) \qquad \text{for } x \in W,$$

$$a_6(x) := \Delta(a, h_3, h_4) \quad = \frac{\varphi(x)}{x} \qquad \text{for } x \in W;$$

$$b_1(x) := \Delta(b, h_1, h_2) \quad = 2 - a_1(x) \qquad \text{for } x \in V,$$

$$b_2(x) := \Delta(b, h_1, h_3) \quad = a_2(x) \qquad \text{for } x \in W,$$

$$b_3(x) := \Delta(b, h_1, h_4) \quad = a_3(x) \qquad \text{for } x \in W$$

$$b_4(x) := \Delta(b, h_2, h_3) \quad = 2 - a_3(x) \qquad \text{for } x \in W,$$

$$b_5(x) := \Delta(b, h_2, h_4) \quad = 2 - a_2(x) \qquad \text{for } x \in W,$$

$$b_6(x) := \Delta(b, h_3, h_4) \quad = a_6(x) \qquad \text{for } x \in W;$$

$$c_1(x) := \Delta(c, h_1, h_2) \quad = 2 - a_1(x) \qquad \text{for } x \in V,$$

$$c_2(x) := \Delta(c, h_1, h_3) \quad = 2 - a_2(x) \qquad \text{for } x \in W,$$

$$c_3(x) := \Delta(c, h_1, h_4) \quad = 2 - a_3(x) \qquad \text{for } x \in W$$

$$c_4(x) := \Delta(c, h_2, h_3) \quad = a_3(x) \qquad \text{for } x \in W,$$

$$c_5(x) := \Delta(c, h_2, h_4) \quad = a_2(x) \qquad \text{for } x \in W,$$

$$c_6(x) := \Delta(c, h_3, h_4) \quad = a_6(x) \qquad \text{for } x \in W;$$

$$f_1(x) := \Delta(h_1, h_2, h_3) \quad = \frac{2(2 - x)(x - 1)^2 x}{(x^2 + 1)(5x^2 + 2x + 1)} \qquad \text{for } x \in W,$$

$$f_2(x) := \Delta(h_1, h_3, h_4) \quad = \frac{(x - 1)^2}{1 + 2x + 5x^2} \frac{\varphi(x)}{x} \qquad \text{for } x \in W,$$

$$f_3(x) := \Delta(h_1, h_2, h_4) \quad = f_1(x) \qquad \text{for } x \in W,$$

$$f_4(x) := \Delta(h_2, h_3, h_4) \quad = f_2(x) \qquad \text{for } x \in W,$$

$$f_5(x) := \Delta(b, c, h_1) \quad = \Delta(b, c, h_2) = x \qquad \text{for } x \in V,$$

$$f_6(x) := \Delta(b, c, h_3) \quad = \Delta(b, c, h_4) = 2 - x \qquad \text{for } x \in W.$$

a1(x)

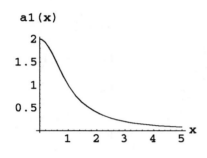

a2(x)

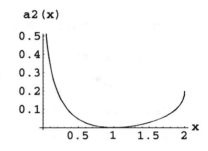

a3(x)

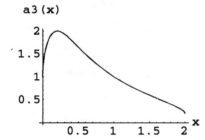

a6(x)

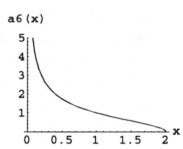

b1(x)

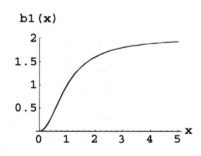

b4(x)

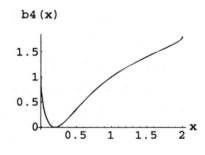

b5(x)

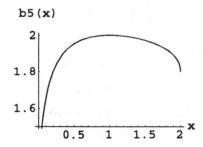

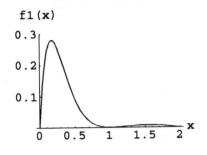

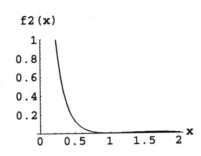

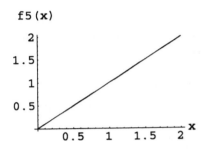

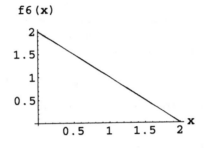

3. Let π be a mapping of M^2 into itself such that the following holds true. If abc is a triangle with $\Delta(a,b,c) = 1$ for $a,b,c \in M^2$, then $\pi(a)\pi(b)\pi(c)$ is a triangle with $\Delta(\pi(a), \pi(b), \pi(c)) = 1$.

(α) Let a,b,c be distinct elements of M^2 such that also $\pi(a), \pi(b), \pi(c)$ are three distinct lines. Then H_{abc} and $H_{\pi(a)\pi(b)\pi(c)}$ are defined and

$$\pi(H_{abc}) \subseteq H_{\pi(a)\pi(b)\pi(c)} \tag{68}$$

holds true.

The proof of (α) follows immediately from the definition of H.

(β) If $a, b \in M^2$ have exactly one point in common, then also $\pi(a), \pi(b)$ intersect in exactly one point.

Proof.   Take $c \in M^2$ such that abc is a triangle with $\Delta(a, b, c) = 1$. This implies that $\pi(a)\pi(b)\pi(c)$ is a triangle of area 1.   □

(γ) π is injective.

Proof.   Assume that $\pi(a) = \pi(b)$ for $a \neq b$ and $a, b \in M^2$. Then a, b must be parallel, in view of (β). Take $g_1, g_2 \in M^2$ such that b, g_1, g_2 are concurrent and such that ag_1g_2 is a triangle of area 1. Hence

$$H_{ag_1g_2} = \emptyset \neq H_{bg_1g_2},$$

in view of (*) (section 2) and (β) (section 1). Now observe that $\pi(a) = \pi(b)$ implies that

$$\Delta\big(\pi(b), \pi(g_1), \pi(g_2)\big) = \Delta\big(\pi(a), \pi(g_1), \pi(g_2)\big) = 1$$

holds true. Hence $H_{\pi(b)\pi(g_1)\pi(g_2)} = \emptyset$. But this contradicts

$$\emptyset \neq \pi(H_{bg_1g_2}) \subseteq H_{\pi(b)\pi(g_1)\pi(g_2)}. \qquad \square$$

(δ) *Let abc be a triangle with* $\Delta(a, b, c) =: x > 0$ *for* $a, b, c \in M^2$. *Then* $\pi(a)\pi(b)\pi(c)$ *is also a triangle of positive area* ξ.

Proof.   Since a, b, c have pairwise exactly one point in common, the same holds true for the images, in view of (β). Hence $\pi(a)\pi(b)\pi(c)$ is a triangle. Assume that $\xi = 0$. Then $x \neq 1$. If $x \in W$, then

$$\#H_{abc} \geq 3 \text{ and } \#H_{\pi(a)\pi(b)\pi(c)} = 2$$

hold true. But this is impossible, since π is injective. If $x > 2$, then (68) and

$$\#H_{abc} = 2 = \#H_{\pi(a)\pi(b)\pi(c)}$$

imply that $\pi(H_{abc}) = H_{\pi(a)\pi(b)\pi(c)}$. The two lines in H_{abc} intersect in exactly one point and the two lines in $H_{\pi(a)\pi(b)\pi(c)}$ are parallel. This contradicts statement (β). $\square$

(ε) *Let abc be a triangle with* $\Delta(a, b, c) =: x \in \left]\dfrac{2}{5}, 2\right]$. *Then*

$$\xi := \Delta\big(\pi(a), \pi(b), \pi(c)\big) \notin \left[0, \dfrac{2}{5}\right].$$

Proof. $x = 1$ implies that $\xi = 1 \notin \left[0, \frac{2}{5}\right]$. So assume that $x \neq 1$. Then $\xi > 0$, in view of (δ).

Case 1: $1 \neq x \in \left]\dfrac{2}{5}, 2\right[$ and $\xi \in \left]0, \dfrac{2}{5}\right]$. Here we have $\#H_{abc} = \#H_{\pi(a)\pi(b)\pi(c)} = 4$, in view of (*), and hence

$$\pi(H_{abc}) = H_{\pi(a)\pi(b)\pi(c)}.$$

Therefore there exist lines $l_1, l_2 \in H_{abc}$ with

$$\pi(l_1) = h_3^{\pi(a),\pi(b),\pi(c)} \text{ and } \pi(l_2) = h_4^{\pi(a),\pi(b),\pi(c)}.$$

Hence

$$\Delta\big(\pi(a), \pi(l_1), \pi(l_2)\big) = \Delta\big(\pi(a), h_3^{\pi(a)\cdots}, h_4^{\pi(a)\cdots}\big) = a_6(\xi) \geq 2,$$

since $\xi \in \left]0, \frac{2}{5}\right]$, and

$$\Delta(a, l_1, l_2) \in \{a_1(x), \ldots, a_6(x)\} \subset (0, 2),$$

since $1 \neq x \in \left]\frac{2}{5}, 2\right[$. This implies that $\#H_{al_1l_2} = 4$ (see $(*)$) holds true, since $\Delta(a, l_1, l_2) = 1$ would lead to $2 \leq \Delta(\pi(a), \pi(l_1), \pi(l_2)) = 1$. Similarly,

$$\#H_{\pi(a)\pi(l_1)\pi(l_2)} \in \{2, 3\},$$

which contradicts

$$\pi(H_{al_1l_2}) \subseteq H_{\pi(a)\pi(l_1)\pi(l_2)}.$$

Case 2: $x = 2$ and $\xi \in \left]0, \frac{2}{5}\right]$. Observe that $\#H_{abc} = 3$ holds true. Put $l_i := h_i^{a,b,c}$, $i = 1, 2, 3$, and moreover $g_i := h_i^{\pi(a),\pi(b),\pi(c)}$ for $i = 1, 2, 3, 4$. (68) implies

$$\{\pi(l_1), \pi(l_2), \pi(l_3)\} \subset \{g_1, g_2, g_3, g_4\}. \tag{69}$$

Observe that

$$\Delta(a, l_1, l_2) = \frac{2}{5} \text{ and } \Delta(a, l_1, l_3) = \frac{1}{5} = \Delta(a, l_2, l_3)$$

is satisfied and therefore

$$\#H_{al_1l_2} = \#H_{al_1l_3} = \#H_{al_2l_3} = 4.$$

$\Delta(\pi(a), g_3, g_4) \geq 2$ implies $\#H_{\pi(a)g_3g_4} \leq 3$. Since π is injective, we get $\{g_3, g_4\} \not\subseteq \{\pi(l_1), \pi(l_2), \pi(l_3)\}$. Otherwise,

$$\pi(H_{al_il_j}) \subseteq H_{\pi(a)g_3g_4}$$

would hold true by putting $\pi(l_i) = g_3$, $\pi(l_j) = g_4$. Hence

$$\{g_1, g_2\} \subset \{\pi(l_1), \pi(l_2), \pi(l_3)\}, \tag{70}$$

in view of (69).

Note that

$$b_1(2) = \frac{8}{5}, \quad b_2(2) = \frac{1}{5}, \quad b_4(2) = \frac{9}{5},$$
$$c_1(2) = \frac{8}{5}, \quad c_2(2) = \frac{9}{5}, \quad c_4(2) = \frac{1}{5}$$

hold true. Also

$$\Delta(\pi(b), g_1, g_2) = \Delta\left(\pi(b), h_1^{\pi(a)\cdots}, h_2^{\pi(a)\cdots}\right) = b_1(\xi) \leq b_1\left(\frac{2}{5}\right) < \frac{2}{5}$$

is satisfied. Since $g_1 = \pi(l_i), g_2 = \pi(l_j)$ with $i, j \in \{1, 2, 3\}$ (see (70)), and

$$\Delta(b, l_i, l_j) = \Delta(b, h_i^{a\cdots}, h_j^{a\cdots}) \in \{b_1(2), b_2(2), b_4(2)\}$$

hold true, and since case 1 implies that a triangle of area $\in \left]\frac{2}{5}, 2\right[\backslash\{1\}$ does not have an image of area $< \frac{2}{5}$, we get $\{\pi(l_1), \pi(l_3)\} = \{g_1, g_2\}$. Similarly, $\{\pi(l_2), \pi(l_3)\} = \{g_1, g_2\}$ because of the fact that $\Delta(\pi(c), g_1, g_2) < \frac{2}{5}$ holds true. This contradicts (γ).   □

REMARKS. 1. $x = 2$ implies that $\#H_{\pi(a)\pi(b)\pi(c)} \geq 3$ and therefore $\xi \in (0, 2], \xi \neq 1$. Case 2 of (ε) then leads to $\xi \in \left]\frac{2}{5}, 2\right]\backslash 1$.

2. Assume that $x = 2$ and that $h_i = h_i^{a,b,c}$, $i = 1, 2, 3$. If $\xi = \Delta(\pi(a), \pi(b), \pi(c)) \in \left[\frac{8}{5}, 2\right[$ and $g_i = h_i^{\pi(a), \pi(b), \pi(c)}$, $i = 1, 2, 3, 4$ hold true, then the statements

$$
\begin{aligned}
\pi(H_{abc}) \quad &\subset \quad H_{\pi(a)\pi(b)\pi(c)}, \\
\Delta(h_1, b, c) \quad &= \quad \Delta(h_2, b, c) \qquad\quad = f_5(x) = x = 2, \\
\Delta(g_1, \pi(b)\pi(c)) \quad &= \quad \Delta(g_2, \pi(b), \pi(c)) = \quad f_5(\xi) = \xi \in \left[\frac{8}{5}, 2\right[, \\
\Delta(g_3, \pi(b), \pi(c)) \quad &= \quad \Delta(g_4, \pi(b), \pi(c)) = \quad f_6(\xi) = 2 - \xi \in \left]0, \frac{2}{5}\right]
\end{aligned}
$$

are satisfied. Hence $\{\pi(h_1), \pi(h_2)\} = \{g_1, g_2\}$.

3. Let a, b, c be distinct and concurrent lines in M^2. Put $\{h_1, h_2\} = H_{abc}$ (see (β) of section 1). If $\xi = \Delta(\pi(a), pi(b), \pi(c)) \in \left]0, \frac{2}{5}\right]$ and $g_i = h_i^{\pi(a), \pi(b), \pi(c)}$, $i = 1, 2, 3, 4$, then

$$
\begin{aligned}
\pi(H_{abc}) \quad &\subset H_{\pi(a)\pi(b)\pi(c)}, \\
\Delta(h_1, b, c) \quad &= \Delta(h_2, b, c) = 2, \\
\Delta(g_1, \pi(b), \pi(c)) \quad &= \Delta(g_2, \pi(b), \pi(c)) = f_5(\xi) = \xi \in \left]0, \frac{2}{5}\right], \\
\Delta(g_3, \pi(b), \pi(c)) \quad &= \Delta(g_4, \pi(b), \pi(c)) = f_6(\xi) = 2 - \xi \in \left[\frac{8}{5}, 2\right[
\end{aligned}
$$

hold true. Hence $\{\pi(h_1), \pi(h_2)\} = \{g_3, g_4\}$.

(ξ) *Let* $a, b, c \in M^2$ *be distinct lines with* $a \nparallel b \parallel c$ *such that* $\pi(a), \pi(b), \pi(c)$ *are sides of a triangle. Then*

$$x := \Delta(\pi(a), \pi(b), \pi(c)) \leq 13.$$

Proof.   Assume that $a, b, c \in M^2$ are distinct lines with $a \nparallel b \parallel c$ and $x = \Delta\big(\pi(a), \pi(b), \pi(c)\big) > 13$.

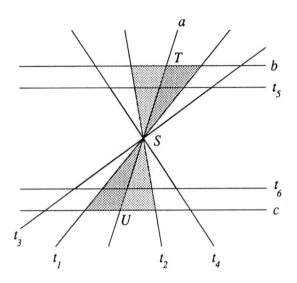

Put $\{t_1, t_2\} = H_{abc}$ (see (γ) of section 1), $\{t_3, a\} = H_{t_1bc}, \{t_4, a\} = H_{t_2bc}$. Without loss of generality we may assume that

$$(0,0) \quad = t_1 \cap t_2 \cap a,$$

$$(m, n) \quad = a \cap b \text{ and hence that}$$

$a \cap c = -(m, n)$. Choose $t_5, t_6 \parallel b$ such that

$$t_5 \cap a = \frac{1}{\sqrt{2}}(m, n) \text{ and } t_6 \cap a = -\frac{1}{\sqrt{2}}(m, n)$$

hold true. Then

$$\Delta(a, t_3, t_5) = \frac{1}{2}\Delta(a, b, t_3) = 1 \text{ and } \Delta(a, t_4, t_5) = \frac{1}{2}\Delta(a, b, t_4) = 1$$

is satisfied and hence $t_5 \in H_{at_3t_4}$. Similarly, $t_6 \in H_{at_3t_4}$. Therefore $\{t_5, t_6\} = H_{at_3t_4}$. Moreover,

$$\Delta(t_1, t_2, t_5) = \frac{1}{2}\Delta(b, t_1, t_2) = 1 \text{ and } \Delta(t_1, t_2, t_6) = \frac{1}{2}\Delta(c, t_1, t_2) = 1$$

hold true. Define

$$C := \pi(a) \cap \pi(b), \ B := \pi(c) \cap \pi(a), \ A := \pi(b) \cap \pi(c).$$

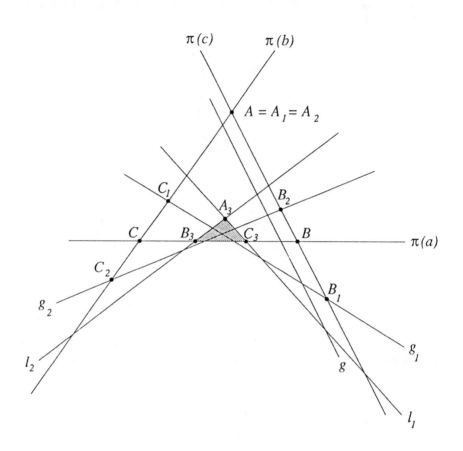

If $g_i := h_i^{\pi(a),\pi(b),\pi(c)}$, $i = 1, 2$, then

$$
\begin{aligned}
g_1 \cap \pi(a) &= \alpha_1(x)(B - C) + C, \\
C_1 := \quad g_1 \cap \pi(b) &= \beta_1(x)(A - C) + C, \\
B_1 := \quad g_1 \cap \pi(c) &= \beta_2(x)(A - B) + B \\
&= \left(1 - \beta_2(x)\right)(B - C) + \beta_2(x)(A - C) + C, \\
g_2 \cap \pi(a) &= \alpha_2(x)(B - C) + C, \\
C_2 := \quad g_2 \cap \pi(b) &= \beta_2(x)(A - C) + C, \\
B_2 := \quad g_2 \cap \pi(c) &= \beta_1(x)(A - B) + B \\
&= \left(1 - \beta_1(x)\right)(B - C) + \beta_1(x)(A - C) + C.
\end{aligned}
$$

Observe that $\Delta(A_1, B_1, C_1) = \Delta\big(g_1, \pi(b), \pi(c)\big)$ and $\Delta(A_2, B_2, C_2) = \Delta\big(g_2, \pi(b), \pi(c)\big)$ with $A_1 := A =: A_2$. If $l_i := h_i^{g_i, \pi(b), \pi(c)}$, $i = 1, 2$, then

$$l_1 \cap g_1 \quad = \alpha_1(x)(B_1 - C_1) + C_1 \quad = \frac{(x+1)^2}{2x(x-1)}(B - C) + \frac{4}{1-x^2}(A - C) + C,$$

$$l_1 \cap \pi(b) \quad = \beta_1(x)(A_1 - C_1) + C_1 \quad = \frac{4x}{(x+1)^2}(A - C) + C$$

and hence

$$C_3 := l_1 \cap \pi(a) = \frac{(x+1)^2}{2(x^2+1)}(B - C) + C.$$

Similarly,

$$l_2 \cap g_2 \quad = \alpha_2(x)(B_2 - C_2) + C_2 \quad = \frac{(x-1)^2}{2x(x+1)}(B - C) + \frac{4}{1-x^2}(A - C) + C,$$

$$l_2 \cap \pi(b) \quad = \beta_2(x)(A_2 - C_2) + C_2 \quad = -\frac{4x}{(x-1)^2}(A - C) + C,$$

and hence

$$B_3 := l_2 \cap \pi(a) = \frac{(x-1)^2}{2(x^2+1)}(B - C) + C.$$

Then

$$A_3 := l_1 \cap l_2 = \frac{(x+1)^2(x-1)^2}{2(x^4+6x^2+1)}(B - C) + \frac{8x^2}{x^4+6x^2+1}(A - C) + C.$$

For the area $\Delta\big(\pi(a), l_1, l_2\big) = \Delta(A_3, B_3, C_3)$ we therefore get

$$y := \Delta\big(\pi(a), l_1, l_2\big) = \frac{16x^4}{(x^2+1)(x^4+6x^2+1)}.$$

It is easy to check that $y(x) < \frac{2}{5}$ for all $x > 13$.

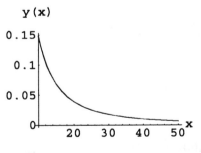

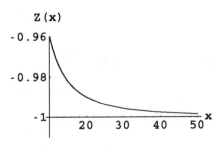

Since

$$\{\pi(t_1), \pi(t_2)\} = \pi(H_{abc}) = H_{\pi(a)\pi(b)\pi(c)} = \{g_1, g_2\},$$

we get

$$\{\pi(t_3), \pi(t_4), \pi(a)\} = \pi(H_{t_1bc}) \cup \pi(H_{t_2bc})$$
$$= H_{\pi(t_1)\pi(b)\pi(c)} \cup H_{\pi(t_2)\pi(b)\pi(c)} = \{l_1, l_2\pi(a)\}$$

and hence $\{\pi(t_3), \pi(t_4)\} = \{l_1, l_2\}$. Therefore $\{t_5, t_6\} = H_{at_3t_4}$, i.e.

$$\pi(t_5), \pi(t_6) \in H_{\pi(a)\pi(t_3)\pi(t_4)} = H_{\pi(a)l_1l_2}.$$

Since $\Delta(a, t_3, t_4) = 0$ and $y = \Delta\big(\pi(a), \pi(t_3), \pi(t_4)\big) \in \left]0, \dfrac{2}{5}\right[$ hold true, we get

$$\{\pi(t_5), \pi(t_6)\} = \{h_3^{\pi(a), l_1, l_2}, h_4^{\pi(a), l_1, l_2}\}$$

from Remark 3. Set $g := h_4^{\pi(a), l_1, l_2}$. Then

$$u_1(x) \cdot (B - C) + C := \quad g \cap \pi(a) \quad = \alpha_4(y)(B_3 - C_3) + C_3,$$
$$g \cap l_1 \quad = \beta_4(y)(A_3 - C_3) + C_3,$$
$$u_2(x) \cdot (A - C) + C := \quad g \cap \pi(b).$$

$u_1(x)$ and $u_2(x)$ are well–defined for $x > 13$. Define $p_i(x), q_i(x), r_i(x)$, $i = 1, 2$, by

$$g_1 \cap g_2 =: p_1(x)(B - C) + p_2(x)(A - C) + C,$$
$$g_2 \cap g =: q_1(x)(B - C) + q_2(x)(A - C) + C,$$
$$g \cap g_1 =: r_1(x)(B - C) + r_2(x)(A - C) + C.$$

Then $\Delta(g, g_1, g_2) = |Z(x)|$ with

$$Z(x) \quad := \quad \begin{vmatrix} p_1(x) & p_2(x) & 1 \\ q_1(x) & q_2(x) & 1 \\ r_1(x) & r_2(x) & 1 \end{vmatrix} \cdot x$$

$$= \quad -\frac{(x^2 - 1)^2(1 + 7x^2 - x^4 + x^6)}{(x^2 + 1)(x^8 + 22x^4 + 8x^2 + 1)}.$$

It is easy to check that $|Z(x)| \neq 1$ for all $x > 13$. Now

$$\Delta(t_5, t_1, t_2) = \Delta(t_6, t_1, t_2)$$

leads to $|Z(x)| = \Delta(g, g_1, g_2) = 1$, since

$$\Delta\big(\pi(t_5), \pi(t_1), \pi(t_2)\big) = \Delta\big(\pi(t_6), \pi(t_1), \pi(t_2)\big) = 1$$

and $\{\pi(t_1), \pi(t_2)\} = \{g_1, g_2\}, g \in \{\pi(t_5), \pi(t_6)\}$ hold true.   □

(η)   *Let $a, b, c \in M^2$ be distinct and concurrent lines. Then $\pi(a), \pi(b)$, $\pi(c)$ are also concurrent.*

Proof.   Assume that $\pi(a), \pi(b), \pi(c)$ are not concurrent. This implies that $\pi(a)\pi(b)\pi(c)$ is a triangle with positive area. Take a line l_1 in H_{abc}.

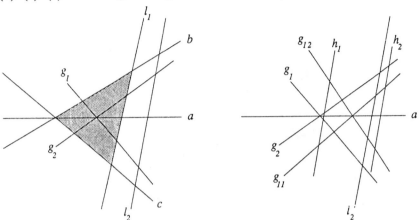

Then $\Delta(l_1, b, c) = 2$. Put $x := \Delta\big(\pi(l_1), \pi(b), \pi(c)\big)$ and observe that x is in $\big]\frac{2}{5}, 2\big]\backslash 1$, in view of Remark 1. If $x = 2$, there exists $g \in H_{l_1 bc}$ with $\pi(g) = h_3^{\pi(l_1), \pi(b), \pi(c)}$. Then $\pi(g), \pi(b), \pi(c)$ must be concurrent and g therefore $\neq a$, since $\pi(a), \pi(b), \pi(c)$ are not concurrent. $g \in H_{l_1 bc}\backslash\{a\}$ now implies that $\Delta(g, b, c) = 2 \neq 0$ holds true which contradicts (δ). The case $x = 2$ is thus impossible and we get $1 \neq x \in \big]\frac{2}{5}, 2\big[$. Put $g_i := h_i^{l_1, b, c}$, $i = 1, 2$, $a = h_3^{l_1, b, c}$. Then

$$\{\pi(a), \pi(g_1), \pi(g_2)\} \subset H_{\pi(l_1)\pi(b)\pi(c)}$$

and hence

$$\Delta\big(\pi(a), \pi(g_1), \pi(g_2)\big) \in \{f_1(x), f_2(x), f_3(x), f_4(x)\}.$$

$1 \neq x \in \big]\frac{2}{5}, 2\big[$ implies $f_i(x) \in \big]0, \frac{2}{5}\big[$ for $i = 1, 2, 3, 4$. Hence

$$\Delta\big(\pi(a), \pi(g_1), \pi(g_2)\big) \in \big]0, \frac{2}{5}\big[. \tag{71}$$

If $l_2 \in H_{ag_1 g_2}$, then $\pi(l_2) \in H_{\pi(a)\pi(g_1)\pi(g_2)}$. The lines a, g_1, g_2 are concurrent. Now Remark 3 and (71) imply that

$$\pi(l_2) \in \{h_i^{\pi(a), \pi(g_1), \pi(g_2)} \mid i \in \{3, 4\}\}.$$

Define

$$\xi := \Delta\big(\pi(l_2), \pi(g_1), \pi(g_2)\big) = 2 - \Delta\big(\pi(a), \pi(g_1), \pi(g_2)\big) \in \left]\tfrac{8}{5}, 2\right[.$$

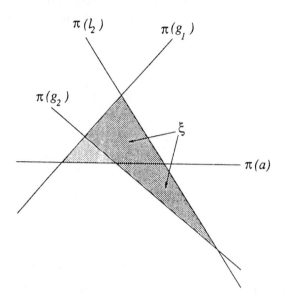

Note that $a = h_3^{l_2, g_1, g_2}$ and choose $g_{1i} := h_i^{l_2, g_1, g_2}$, $i = 1, 2$. Now

$$\Delta(l_2, g_1, g_2) = 2, \ \xi \in \left]\tfrac{8}{5}, 2\right[$$

and Remark 2 imply that

$$\{\pi(g_{11}), \pi(g_{12})\} = \big\{ h_i^{\pi(l_2), \pi(g_1), \pi(g_2)} \mid i \in \{1, 2\} \big\}$$

holds true and hence

$$0 \neq \Delta\big(\pi(a), \pi(g_{11}), \pi(g_{12})\big) = f_1(\xi) < \frac{1}{100}.$$

a, g_{11}, g_{12} are concurrent lines. Put $\{h_1, h_2\} = H_{ag_{11}g_{12}}$. Remark 3 for $\Delta(a, g_{11},$
$g_{12})$ then implies that

$$\{\pi(h_1), \pi(h_2)\} = \big\{ h_i^{\pi(a), \pi(g_{11}), \pi(g_{12})} \mid i \in \{3, 4\} \big\}$$

and hence

$$\Delta\big(\pi(a), \pi(h_1), \pi(h_2)\big) = \Delta\left(\pi(a), h_3^{\pi(a), \pi(g_{11}), \pi(g_{12})}, h_4^{\pi(a), \pi(g_{11}), \pi(g_{12})} \right).$$

Thus

$$\Delta\big(\pi(a), \pi(h_1), \pi(h_2)\big) = a_6\big(f_1(\xi)\big) = \frac{\varphi\big(f_1(\xi)\big)}{f_1(\xi)} \geq \sqrt{199} > 13$$

together with $f_1(\xi) < \frac{1}{100}$. Now $h_2 \parallel h_1 \nparallel a$ contradicts (ξ). $\qquad\square$

(ϑ)   *There exists an equiaffine mapping τ of $\mathbb{R}^2$ such that*

$$\pi(l) = \{\tau(P) \mid P \in l\}$$

holds true for every line l of $\mathbb{R}^2$.

Proof.   (η) implies that to every $P \in \mathbb{R}^2$ there exists exactly one point in $\mathbb{R}^2$, say $\tau(P)$, such that $\pi(l)$ contains $\tau(P)$ whenever P is a point of l. This mapping τ must be equiaffine, in view of Martin's theorem (see section 5.3.1). $\square$

4. With (ϑ) we established the Theorem of Wen–ling Huang in the case $n = 2$. Let us now assume that $n \geq 3$ holds true.

(1) *Let ε_0 be a plane of $\mathbb{R}^n$. Then there exists a uniquely determined plane ε of $\mathbb{R}^n$ such that $\pi(l) \subset \varepsilon$ holds true whenever l is a line in ε_0.*

Proof.   Choose a triangle abc in ε_0 with $\Delta(a, b, c) = 1$.   Then $\Delta\big(\pi(a), \pi(b), \pi(c)\big) = 1$ and $\pi(a), \pi(b), \pi(c)$ are contained in a uniquely determined plane ε. Let $l \notin \{a, b, c\}$ be a line in ε_0.

Case 1. None of the lines a, b, c is parallel to l.

Similar to (β) one shows that $\#[\pi(l_1) \cap \pi(l_2)] = 1$ is a consequence of $\#[l_1 \cap l_2] = 1$ for lines l_1, l_2. The line $\pi(l)$ is therefore contained in ε.

Case 2. The line l is parallel to one of the lines a, b, c.

Without loss of generality assume that $l \parallel a$. This implies $l \nparallel b$ and $l \nparallel c$. Choose a line $g \subset \varepsilon_0$ with

$$\Delta(g, b, c) = 1 \text{ and } g \nparallel a.$$

Then $\pi(g) \subset \varepsilon$, in view of case 1.

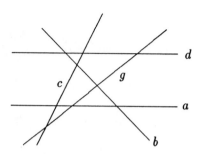

$g \nparallel a$ implies $g \nparallel l$. Then case 1 leads to $\pi(l) \subset \varepsilon$.   □

(2) $a, b \in M^n$ and $a \parallel b \neq a$ imply $\pi(a) \parallel \pi(b) \neq \pi(a)$.

Proof. Denote by ε_0 the plane through a, b. Let ε be the plane as defined in (1). The restriction $\pi \mid \varepsilon_0$ from ε_0 into ε may be considered as a mapping of M^2 into itself, by identifying ε_0 with $\mathbb{R}^2$ and also ε with $\mathbb{R}^2$. Then $\pi \mid \varepsilon_0$ must be equiaffine and it maps especially parallel lines a, b in lines $\pi(a) \parallel \pi(b)$.   □

(3) π is injective.

Proof.   Let $a \neq b$ be lines in M^n with $\pi(a) = \pi(b)$. If a, b are in the same plane ε_0, then, in view of (2), $\pi \mid \varepsilon_0$ is injective, which leads to $\pi(a) \neq \pi(b)$. So the lines a, b are not in a common plane. Let $\varepsilon_1, \varepsilon_2$ be parallel planes with $a \subset \varepsilon_1$ and $b \subset \varepsilon_2$, and let c be a line in ε_2 with $a \parallel c \nparallel b$.

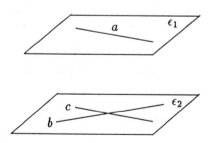

Then (2) implies that $\pi(a) \parallel \pi(c) \neq \pi(a)$. Now $\pi(b) \nparallel \pi(c)$ contradicts $\pi(a) = \pi(b)$.   □

(4) If $a, b, c \in M^n$ are distinct and concurrent lines, then $\pi(a), \pi(b), \pi(c)$ are also concurrent.

Proof.   If $\pi(a), \pi(b), \pi(c)$ are not concurrent, then $\pi(a)\pi(b)\pi(c)$ must be a triangle with positive area. Let $d \in M^n$ be a line $\not\subset \{a, b, c\}$ through $X :=$ $a \cap b \cap c$. Then $\pi(d)$ intersects each of the lines $\pi(a), \pi(b), \pi(c)$. Therefore $\pi(d) \subset \varepsilon$, where ε denotes the plane through $\pi(a), \pi(b), \pi(c)$. If $g \in M^n$ does not contain X, we may choose $l_1, l_2 \in M^n$ with

$$l_1 \cap l_2 = X \text{ and } \Delta(l_1, l_2, g) = 1.$$

The lines $\pi(l_1), \pi(l_2), \pi(g)$ must therefore be in the same plane. Since $\pi(l_1), \pi(l_2)$ are in ε, so is $\pi(g)$. This implies that all lines $l \in M^n$ have their image in ε.

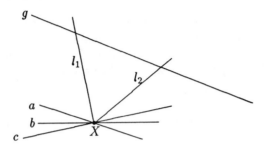

Especially all the lines in ε have their image in ε. But this mapping is already established as equiaffine and hence as bijective. Since π is injective, there would thus not exist images for lines in M^n which are not in ε.   □

(5) *There exists a euclidean motion τ of $\mathbb{R}^n$ such that*

$$\pi(l) = \{\tau(P) \mid P \in l\}$$

holds true for every line l of $\mathbb{R}^n$.

Proof.   (4) implies that to every $P \in \mathbb{R}^n$ there exists exactly one point in $\mathbb{R}^n$, say $\tau(P)$, such that $\pi(l)$ contains $\tau(P)$ whenever P is a point of l. A theorem of June Lester (Theorem 2 of chapter 5) then implies that τ must be a euclidean motion.   □

This finishes the proof of Theorem 20.

6.5   Proportion geometries

6.5.1   Proportion relations, 1–point–invariants

Let $\Sigma^{n,m}$ be the set of all n–dimensional boxes of $\mathbb{R}^m$ ($m \geq n \geq 2$) and let $' \sim '$ be an equivalence relation on $\Sigma^{n,m}$. Two boxes $Q, Q' \in \Sigma^{n,m}$ are called *reciprocal* (see C. Alsina, E. Trillas [1], C. Alsina, W. Benz [1], 293) if they are similar (in the sense that there exists a similarity transformation σ of $\mathbb{R}^m$ with $\sigma(Q) = Q'$), and if there exists an edge of Q which is congruent to an edge of Q'. Reciprocal rectangles are important in arts and in architecture. Examples can be found in many building designs since ancient times. As to the opinion of the artist it is impressive from an aesthetical point of view to see reciprocal rectangles together at a wall, a floor, in a building design. We will call $(\Sigma^{n,m}, \sim)$ a *proportion relation iff*

(*)   *Reciprocal boxes $Q, Q' \in \Sigma^{n,m}$ are always equivalent*

is satisfied. If μ is a euclidean motion of $\mathbb{R}^m$ and if $Q \in \Sigma^{n,m}$, then obviously $Q \sim \mu(Q)$. It is therefore sufficient to represent Q by $(x_1, \ldots, x_n)$, where the x_i, $i = 1, \ldots, n$, are the lengths of the edges of Q. Obviously, a proportion relation $(\Sigma^{n,m}, \sim)$ can also be defined as follows.

Let ' $\sim$ ' be an equivalence relation on

$$S^n := \{(x_1, \ldots, x_n) \in \mathbb{R}^n \mid all\ x_i\ positive\} \qquad (72)$$

such that

(1) $x = (x_1, \ldots, x_n) \sim (x_{\sigma(1)}, \ldots, x_{\sigma(n)})$ *for all $x \in S^n$ and all permutations σ of $\{1, \ldots, n\}$,*

(2) $(x_1, \ldots, x_n) \sim \dfrac{x_n}{x_1} \cdot x$ *for all $x \in S^n$*

hold true.

From now on we prefer to work with $(S^n, \sim)$ instead of $(\Sigma^{n,m}, \sim)$. The structure $(S^n, \sim)$ will also be called a proportion relation.

PROPOSITION 21. *Let G be a group of bijections of $S^n (n \geq 2)$ such that*

(i) *For every permutation σ of $\{1, \ldots, n\}$,*

$$g_\sigma(x) := (x_{\sigma(1)}, \ldots, x_{\sigma(n)})$$

(for all $x = (x_1, \ldots, x_n) \in S^n$) is in G,

(ii) $g_0(x) = \dfrac{x_n}{x_1} \cdot x$ *(for all $x \in S^n$) is in G*

hold true. Then $(S^n, \sim)$ *is a proportion relation where we put*

$$x \sim y \Leftrightarrow \exists_g \in G \quad y = g(x)$$

for all $x, y \in S^n$.

Proof. Obvious.

Let G be a group as described in Proposition 21. We then call (S^n, G) a *proportion geometry*. An important notion for proportion geometries is that of a 1–*point–invariant*. Obviously, S^n is an invariant notion of (S^n, G). A 1–point–invariant

$$h : S^n \to W,$$

where $W \neq \emptyset$ is a set, has to satisfy

(i)* $h(x_1, \ldots, x_n) = h(x_{\sigma(1)}, \ldots, x_{\sigma(n)}),$

and

(ii)* $h(x_1, \ldots, x_n) = h\left(\dfrac{x_n}{x_1} \cdot x_1, \ldots, \dfrac{x_n}{x_1} \cdot x_n\right)$

for all $(x_1, \ldots, x_n) \in S^n$ and for all permutations σ of $\{1, 2, \ldots, n\}$. This is obvious because

$$h(x) = h\big(g(x)\big)$$

holds true for all $x \in S^n$ and for all $g \in G$. In the case $n = 2$ the equations (i)*, (ii)* reduce to

$$h(x, y) = h(y, x)$$

and

$$h(x, y) = h\left(y, \dfrac{y^2}{x}\right)$$

for all $(x, y) \in S^2$.

REMARKS. 1) Other groups may be defined in our context: let $G(\sim)$ be the group of all bijections γ of S^n of a proportion relation $(S^n, \sim)$ such that $x \sim x'$ holds true iff $\gamma(x) \sim \gamma(x')$ is satisfied for all $x, x' \in S^n$. The group $G(\sim)$ is the group $G(N)$ (in the sense of section 1.2) where N is the set of all equivalence classes of $(S^n, \sim)$ with

$$\varphi(\pi, T) := \{\pi(t) \mid t \in T\}$$

for $T \subseteq S^n$ and $\pi \in \text{Perm } S^n$. Also the group $G(h)$ may be considered in the case that $h : S^n \to W$ satisfies (i)* and (ii)*.

2) Every $h : S^n \to W$ which satisfies (i)* and (ii)* induces a proportion relation: put $x \sim y$ for $x, y \in S^n$ iff $h(x) = h(y)$ holds true. Conversely, if $(S^n, \sim)$ is a proportion relation, define W to be the set of all equivalence classes and put

$$h(x) = w \in W \Leftrightarrow x \in w$$

for all $x \in S^n$. Then $h : S^n \to W$ satisfies (i)* and (ii)*.

6.5.2 Proportion functions in two variables

The following definition is due to C. Alsina, E. Trillas [1] and C. Alsina [1]: *let I be the intervall*

$$I = [1, \infty[:= \{t \in \mathbb{R} \mid 1 \le t\}$$

and let D be the set S^2. A proportion function in two variables is then a function

$$f : D \to I$$

which satisfies

$$f(x, y) = f\left(\frac{y^2}{x}, y\right), \tag{73}$$

$$f(x, y) = f(y, x), \tag{74}$$

$$f(x, x) = 1 \tag{75}$$

for all positive x and y.

Suppose that x and y are positive real numbers. Then the classical proportion function in two variables, the so-called rectangle proportion, is given by

$$p(x, y) := \frac{\max\{x, y\}}{\min\{x, y\}}. \tag{76}$$

This is certainly the classical proportion of x, y with the agreement that the maximal number of $x \ne y$ is written in the nominator and the remaining one in the denominator. Obviously, $p(x, y)$ is a solution of the functional equations (73), (74), (75). Two rectangles Q, Q' of $\mathbb{R}^2$ are *reciprocal* if they are similar and if there exists an edge e of Q which is congruent to an edge e' of Q'. Let us put Q and Q' together in $\mathbb{R}^2$ such that e and e' coincide.

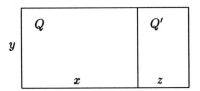

Since Q, Q' are similar, we get with the notations of the figure above

$$\frac{y}{x} \in \left\{ \frac{y}{z}, \frac{z}{y} \right\},$$

i.e. $z = x$ or $z = \dfrac{y^2}{x}$. So in the nontrivial case $z \neq x$ we obtain

$$z = \frac{y^2}{x} \text{ and } x \neq y.$$

This case of two reciprocal rectangles can easily be constructed.

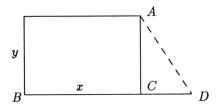

Let D be the point on the line B, C such that D, A is orthogonal to A, B. The distance between C and D is then $\dfrac{y^2}{x}$.

We would now like to characterize all proportion functions. Define

$$G := \{(x, \gamma x^2) \in \mathbb{R}^2 \mid 0 < x \leq 1 \text{ and } 0 < \gamma < 1\}.$$

The following theorem is due to W. Benz [6], Z. Moszner [1]:

THEOREM 22. *Suppose that $\varphi : G \to I$ is an arbitrary function. Then there exists one and only one proportion function $f = f(\varphi)$ such that the restriction of f on G is φ.*

Proof.   1) Denote as usual by $[a]$ the greatest integer less than or equal to $a \in \mathbb{R}$. Let $\varphi : G \to I$ be a function and assume that there exists a proportion function f such that the restriction $f \mid G$ of f on G is equal to φ. We would like to show that f is uniquely determined. If $x = y > 0$, we have $f(x, y) = 1$ because of (75). Put

$$\nu := -\left[\frac{\ln x}{\ln \frac{y}{x}}\right] \tag{77}$$

for $x > y > 0$. Then ν is the only integer satisfying

$$\frac{y}{x} < \left(\frac{y}{x}\right)^{\nu} \cdot x \le 1. \tag{78}$$

Put $t := \frac{y}{x}$. Then (73), (74) imply that

$$f(x, tx) = f(tx, t^2 x) = f(t^2 x, t^3 x) = \ldots$$

and

$$f(x, tx) = f(t^{-1} x, x) = f(t^{-2} x, t^{-1} x) = \ldots \,.$$

We hence have

$$f(x, y) = f(t^{\nu} x, t^{\nu+1} x)$$

and thus

$$f(x, y) = \varphi(t^{\nu} x, t^{\nu+1} x)$$

in view of $(t^{\nu} x, t^{\nu+1} x) \in G$ from (78). The remaining case $y > x > 0$ can be reduced to the former one, since $f(x, y) = f(y, x)$. The function f is therefore uniquely determined by φ.

2) Suppose that $\varphi : G \to I$ is a function. We then would like to construct a proportion function f with $f \mid G = \varphi$. For this purpose put $f(x, x) = 1$ for all $x > 0$, and in the case $x > y > 0$ put

$$f(x, y) := \varphi(t^{\nu} x, t^{\nu+1} x), \; t := \frac{y}{x}$$

with the integer ν of (77). When $y > x > 0$ define $f(x, y) := f(y, x)$. We shall then show that $f : D \to I$ is a proportion function. Notice first of all that f is well–defined: this is a consequence of the fact that the integer ν in (78) is uniquely determined in dependence of x, y with $x > y > 0$. Equations (74), (75) hold true. For a point $(x, y) \in G$ we have $x > y > 0$ and

$$\nu = -\left[\frac{\ln x}{\ln \frac{y}{x}}\right] = 0.$$

Hence $f(x, y) = \varphi(t^0 x, t^{0+1} x) = \varphi(x, y)$ and $f \mid G = \varphi$. Equation (73) holds true for $x = y$. Case $x > y > 0$. Here we have $f(x, y) = \varphi(t^{\nu} x, t^{\nu+1} x)$ with $t := \frac{y}{x}$, $\nu \in \mathbb{Z}$,

$$\frac{y}{x} < \left(\frac{y}{x}\right)^{\nu} \cdot x \le 1.$$

Obviously,

$$\frac{y^2/x}{y} < \left(\frac{y^2/x}{y}\right)^{\nu-1} \cdot y \le 1.$$

Hence by observing that $y > y^2/x$,

$$f\left(\frac{y^2}{x}, y\right) = f\left(y, \frac{y^2}{x}\right) = \varphi\left(\left(\frac{y^2/x}{y}\right)^{\nu-1} \cdot y, \left(\frac{y^2/x}{y}\right)^{\nu} \cdot y\right)$$

$$= \varphi\left(\left(\frac{y}{x}\right)^{\nu} \cdot x, \left(\frac{y}{x}\right)^{\nu+1} \cdot x\right) = f(x, y).$$

For $y > x > 0$ we get $y^2/x > y$ and hence

$$f\left(\frac{y^2}{x}, y\right) = f\left(\frac{y^2}{y^2/x}, y\right) = f(x, y)$$

by applying the case before. Thus (73) holds true for all $(x, y) \in D$. □

Let $g : I \to I$ be a function with $g(1) = 1$ and let $p(x, y)$ be the classical proportion function (76). Then

$$f(x, y) := g\Big(p(x, y)\Big) \tag{79}$$

is obviously a proportion function. The following proposition characterizes these functions:

PROPOSITION 23. *A proportion function f is of the form (79) if and only if*

$$\lim_{x \to 0+} f(x, tx) \tag{80}$$

exists for all $t \in]0, 1[$.

Proof. Suppose that f is a proportion function such that (80) exists for all t with $0 < t < 1$. Define

$$g(s) := \lim_{x \to 0+} f\left(x, \frac{1}{s} \cdot x\right) \text{ for } s \in I. \tag{81}$$

g is a function from I into I with $g(1) = 1$, since (80) exists also for $t = 1$ from (75). Hence (79) holds true for $x = y > 0$. For a point $(x, y) \in D$ with $x > y$ put again $t := \frac{y}{x}$. Then $0 < t < 1$ and

$$f(x, y) = f(x, tx) = \ldots = f(t^n x, t^{n+1} x)$$

for all $n \in \{0, 1, 2, \ldots\}$. Hence

$$f(x, y) = \lim_{n \to \infty} f(t^n x, t \cdot t^n x) = g\left(\frac{1}{t}\right)$$

by (81), i.e.

$$f(x, y) = g\left(\frac{x}{tx}\right) = g\left(\frac{\max\{x, y\}}{\min\{x, y\}}\right). \tag{82}$$

For $y > x > 0$ we get

$$f(x, y) = f(y, x) = g\Big(p(x, y)\Big)$$

by applying (82). $\square$

REMARK. Let $\varphi : G \to I$ be a function and denote by f the proportion function with $f \mid G = \varphi$. Then, obviously, the following statements are equivalent

(a) f is of the form (79),

(b) φ is homogeneous in G, i.e. $\varphi(x, y) = \varphi(sx, sy)$ holds true for all real x, y, s such that (x, y) and (sx, sy) are points in G,

(c) $\varphi(x, y) = \varphi(sx, sy)$ is satisfied for all $(x, y) \in G$ and $s \in \;] \frac{y}{x^2}, \frac{1}{x} \,]$.

REMARK. Proposition 23 is due to W. Benz [7], Z. Moszner, B. Nawolska [1].

6.5.3   A generalization

Suppose that $D \neq \emptyset$ and $I \neq \emptyset$ are abstract sets and that $B \neq \emptyset$ is a set of bijections β of D. Define

$$F := \{x \in D \mid x = \beta(x) \text{ for all } \beta \in B\}. \tag{83}$$

Let M be a subset of F and let ε be a fixed element of I. We then ask for all functions $f : D \to I$ such that

$$
\begin{aligned}
f(x) &= f\Big(\beta(x)\Big) \text{ for all } x \in D \text{ and all } \beta \in B, &\tag{84}\\
f(x) &= \varepsilon \text{ for all } x \in M &\tag{85}
\end{aligned}
$$

hold true.

In the special case $D := S^2$ and $I := [1,\infty[$ and furthermore $\varepsilon := 1$, $B := \{\alpha, \beta\}$ with

$$\alpha(x, y) := (y, x), \quad \beta(x, y) := \left(\frac{y^2}{x}, y\right) \tag{86}$$

we get the proportion functions f if we put

$$M := \{(x, x) \in \mathbb{R}^2 \mid x > 0\}.$$

Notice that in this special case $\alpha = \alpha^{-1}$ and $\beta = \beta^{-1}$ hold true.

Returning to the general situation, (84) yields

$$f\Big(\beta^{-1}(x)\Big) = f\Big(\beta\big(\beta^{-1}(x)\big)\Big) = f(x)$$

for all $x \in D$ and $\beta \in B$. Denoting

$$B \cup \{\beta^{-1} \mid \beta \in B\}$$

by B' we obtain

$$f(x) = f\Big(\gamma(x)\Big) \text{ for all } x \in D \text{ and all } \gamma \in B'.$$

If $\gamma_1, \gamma_2 \in B'$ then also

$$f\Big(\gamma_1\big(\gamma_2(x)\big)\Big) = f\Big(\gamma_2(x)\Big) = f(x).$$

Let $\overline{B}$ be the group of bijections generated by the set B and denote by $[x]$ the orbit

$$[x] := \{\delta(x) \mid \delta \in \overline{B}\}$$

of $x \in D$ under $\overline{B}$. Obviously, $[x] = \{x\}$ for all $x \in F$. We therefore have

PROPOSITION 24. *All functions $f : D \to I$ satisfying (84), (85) are given as follows: let*

$$\Phi : \{[x] \mid x \in D\} \to I$$

be an arbitrary function with

$$\Phi([x]) = \varepsilon \text{ for all } x \in M.$$

Then define $f : D \to I$ by means of

$$f(x) := \Phi\big([x]\big) \text{ for } x \in D.$$

The following proposition can easily be verified:

PROPOSITION 25: *The group $\overline{B}$ generated by the mappings α, β of (86) is given by*

$$\overline{B} = C \cup \alpha C,$$

where $C := \{(\alpha\beta)^n \mid n \in \mathbb{Z}\}$ is a subgroup of $\overline{B}$ of index 2. It is

$$(\alpha\beta)^n (x, y) = \left(\frac{y}{x}\right)^n \cdot (x, y)$$

and

$$(\alpha\beta)^n \alpha = \alpha \cdot (\alpha\beta)^{-n}$$

satisfied for all $n \in \mathbb{Z}$ and all $(x, y) \in D$. The group $\overline{B}$ is a group of birational transformations, acting on D.

REMARK. If $x > y > 0$, then

$$(\alpha\beta)^\nu (x, y) \in G$$

holds true where ν is the number as defined in (77).

6.5.4   Continuous proportion functions

Define

$$H := \{(x, \gamma x^2) \in \mathbb{R}^2 \mid 0 < x \le 1 \text{ and } 0 < \gamma \le 1\}.$$

With the set G of section 6.5.2 we get

$$H = G \cup \{(x, x^2) \in \mathbb{R}^2 \mid 0 < x \le 1\}$$

and

$$H = \overline{G} \backslash \{(x, 0) \in \mathbb{R}^2 \mid x \in [0, 1]\},$$

where $\overline{G}$ denotes the topological closure of G. Suppose that the proportion function $f : D \to I$ is continuous in D. Then the restriction $\varphi := f \mid H$ of f on H satisfies

(i) $\varphi(1, 1) = 1$,

(ii) $\varphi(t, t^2) = \varphi(1, t)$ for all $t \in \,]0, 1[$,

(iii) φ is continuous in H.

THEOREM 26. *Suppose that* $\varphi : H \to I$ *is an arbitrary function satisfying* (i), (ii), (iii). *Then* $f = f(\varphi \mid G)$ *must be continuous and* $f \mid H = \varphi$.

Proof.   In view of Theorem 22 there exists exactly one proportion function f with $f \mid G = \varphi \mid G$. Because of (i) and (ii) we also have $f \mid H = \varphi$. It remains to prove that f is continuous in D. In view of (74) it remains to show that

a) f is continuous in (x, y) with $x > y > 0$,

b) f is continuous in (x, x) with $x > 0$.

Case a).   Let (x_μ, y_μ), $\mu = 1, 2, 3, \ldots$, be a sequence with $x_\mu > y_\mu > 0$ such that (x_μ, y_μ) tends to (x, y). Put

$$\nu := - \left[\frac{ln\, x}{ln\, y/x} \right] \text{ and } \nu(\mu) := - \left[\frac{ln\, x_\mu}{ln\, y_\mu/x_\mu} \right].$$

Since ln is a continuous function, we have

$$\nu(\mu) \in \{\nu, \nu + 1\}$$

from a positive integer μ_0 on.

Case a$_1$). $\frac{ln\, x}{ln\, y/x}$ is not an integer.

Then we have $\nu(\mu) = \nu$ from μ_0 on. Hence

$$f(x_\mu, y_\mu) = \varphi \left(\left(\frac{y_\mu}{x_\mu} \right)^{\nu(\mu)} \cdot x_\mu, \left(\frac{y_\mu}{x_\mu} \right)^{\nu(\mu)+1} \cdot x_\mu \right) \to f(x, y)$$

because of (iii).

Case a$_2$). $\frac{ln\, x}{ln\, y/x} = -\nu$.

Here we have $(y/x)^\nu \cdot x = 1$ and hence

$$f(x, y) = \varphi \left(\left(\frac{y}{x} \right)^\nu \cdot x, \left(\frac{y}{x} \right)^{\nu+1} \cdot x \right) = \varphi \left(1, \frac{y}{x} \right).$$

If necessary, we shall divide the sequence (x_ν, y_ν) in two sequences

$$(x_{\mu(i_1)}, y_{\mu(i_1)}), \quad (x_{\mu(i_2)}, y_{\mu(i_2)}), \quad \cdots$$
$$(x_{\mu(j_1)}, y_{\mu(j_1)}), \quad (x_{\mu(j_2)}, y_{\mu(j_2)}), \quad \cdots$$

according to $\nu(\mu) = \nu$ or $\nu(\mu) = \nu+1$. For the members of the first subsequence we obtain

$$f(x_\mu, y_\mu) \;=\; \varphi\left(\left(\frac{y_\mu}{x_\mu}\right)^{\nu(\mu)} \cdot x_\mu, \left(\frac{y_\mu}{x_\mu}\right)^{\nu(\mu)+1} \cdot x_\mu\right)$$

$$=\; \varphi\left(\left(\frac{y_\mu}{x_\mu}\right)^{\nu} \cdot x_\mu, \left(\frac{y_\mu}{x_\mu}\right)^{\nu+1} \cdot x_\mu\right) \to \varphi\left(1, \tfrac{y}{x}\right) = f(x, y),$$

and for the members of the second subsequence

$$f(x_\mu, y_\mu) \;=\; \varphi\left(\left(\frac{y_\mu}{x_\mu}\right)^{\nu+1} \cdot x_\mu, \left(\frac{y_\mu}{x_\mu}\right)^{\nu+2} \cdot x_\mu\right) \to \varphi\left(\frac{y}{x}, \left(\frac{y}{x}\right)^2\right)$$

$$=\; \varphi\left(1, \tfrac{y}{x}\right) = f(x, y)$$

by observing (ii). Hence together $f(x_\mu, y_\mu) \to f(x, y)$.

Case b). We start again with a sequence $(x_\mu, y_\mu) \to (x, x)$ with $x_\mu > y_\mu > 0$ without loss of generality. Observe (78), i.e.

$$\frac{y_\mu}{x_\mu} < \left(\frac{y_\mu}{x_\mu}\right)^{\nu(\mu)} \cdot x_\mu \leq 1.$$

Hence

$$\lim_{\mu \to \infty} \left(\frac{y_\mu}{x_\mu}\right)^{\nu(\mu)} \cdot x_\mu = 1$$

and thus

$$f(x_\mu, y_\mu) = \varphi\left(\left(\frac{y_\mu}{x_\mu}\right)^{\nu(\mu)} \cdot x_\mu, \left(\frac{y_\mu}{x_\mu}\right)^{\nu(\mu)+1} \cdot x_\mu\right) \to \varphi(1, 1). \qquad \square$$

REMARK. Concerning Theorem 26 see W. Benz [7], Z. Moszner [1], Z. Moszner, B. Nawolska [1].

6.5.5   Proportion polynomials

A polynomial in two variables with real coefficients is said to be a proportion polynomial of class C^0 iff $\varphi(1, 1) = 1$, $\varphi(\xi, \eta) \geq 1$ for all $(\xi, \eta) \in H$, and $\varphi(t, t^2) = \varphi(1, t)$ for all $t \in \,]0, 1[$. Since a polynomial is continuous in H, proportion polynomials define continuous proportion functions. An example is the polynomial

$$\varphi(x, y) = 1 + (1 - x)(x^2 - y). \tag{87}$$

The most general polynomial $\varphi(x,y)$ of degree ≤ 3 over $\mathbb{R}$ which satisfies $\varphi(1,1) = 1$ and $\varphi(t,t^2) = \varphi(1,t)$ for all $t \in]0,1[$ is given by

$$\varphi(x,y) = 1 + (a + bx + c)(1 - x) + (ax + by + c)(x^2 - y), \qquad (88)$$

where a, b, c are real numbers.

Because of Theorem 26 there exists exactly one continuous proportion function f such that $f \mid H = \varphi$, where φ is supposed to be polynomial (87). We would like to show that f is not of the form (79). In view of Proposition 23, this will be proved if we find a $t \in]0,1[$ such that

$$\lim_{x \to 0+} f(x, tx) \qquad (89)$$

does not exist. We would like to show more: for every $t \in]0,1[$ (89) does not exist. In fact, take a $t \in]0,1[$ and a positive real number λ which is supposed to be unequal to t^g for all $g \in \mathbb{Z}$. Then

$$f(t^n, t \cdot t^n) = f(1, t) \to f(1, t) = \varphi(1, t) = 1$$

for $n \to \infty$ and

$$f\left(\frac{1}{\lambda}t^n, t \cdot \frac{1}{\lambda}t^n\right) = f\left(\frac{1}{\lambda}, \frac{1}{\lambda}t\right) \xrightarrow[n\to\infty]{} f\left(\frac{1}{\lambda}, \frac{1}{\lambda}t\right)$$
$$= \varphi\left(t^\nu \cdot \frac{1}{\lambda}, t^{\nu+1} \cdot \frac{1}{\lambda}\right)$$

with $t < t^\nu \cdot \frac{1}{\lambda} \leq 1$ and $\nu \in \mathbb{Z}$. Because of the construction of λ we obtain $t^\nu \cdot \frac{1}{\lambda} < 1$ and hence

$$\varphi\left(t^\nu \cdot \frac{1}{\lambda}, t^{\nu+1} \cdot \frac{1}{\lambda}\right) = 1 + t^\nu \cdot \frac{1}{\lambda}\left(t^\nu \cdot \frac{1}{\lambda} - t\right) \cdot \left(1 - t^\nu \cdot \frac{1}{\lambda}\right) > 1.$$

Thus $\lim_{x \to 0+} f(x, tx)$ does not exist.

A polynomial $\varphi(x,y)$ of the ring $\mathbb{R}[x,y]$ of all polynomials in two variables over $\mathbb{R}$ is said to be a proportion polynomial of class C^i where i is a non–negative integer if and only if the proportion function $f(\varphi)$ is of class $C^i(D)$.

According to (88), the extension $f(\varphi)$ of $\varphi(x,y) = 1 + x^2 - y$ is not of class C^0. In section 6.5.6 we shall realize that the extension of the polynomial (87) which is of class C^0, is not of class C^1.

6.5.6   The general C^1–solution

PROPOSITION 27. *Suppose that the proportion function f has continuous partial derivatives f_x, f_y in D. Define $\varphi := f \mid H$. Then the following properties hold true: (i), (ii), (iii) (see section 6.5.4) and*

(iv) φ_x, φ_y exist and are continuous in $H_1 := H\backslash\{(1,1)\}$,

(v) the limits of $\dfrac{\varphi(x,y)-1}{x-y}, \varphi_x(x,y), \varphi_y(x,y)$ and $\dfrac{x\varphi_x(x,y)+y\varphi_y(x,y)}{x-y}$ exist for $(x,y) \to (1,1)$ with $(x,y) \in H_1$ and they are all 0,

(vi) $\left(\varphi_x(t,t^2), \varphi_y(t,t^2)\right) = \left(\varphi_x(1,t), \varphi_y(1,t)\right) \begin{pmatrix} \dfrac{2}{t} & -\dfrac{1}{t^2} \\ 1 & 0 \end{pmatrix}$ for all $t \in\,]0,1[$.

Proof.   Properties (i) to (iv) are obvious. The equation

$$f(x,y) = f(y,x) = f\left(\frac{x^2}{y}, x\right)$$

implies that

$$\left(f_x(x,y), f_y(x,y)\right) = \left(f_x\left(\frac{x^2}{y}, x\right), f_y\left(\frac{x^2}{y}, x\right)\right) \cdot \begin{pmatrix} \dfrac{2x}{y} & -\dfrac{x^2}{y^2} \\ 1 & 0 \end{pmatrix}$$

for all $(x,y) \in D$ and hence (vi) for $x = t$ and $y = t^2$ with $t \in\,]0,1[$. The matrix equation also yields $f_y(a,a) = -f_x(a,a)$, i.e. $f_x(a,a) = 0 = f_y(a,a)$, since $f(x,y) = f(y,x)$ implies that $f_x(x,y) = f_y(y,x)$. Therefore

$$\varphi_x(x,y) = f_x(x,y) \to 0 \text{ and } \varphi_y(x,y) = f_y(x,y) \to 0$$

for $(x,y) \to (1,1)$ with $(x,y) \in H_1$. Observe furthermore that

$$f(x,y) = f(1,1) + (x-1)f_x(q) + (y-1)f_y(q)$$

with $q := \left(1 + \delta \cdot (x-1), 1 + \delta \cdot (y-1)\right)$ and $\delta(x,y) \in\,]0,1[$ for $(x,y) \in D$. Hence

$$\frac{\varphi(x,y)-1}{x-y} = \frac{x-1}{x-y}f_x(q) + \frac{y-1}{x-y}f_y(q)$$

for $(x,y) \in H_1$. Now $0 < x \le 1$ and $y \le x^2$ with $(x,y) \ne (1,1)$ imply $0 \le 1-x \le 1-\frac{y}{x} > 0$ and hence

$$\left|\frac{x-1}{x-y}\right| = \frac{1}{x} \cdot \frac{1-x}{1-\frac{y}{x}} \le \frac{1}{x},$$

$$\left|\frac{y-1}{x-y}\right| = \left|\frac{x-1}{x-y} - 1\right| \le \frac{1}{x} + 1.$$

Consequently, $\frac{\varphi(x,y)-1}{x-y} \to 0$ for $(x,y) \to (1,1), (x,y) \in H_1$, since

$$f_x(q) \to f_x(1,1) = 0, \quad f_y(q) \to f_y(1,1) = 0.$$

We finally have to prove

$$\lim \frac{u\varphi_x(u,v) + v\varphi_y(u,v)}{u-v} = 0$$

for $(u,v) \to (1,1)$ with $(u,v) \in H_1$. This will be done in two steps. 1) Put

$$q_n := \left(\frac{y}{x}\right)^n \cdot (x,y)$$

for $n \in \mathbb{Z}$ and $(x,y) \in D$. Then $f(x,y) = f(q_n)$ and hence

$$f_x(x,y) = f_x(q_n) \cdot (1-n)\left(\frac{y}{x}\right)^n - f_y(q_n) \cdot n \left(\frac{y}{x}\right)^{n+1}. \tag{90}$$

Assume from now on that $x > y$ and take for n in (90) one of the integers ν or $\nu + 1$ (see (77)). Consider a sequence $(x,y) \to (2,2)$ (we omit the indices of the sequence). Hence

$$f_x(x,y) \to f_x(2,2) \;= 0, \left(\frac{y}{x}\right)^n \cdot x \to 1,$$

$$f_x(q_n) \to f_x(1,1) \;= 0, \left(\frac{y}{x}\right)^n \to \frac{1}{2}$$

and (90) imply that

$$n \cdot \left[\varphi_x(q_n) + \frac{y}{x}\varphi_y(q_n)\right] \to 0 \tag{91}$$

from $f_t(q_n) = \varphi_t(q_n)$ for $t \in \{x,y\}$. (77) yields

$$n =: \frac{\ln x}{\ln x/y} + \delta(x,y), \quad \delta(x,y) \in [0,1].$$

This and (91) imply that

$$\frac{1}{\ln x/y}\left[\varphi_x(q_n) + \frac{y}{x}\varphi_y(q_n)\right] \to 0, \tag{92}$$

since $\ln x \to \ln 2 \neq 0$ and $\varphi_t(q_n) \to 0$ for $t \in \{x,y\}$. Observing that $x > y > 0$ and that

$$\frac{\ln x/y}{\left(\frac{y}{x}\right)^n x - \left(\frac{y}{x}\right)^{n+1} x} \to 1,$$

we get

$$\frac{\left(\frac{y}{x}\right)^n x \cdot \varphi_x(q_n) + \left(\frac{y}{x}\right)^{n+1} x \cdot \varphi_y(q_n)}{\left(\frac{y}{x}\right)^n x - \left(\frac{y}{x}\right)^{n+1} x} \to 0 \tag{93}$$

for $(x, y) \to (2, 2)$ from (92).

2) Let now $(u, v) \to (1, 1)$ be an arbitrary sequence (we again omit the indices of the sequence) such that all (u, v) are in H_1. Because of $u > v$ and $(u, v) \to (1, 1)$ we may assume that $\frac{u}{v} > \frac{1}{2}$ without loss of generality. Define

$$\mu := \min\left\{ m \in \{1, 2, 3, \ldots\} \,\Big|\, \left(\frac{v}{u}\right)^m \le \frac{1}{2}\right\}.$$

Then $\mu > 1$. The inequality

$$\left(\frac{v}{u}\right)^{\mu-1} > \frac{1}{2}$$

implies that

$$\frac{v}{2u} < \left(\frac{v}{u}\right)^{\mu-1} \cdot \frac{u}{v} \le \frac{1}{2}.$$

Hence (note $(u, v) \to (1, 1)$)

$$\left(\frac{v}{u}\right)^{\mu} \to \frac{1}{2}.$$

Define new sequences x, y by

$$x := u \cdot \left(\frac{u}{v}\right)^{\mu}, \quad y := \frac{v}{u} \cdot x.$$

Therefore we have $x \to 2$, $y \to 2$ and always $x > y > 0$. Moreover,

$$u = \left(\frac{y}{x}\right)^{\mu} \cdot x, \quad v = \left(\frac{y}{x}\right)^{\mu+1} \cdot x, \quad \frac{y}{x} \le \left(\frac{y}{x}\right)^{\mu} \cdot x \le 1 \tag{94}$$

from $u \le 1$ and $\frac{y}{x} = \frac{v}{u} \le u$, because of $(u, v) \in H_1$. Inequality (94) implies that $\mu = \nu$ in the case $\frac{y}{x} < \left(\frac{y}{x}\right)^{\mu} \cdot x$ and $\mu = \nu + 1$ in the case $\frac{y}{x} = \left(\frac{y}{x}\right)^{\mu} \cdot x$. We hence have

$$\frac{u \cdot \varphi_x(u, v) + v \cdot \varphi_y(u, v)}{u - v} \to 0$$

by means of (93). This finally proves Proposition 27. $\qquad\square$

THEOREM 28. *Suppose that* $\varphi : H \to I$ *is an arbitrary function satisfying properties* (i), (ii), (iii), (iv), (v), (vi). *Then* $f = f(\varphi \mid G)$ *has continuous derivatives* f_x, f_y *in* D *and* $f \mid H = \varphi$.

Proof.   According to Theorem 26 there exists exactly one continuous proportion function f with $f|H = \varphi$. We have to show that f_x, f_y exist in D and that they are continuous there. Let (x, y) be a point of D. We would like to prove that f_x, f_y exist in (x, y). We shall assume $x \geq y > 0$ without loss of generality.

Case a): $x > y > 0$ and $\frac{y}{x} < \left(\frac{y}{x}\right)^\nu \cdot x < 1$, $\nu \in \mathbb{Z}$. In this situation, $q_\nu := \left(\frac{y}{x}\right)^\nu \cdot (x, y)$ must be an inner point of H. Because of

$$L(x, y) := \frac{\ln x}{\ln x/y} < \nu$$

there exists a neighbourhood

$$U \subseteq \{(\xi, \eta) \in \mathbb{R}^2 \mid \xi > \eta > 0\}$$

of (x, y) such that

$$L(\xi, \eta) < \nu < 1 + L(\xi, \eta) \tag{95}$$

holds true for all $(\xi, \eta) \in U$. Hence

$$f(\xi, \eta) = \varphi(\gamma_\nu) \tag{96}$$

with $\gamma_\nu := \left(\frac{\eta}{\xi}\right)^\nu \cdot (\xi, \eta)$ for all $(\xi, \eta) \in U$. All these points γ_ν are inner points of H because of (95). Now (96) and (iv) imply that f_ξ, f_η exist in U and are continuous in U.

Case b): $x > y > 0$ and $\frac{y}{x} < \left(\frac{y}{x}\right)^\nu \cdot x = 1$, $\nu \in \mathbb{Z}$. Here we have $L(x, y) = \nu$. Choose a neighbourhood

$$V \subseteq \{(\xi, \eta) \in \mathbb{R}^2 \mid \xi > \eta > 0\}$$

of (x, y) such that

$$\mid L(\xi, \eta) - \nu \mid < \frac{1}{3} \tag{97}$$

holds true for all $(\xi, \eta) \in V$. For the points $(\xi, \eta) \in V$ we have

$$\frac{\eta}{\xi} < \left(\frac{\eta}{\xi}\right)^{\nu(\xi, \eta)} \cdot \xi \leq 1, \quad \nu(\xi, \eta) \in \mathbb{Z},$$

i.e. $L(\xi, \eta) \leq \nu(\xi, \eta) < 1 + L(\xi, \eta)$. Hence (97) implies that $\nu(\xi, \eta) \in \{\nu, \nu + 1\}$. Define

$$V_- := \{(\xi, \eta) \in V \mid L(\xi, \eta) \leq \nu\} \text{ and } V_+ := V \backslash V_-.$$

For a point $(\xi, \eta) \in V$ we hence have $(\xi, \eta) \in V_-$ iff $\nu(\xi, \eta) = \nu$ and $(\xi, \eta) \in V_+$ iff $\nu(\xi, \eta) = \nu + 1$. We obtain

$$f(\xi, \eta) = \begin{cases} \varphi(\gamma_\nu) & (\xi, \eta) \in V_- \\ \varphi(\gamma_{\nu+1}) & (\xi, \eta) \in V_+ \end{cases} \quad \text{for} \quad .$$

Observe that $(x, y) \in V_-$. Therefore

$$f(x, y) = \varphi(q_\nu) = \varphi(q_{\nu+1})$$

from $\left(\dfrac{y}{x}\right)^\nu \cdot x = 1$ and (ii). Assume that

$$(x_\mu, y) \to (x, y) \quad \text{with } (x_\mu, y) \in V_- \quad \text{and } x_\mu \neq x \quad \text{for all } \mu = 1, 2, 3, \ldots,$$
$$(\xi_\mu, y) \to (x, y) \quad \text{with } (\xi_\mu, y) \in V_+ \quad \text{and } \xi_\mu \neq x \quad \text{for all } \mu = 1, 2, 3, \ldots$$

are sequences.

Then

$$\frac{f(x_\mu, y) - f(x, y)}{x_\mu - x} = \frac{\left(\left(\frac{y}{x_\mu}\right)^\nu x_\mu, \left(\frac{y}{x_\mu}\right)^{\nu+1} x_\mu\right) - \varphi(q_\nu)}{x_\mu - x}$$

$$\to \varphi_x(1, t) \cdot \frac{1 - \nu}{x} + \varphi_y(1, t) \cdot \left(\frac{-\nu t}{x}\right) \quad \text{with } t := \frac{y}{x}$$

and

$$\frac{f(\xi_\mu, y) - f(x, y)}{\xi_\mu - x} = \frac{\varphi\left(\left(\frac{y}{\xi_\mu}\right)^{\nu+1} \xi_\mu, \left(\frac{y}{\xi_\mu}\right)^{\nu+2} \xi_\mu\right) - \varphi(q_\nu)}{\xi_\mu - x}$$

$$\to \varphi_x(t, t^2) \cdot \left(\frac{-\nu t}{x}\right) + \varphi_y(t, t^2) \cdot \left(\frac{-(\nu+1)t^2}{x}\right).$$

Both limits are equal according to (vi). Hence f_x exists. A similar consideration leads to the existence of f_y. We have $\left(t = \frac{y}{x}\right)$

$$\left(f_x(x, y), f_y(x, y)\right) = \left(\varphi_x(1, t), \varphi_y(1, t)\right) \begin{pmatrix} \dfrac{1 - \nu}{x} & \dfrac{\nu}{y} \\ -\dfrac{\nu t}{x} & \dfrac{1 + \nu}{x} \end{pmatrix} \tag{98}$$

in the case b). We now would like to prove that f_x, f_y are also continuous in (x, y). Let $(\xi, \eta) \to (x, y)$ be a sequence (we omit again the indices of the sequence) such that all (ξ, η) are in V. We will divide the sequence in three subsequences (ξ, η) by means of

1) $\left(\dfrac{\eta}{\xi}\right)^{\nu(\xi,\eta)} \cdot \xi < 1$ and $(\xi,\eta) \in V_-$,

2) $\left(\dfrac{\eta}{\xi}\right)^{\nu(\xi,\eta)} \cdot \xi < 1$ and $(\xi,\eta) \in V_+$,

3) $\left(\dfrac{\eta}{\xi}\right)^{\nu(\xi,\eta)} \cdot \xi = 1$ and $(\xi,\eta) \in V_-$.

The case $\left(\frac{\eta}{\xi}\right)^{\nu(\xi,\eta)} \cdot \xi = 1$ and $(\xi,\eta) \in V_+$ cannot occur since $\left(\frac{\eta}{\xi}\right)^{\nu+1} \cdot \xi = 1$, i.e. $\nu + 1 = L(\xi,\eta)$, contradicts (97). Restricting ourselves on f_x we obtain from a), b)

1) $f_x(\xi,\eta) = \varphi_x(\gamma_\nu) \cdot (1-\nu) \left(\dfrac{\eta}{\xi}\right)^{\nu} + \varphi_y(\gamma_\nu) \cdot (-\nu) \left(\dfrac{\eta}{\xi}\right)^{\nu+1}$,

2) $f_x(\xi,\eta) = \varphi_x(\gamma_{\nu+1})(-\nu) \left(\dfrac{\eta}{\xi}\right)^{\nu+1} + \varphi_y(\gamma_{\nu+1})(-\nu-1) \left(\dfrac{\eta}{\xi}\right)^{\nu+2}$,

3) $f_x(\xi,\eta) = \dfrac{1-\nu}{\xi} \varphi_x \left(1, \dfrac{\eta}{\xi}\right) - \dfrac{\nu\eta}{\xi^2} \varphi_y \left(1, \dfrac{\eta}{\xi}\right)$.

But all these $f_x(\xi,\eta)$ tend to $f_x(x,y)$ of (98) in view of (iv) and (vi).

Case c): $x = y > 0$.

Let $x_\mu \to x$ be a sequence with $(x_\mu, y) \in D\backslash\{(x,y)\}$. We would like to prove

$$\frac{f(x_\mu, y) - f(x,y)}{x_\mu - x} \to 0. \tag{99}$$

Observe that $f(x,y) = 1$ because of $x = y$. We will divide the sequence x_μ in two subsequences

1) $x_\mu > x = y$,

2) $x_\mu < x = y$.

In the case 1) we obtain (observe that $\frac{y}{x_\mu} < \left(\frac{y}{x_\mu}\right)^{\nu(\mu)} \cdot x_\mu \leq 1, \nu(\mu) \in \mathbb{Z}$)

$$\frac{f(x_\mu, y) - 1}{x_\mu - x} = \frac{\varphi\left(\left(\frac{y}{x_\mu}\right)x_\mu, \left(\frac{y}{x_\mu}\right)^{\nu(\mu)+1} x_\mu\right) - 1}{x_\mu - x}$$

$$= \left(\frac{y}{x_\mu}\right)^{\nu(\mu)} \cdot \frac{\varphi\left(\left(\frac{y}{x_\mu}\right)^{\nu(\mu)} x_\mu, \left(\frac{y}{x_\mu}\right)^{\nu(\mu)+1} x_\mu\right) - 1}{\left(\frac{y}{x_\mu}\right)^{\nu(\mu)} x_\mu - \left(\frac{y}{x_\mu}\right)^{\nu(\mu)+1} x_\mu} \to 0,$$

in view of (v), $y = x$ and $\left(\frac{y}{x_\mu}\right)^{\nu(\mu)} x_\mu \to 1$. In the case 2) we get similar expressions by starting with

$$\frac{f(x_\mu, y) - 1}{x_\mu - x} = \frac{f(y, x_\mu) - 1}{x_\mu - x}.$$

Hence $f_x = 0$ exists in (x, y) with $x = y > 0$. Exactly the same considerations lead to the existence of $f_y = 0$ in (x, y), $x = y > 0$.

We finally have to prove that f_t is continuous in (a, a), $a > 0$, for $t \in \{x, y\}$. For this purpose take a sequence $(\xi, \eta) \to (a, a)$ with $(\xi, \eta) \in D$. Since $f_t(\xi, \xi) = 0 = f_t(a, a)$ we may assume that for all members (ξ, η) of our sequence $\xi \neq \eta$ holds true. Because of $f_t(\xi, \eta) = f_t(\eta, \xi)$ for $\xi \neq \eta$ and $t \in \{x, y\}$ we moreover may assume that $\xi > \eta$ for all (ξ, η) of the sequence. So it remains to prove that

$$f_t(\xi, \eta) \to 0 \qquad\qquad (100)$$

for a sequence $(\xi, \eta) \to (a, a)$ with $\xi > \eta > 0$ for all members (ξ, η) of the sequence. Because of

$$\frac{\eta}{\xi} < \left(\frac{\eta}{\xi}\right)^{\nu(\xi, \eta)} \cdot \xi \leq 1, \; \nu(\xi, \eta) \in \mathbb{Z}, \qquad\qquad (101)$$

we get

$$f_x(\xi, \eta) = \varphi_x(\gamma_\nu)(1 - \nu)\left(\frac{\eta}{\xi}\right)^\nu - \varphi_y(\gamma_\nu)\nu\left(\frac{\eta}{\xi}\right)^{\nu+1}, \qquad\qquad (102)$$

$$f_y(\xi, \eta) = \varphi_x(\gamma_\nu)\nu\left(\frac{\eta}{\xi}\right)^{\nu-1} + \varphi_y(\gamma_\nu)(\nu+1)\left(\frac{\eta}{\xi}\right)^\nu \qquad\qquad (103)$$

or

$$f_x(\xi, \eta) = \frac{1 - \nu}{\xi}\varphi_x\left(1, \frac{\eta}{\xi^2}\right) - \frac{\nu\eta}{\xi^2}\varphi_y\left(1, \frac{\eta}{\xi}\right), \qquad\qquad (104)$$

$$f_y(\xi, \eta) = \frac{\nu}{\eta}\varphi_x\left(1, \frac{\eta}{\xi}\right) + \frac{1 + \nu}{\xi}\varphi_y\left(1, \frac{\eta}{\xi}\right) \qquad\qquad (105)$$

according to case a) or case b). In order to prove (100) we thus have to verify
that

$$\nu(\xi, \eta) \cdot \left[\varphi_x(\gamma_\nu) + \frac{\eta}{\xi} \varphi_y(\gamma_\nu) \right] \to 0 \qquad (106)$$

in the case (102), (103), and

$$\nu \cdot \left[\varphi_x \left(1, \frac{\eta}{\xi} \right) + \frac{\eta}{\xi} \varphi_y \left(1, \frac{\eta}{\xi} \right) \right] \to 0 \qquad (107)$$

in the case (104), (105). Because of (observe (101))

$$L(\xi, \eta) \leq \nu < 1 + L(\xi, \eta)$$

and

$$\frac{\ln \dfrac{\xi}{\eta}}{\dfrac{\xi}{\eta} - 1} \to 1$$

properties (106), (107) will be established when

$$\frac{1}{\xi - \eta} \left[\varphi_x(\gamma_\nu) + \frac{\eta}{\xi} \varphi_y(\gamma_\nu) \right] \to 0,$$

$$\frac{1}{\xi - \eta} \left[\varphi_x \left(\frac{\eta}{\xi} \right) + \frac{\eta}{\xi} \varphi_y \left(1, \frac{\eta}{\xi} \right) \right] \to 0,$$

respectively, can be verified. But this follows from

$$\frac{u \varphi_x(u, v) + v \varphi_y(u, v)}{u - v} \to 0$$

$\left((u, v) \to (1, 1), (u, v) \in H_1 \right)$ by putting

$$u = \left(\frac{\eta}{\xi} \right)^\nu \xi, \quad v = \left(\frac{\eta}{\xi} \right)^{\nu+1} \xi,$$

$$u = 1, \qquad v = \frac{\eta}{\xi},$$

respectively. This finally proves Theorem 28. □

REMARKS 1) If φ is the polynomial $1 + (1 - x)(x^2 - y)$, then $f(\varphi)$ is not
of class C^1.

2) $f(\varphi)$ is of class C^1 for

$$\varphi(x, y) := 1 + \left[(x - y)(x^2 - y)(1 - x) \right]^2.$$

This $f(\varphi)$ cannot be written in the form (79), in view of Proposition 23.

3) If we define

$$\varphi(x,y) := 1 + \left(1 - \frac{y}{x}\right)^2 \text{ for } (x,y) \in H,$$

then $f(\varphi)$ is of class C^1 and it has the form (79). This example shows that the condition

$$\frac{x\varphi_x(x,y) + y\varphi_y(x,y)}{x - y} \to 0$$

of Proposition 27 cannot be replaced by

$$\frac{\varphi_x(x,y)}{x - y} \to 0 \text{ and } \frac{\varphi_y(x,y)}{x - y} \to 0$$

for $(x,y) \to (1,1)$ with $(1,1) \neq (x,y) \in H$.

4) Theorem 28 is due to W. Benz [7].

6.5.7 Rectangle patterns

Let $(\Sigma^{2,2}, \sim)$ be a proportion relation and let Σ be an equivalence class. A finite subset Π of Σ is then called a *rectangle pattern* with respect to $(\Sigma^{2,2}, \sim)$. If f is a proportion function in two variables, we obtain, as we already know, a proportion relation (see Remark 2 of section 6.5.1). So if f is a proportion function, and if Π is a finite set of rectangles of $\mathbb{R}^2$, then Π must be a rectangle pattern with respect to f (more precisely: with respect to the proportion relation induced by f) iff

(∗) $R_1, R_2 \in \Pi$ implies $f(R_1) = f(R_2)$, where we put $f(R) := f(x,y)$ in the case that x, y are the lengths of the sides of R

holds true.

Interesting questions may be posed in connection with rectangle patterns. For instance, let f be a proportion function and let A be an area of $\mathbb{R}^2$, say the area of an apartment. Ask for subdivisions of A into rectangles (rooms) $R_1, \ldots, R_n$ with $f(R_i) = f(R_j)$ for all $i, j \in \{1, \ldots, n\}$. Another question could be the following: let

$$R_1(x_1, y_1), \ R_2(x_2, y_2), \ldots, R_n(x_n, y_n)$$

be rooms of a villa. Does there exist a proportion function $f(\varphi)$ with a polynomial φ of degree, say, d such that $R_1, \ldots, R_n$ is a rectangle pattern with respect to $f(\varphi)$?

D. Gronau [1] has developed computer graphics for rectangle patterns.

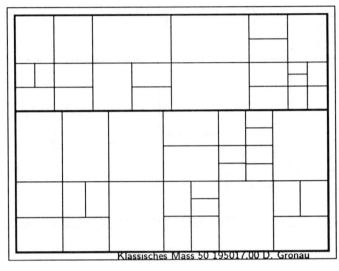

Klassisches Mass 50 19501/.00 D. Gronau

$$\varphi(x, y) = p(x, y)$$

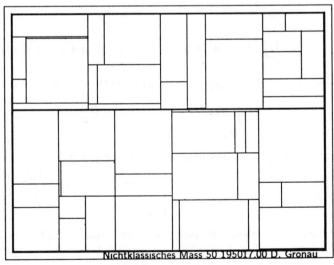

Nichtklassisches Mass 50 19501/.00 D. Gronau

$$\varphi(x, y) = 1 + (x^2 - y) \cdot (1 - x)$$

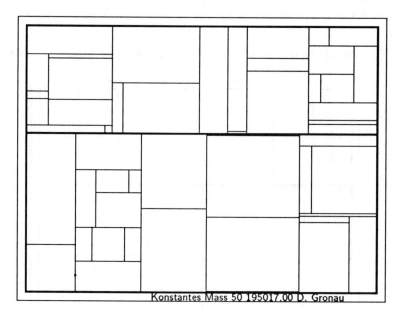

Konstantes Mass 50 195017.00 D. Gronau

$$\varphi(x, y) = \text{const}$$

6.5.8   Three and more variables

Define

$$M = \bigcup_{0<x<1} \{(xz, yz, z) \in S^3 \mid x \le y \le 1 \text{ and } x < z \le 1\}$$

and observe that the boundary of M consists of the developable surface

$$\bigcup_{0<z<1} \{(z^2, \lambda, z) \in S^3 \mid z^2 \le \lambda \le z\}$$

and of parts of the planes of equations $x = 0$, $x = y$, $z = 1$.

Call two points (xz, yz, z) and $(x'z', y'z', z')$ of M equivalent iff there exist integers ν, μ with

$$x = x', y = y', z' = x^\nu y^\mu z.$$

The associated equivalence classes are called *tracks*. The track through $z \cdot (x, y, 1)$ (observe that $0 < x < 1$, $x \le y \le 1$ and $x \le z \le 1$) is given by

$$\{x^\nu y^\mu z \cdot (x, y, 1) \mid \nu, \mu \in \mathbb{Z} \text{ and } x < x^\nu y^\mu z \le 1\};$$

it is part of the line joining $z \cdot (x, y, 1)$ with the origin.

The following theorem is due to C. Alsina, W. Benz [1].

THEOREM 29. *Let ψ be an arbitrary function from M into $I = [1, \infty)$ with always $\psi(P) = \psi(Q)$ in the case that P, Q are in the same track. Then there exists exactly one function $f : S^3 \to I$ such that $f \mid M = \psi$ and such that the following properties hold true:*

$$f(x, y, z) = f\left(z, \tfrac{zy}{x}, \tfrac{z}{x}^2\right) \qquad\qquad for\ all\ (x, y, z) \in S^3,$$

$$f(x_1, x_2, x_3) = f\left(x_{\sigma(1)}, x_{\sigma(2)}, x_{\sigma(3)}\right) \qquad\qquad for\ all\ (x_1, x_2, x_3) \in S^3\ and$$

for any permutation σ of the set $\{1, 2, 3\}$,

$$f(x, x, x) = 1\ for\ all\ x > 0.$$

The following theorem is due to the author [9].

THEOREM 30. *Let $(\Sigma^{n,n}, \sim)$ be a proportion relation such that the following property holds true: whenever $Q_1, Q_2, \ldots \to Q$ and $Q_1', Q_2', \ldots \to Q'$ are convergent sequences of boxes $Q_\nu, Q_\nu' \in \Sigma^{n,n}$ with limit boxes $Q, Q' \in \Sigma^{n,n}$ such that $Q_\nu \sim Q_\nu'$ is satisfied for all positive integers ν, then $Q \sim Q'$. Suppose moreover that $n \geq 3$. Then two similar boxes Q, Q' of $\Sigma^{n,n}$ must always be equivalent.*

REMARKS. 1) One step of our proof (see loc. cit.) of Theorem 30 depends on a result of H. Weyl [1] on equidistribution.

2) A proportion relation as described in Theorem 30 is called continuous. In the case $n = 2$ there exist continuous proportion relations for which Theorem 30 does not hold true: take for instance the relation belonging to $f(\varphi)$ with

$$\varphi(x, y) = 1 + (1 - x)(x^2 - y).$$

3) Suppose that

$$h : S^n \to W,\ n \geq 2, \tag{108}$$

satisfies (i)* and (ii)* of section 6.5.1. If W is a topological Hausdorff space, we will call h of (108) an n–place proportion function. Note that we do not require the normalization axiom

$$h(x_1, \ldots, x_n) = \text{const for all } x_1 = \ldots = x_n > 0 \tag{109}$$

for an n–place proportion function. However, continuity of f implies (109) for $n \geq 3$.

Writing the real numbers $x_1, \ldots, x_n$ in their natural order, $x_1' \leq x_2' \leq \ldots \leq x_n'$, we put

$$\mathrm{med}_i \, (x_1, \ldots, x_n) := x_{i+1}' \text{ for } i = 1, \ldots, n-2,$$

where med stands for medium. If now

$$g : \big\{ (y_1, \ldots, y_{n-1}) \in \mathbb{R}^{n-1} \mid 1 \leq y_1 \leq \ldots \leq y_{n-1} \big\} \rightarrow W$$

is taken arbitrarily, then

$$f(x) := g \left(\frac{\mathrm{med}_1 x}{\min x}, \ldots, \frac{\mathrm{med}_{n-2} \, x}{\min x}, \frac{\max x}{\min x} \right) \tag{110}$$

must be an n–place proportion function with $x := (x_1, \ldots, x_n) \in S^n$. A corollary of Theorem 30 (see W. Benz [9]) is the statement that every continuous n–place proportion function has the form (110) whenever $n \geq 3$. In the case $n = 2$ there exist proportion functions $f(x, y)$ which are continuous, but which are not of the form (108), i.e. the form (79), for instance $f(\varphi)$ with

$$\varphi(x, y) = 1 + (1 - x)(x^2 - y).$$

Bibliography

ACZÉL, J.:

[1] Lectures on functional equations and their applications. Academic Press, New York — London, 1966.

[2] Quasigroups, Nets, and Nomograms. Advances in Math. 1 (1965) 383–450.

[3] Collineations on three and on four lines of projective planes over fields. Mathematica, Cluj 8 (1966) 7–13.

ACZÉL, J. and BENZ, W.:

[1] Kollineationen auf Drei– und Vierecken in der Desargues'schen projektiven Ebene und Äquivalenz der Dreiecksnomogramme und der Dreigewebe von Loops mit der Isotopie–Isomorphie–Eigenschaft. Aequat. Math. 3 (1969) 86–92.

ACZÉL, J. and DHOMBRES, J.:

[1] Functional equations in several variables. New York, 1989.

ACZÉL, J. and MC KIERNAN, M.A.:

[1] On the characterization of plane projective and complex Möbius–transformation. Math. Nachr. 33 (1967) 317–337.

AL–DHAHIR, M.W. and BENZ, W. and GHALIEH, K.:

[1] A Groupoid of the Ternary Ring of a Projective Plane. Journ. Geom. 42 (1991) 3–16.

ALEXANDROV, A.D.:

[1] Seminar Report. Uspehi Mat. Nauk. 5 (1950), no. 3 (37), 187.

[2] A contribution to chronogeometry. Canad. J. Math. 19 (1967) 1119–1128.

[3] Mappings of Spaces with Families of cones and Space–Time–Transformations. Annali di Matematica 103 (1975) 229–257.

ALSINA, C.:

[1] Problems and Remarks, # 27. Aequat. Math. 29 (1985) 100.

ALSINA, C. and BENZ, W.:

[1] Proportion functions in three dimensions. Aequat. Math. 37 (1989) 293–305.

ALSINA, C. and GARCIA-ROIG, J.L.:

[1] On proportion functions of convex domains. Archiv Math. 54 (1990) 594–600.

ALSINA, C. and TRILLAS, E.:

[1] Lecciones de Algebra y Geometria (Curso para estudiantes de Arquitectura). Ed. Gustavo Gili, S.A., Barcelona 1984.

ARTZY, R.:

[1] Linear Geometry. Addison–Wesley, New York, 1965.

[2] Geometry. BI Wissenschaftsverlag, Mannheim, Leipzig, Wien, Zürich, 1992.

[3] Dynamics of quadratic functions in cycle planes. Journ. Geom. 44 (1992) 26–32.

BAER, R.:

[1] Linear algebra and projective geometry. New York 1952.

BAKER, J.A.:

[1] Isometries in normed spaces. Amer. Math. Monthly 78 (1971) 655–658.

[2] Some propositions related to a dilatation theorem of W. Benz, to appear.

BARLOTTI, A.:

[1] Sulle m–strutture di Möbius. Rend. Ist. di Matem. Univ. Trieste 1 (1969) 35–46.

BARTOLONE, C. and BARTOLOZZI, F.:

[1] Topics in Geometric Algebra over rings. In: Rings and Geometry, ed. R. Kaya, P. Plaumann, K. Strambach, 1985, 353–389.

BECKMANN, F.S. and QUARLES JR., D.A.:

[1] On Isometries of Euclidean Spaces. Proc. Amer. Math. Soc. 4 (1953) 810–815.

BENZ, W.:

[1] Geometrische Transformationen (unter besonderer Berücksichtigung der Lorentztransformationen). BI Wissenschaftsverlag, Mannheim, Leipzig, Wien, Zürich, 1992.

[2] Vorlesungen über Geometrie der Algebren. Die Grundlehren der math. Wissensch. in Einzeldarstellungen, Bd. 197, Springer–Verlag, Berlin, New York, 1973.

[3] Grundlagen der Geometrie. Dokumente zur Geschichte der Math. 6 (1990) 231–267 (Festschrift zum hundertjährigen Jubiläum der Deutsch. Math. Verein., Vieweg Verlag).

[4] On a general principle in geometry that leads to functional equations. Aequat. Math. 46 (1993) 3–10.

[5] Eine Kennzeichnung des Büschelsatzes in Kettengeometrien. Journ. Geom. 31 (1988) 22–31.

[6] Remark P 272 S 1. Aequat. Math. 29 (1985) 101–102.

[7] A Functional Equations Problem in Architecture. Arch. d. Math. 47 (1986) 165–181.

[8] Ästhetische Rechtecksmaße, die maßstabsunabhängig sind. Math. Meth. in the Appl. Sci. 9 (1987) 53–58.

[9] Continuous proportion relations and functions. Geom. Ded. 36 (1990) 139–149.

[10] Eine Beckman–Quarles–Charakterisierung der Lorentztransformationen des $\mathbb{R}^n$. Archiv d. Math. 34 (1980) 550–559.

[11] A Beckman Quarles type theorem for plane Lorentz transformations. Math. Z. 177 (1981) 101–106.

[12] Über eine Charakterisierung des hyperbolischen Flächeninhaltes und eine Funktional-gleichung. Publ. Math. Debrecen 28 (1981) 259–263.

[13] A Functional Equation in Connection with Derivations. Math. Zeitschr. 183 (1983) 495–501.

[14] On Lorentz Transformations in Geometry. Giornate di Geometrie Combinatorie, Univ. di Perugia, 1993, 81–86.

[15] All 2–point–invariants of Einstein's Cylinder Universe. Journ. Geom. 48 (1993) 5–9.

[16] Bewegungen in der Einsteinschen Zylinderwelt, to appear.

[17] Characterizations of geometrical mappings under mild hypotheses — Über ein modernes Forschungsgebiet der Geometrie. In: Festband aus Anlaß des 75jährigen Bestehens der Universität Hamburg, Hamburg 1994.

BENZ, W. and BERENS, H.:

[1] A Contribution to a Theorem of Ulam and Mazur. Aequat. Math. 34 (1987) 61–63.

BEUTELSPACHER, A. and ROSENBAUM, U.:

[1] Projektive Geometrie. Vieweg Verlag, 1992.

BLASCHKE, W.:

[1] Gesammelte Werke, Band 1. Thales Verlag, Essen, 1982.

[2] Vorlesungen über Differentialgeometrie und geometrische Grundlagen von Einsteins Relativitätstheorie III. Differenetialgeometrie der Kreise und Kugeln. Bearbeitet von G. Thomsen. Grundlehren der math. Wissenschaften in Einzeldarstellungen. Bd. 29. Berlin, Springer, 1929.

BLUNCK, A.:

[1] Cross–ratios over local alternative rings. Results Math. 19 (1991) 246–256.

BORSUK, K.:

[1] Multidimensional analytic geometry. Monografie Matematyczne, Tom 50, Warszawa, 1969.

BUEKENHOUT, F.:

[1] Inversions in locally affine circular spaces I, II. Math. Zeitschr. 119 (1971) 189–202, 120 (1971) 165–177.

[2] Handbook of Incidence Geometry, to appear.

362

BURAU, W.:

[1] Mehrdimensionale projektive und höhere Geometrie. Berlin, 1961.

CECCHERINI, P.V.:

[1] Graphs, lattices, and projective spaces. Giornate di Geometrie Combinatorie, Univ. di Perugia, 1993, 133–161.

CHEN, Y.:

[1] Der Satz von Miquel in der Möbiusebene. Math. Ann. 186 (1970) 81–100.

CHOW, W.-L.:

[1] On the geometry of algebraic homogeneous spaces. Ann. of Math. 50 (1949) 32–67.

COXETER, H.S.M.

[1] Projective geometry. University of Toronto Press, 1974.

[2] A Geometrical Background for de Sitter's World. Am. Math. Monthly 50 (1943) 217–228.

DOMIATY, R.Z.:

[1] On bijections of Lorentz manifolds, which leave the class of spacelike paths invariant. Topology and its Appl. 20 (1985) 39–46.

DOMIATY, R.Z. and LABACK, O.:

[1] Semimetric spaces in general relativity. Uspekhi Mat. Nauk 35:3 (1980) 50–60.

EWALD, G.:

[1] Geometry: An Introduction. Belmont, Calif.: Wadsworth Publ. Comp., 1971.

FAINA, G.:

[1] Geometric and Algebraic Theory of B-ovals. Results and problems. Giornate di Geometrie Combinatorie, Univ. di Perugia, 1993, 175–212.

FARRAHI, B.:

[1] A characterization of isometries of absolute planes. Resultate Math. 4 (1981) 34–38.

[2] On cone preserving transformations of metric affine spaces. Bull. Iranian Math. Soc. 9 (1978) 50–54.

FISHER, J.CH.:

[1] Models and Theorems of the Classical Circle Planes. Abhdlgn. Math. Sem. Hamburg 63 (1993) 245–264.

FISSER, M.:

[1] Beckman–Quarles–Kennzeichnungen orthogonaler Gruppen. Dissertationsschrift Hamburg, 1989.

GANS, D.:

[1] Transformations and Geometries. New York, 1969.

GIERING, O.:

[1] Vorlesungen über höhere Geometrie. Vieweg–Verlag, Braunschweig, Wiesbaden, 1982.

GRAF, U.:

[1] Über Laguerresche Geometrie in Ebenen mit nichteuklidischer Maßbestimmung und den Zusammenhang mit Raumstrukturen der Relativitätstheorie. Tôhoku Math. J. 39 (1934) 279–291.

[2] Über Laguerresche Geometrie in Ebenen und Räumen mit nichteuklidischer Metrik. Jahresber. DMV 45 (1935) 212–234.

[3] Über eine Darstellung der kosmologischen Struktur mit zeitlich veränderlicher Raumkrümmung in der Laguerreschen Kugelgeometrie. Jahresber. DMV 46 (1936) 20–26.

GRAUSTEIN, W.C.:

[1] Introduction to Higher Geometry. New York, 1930.

GRONAU, D.:

[1] Remark 4 (p. 99) in Report of Meeting, the 26th Internat. Symp. on Funct. Equats, 1988, Sant Feliu de Guixols, Catalonia, Spain, Aequat. Math. 37 (1989) 57–127.

GUTS, A.K.:

[1] On mappings preserving cones in Lobachevsky space. Mat. Zametki 13 (1973) 687–694.

[2] Axiomatic relativity theory. Russian Math. Surveys 37:2 (1982) 41–89.

HALDER, H.R. and HEISE, W.:

[1] Einführung in die Kombinatorik. Hanser–Verlag, München, Wien, 1976.

HAVEL, V.:

[1] On collineations on three and four lines in a projective plane. Aequat. Math. 4 (1970) 51–55.

HAVLICEK, H.:

[1] Eine affine Beschreibung von Ketten. Abhdlgn. Math. Sem. Hamburg 53 (1983) 266–275.

[2] Dual spreads generated by collineations. Simon Stevin 64 (1990) 339–349.

[3] On the geometry of field extensions. Aequat. Math. 45 (1993) 232–238.

HERZER, A.:

[1] Chain geometries, in: Buekenhout, F. (ed.), Handbook of Incidence Geometry. Reidel, Dordrecht, Boston, to appear.

[2] On a projective representation of chain geometries. Journ. Geom. 22 (1984) 83–99.

364

[3] Über rationale Darstellungen von Kettengeometrien als projektive Varietäten. Archiv Math. 47 (1986) 573–576, 48 (1987) 550–551.

HILBERT, D.:

[1] Grundlagen der Geometrie. 1. Aufl. Berlin, 1899, 11. Aufl. Stuttgart, 1972.

HIRSCHFELD, J.W.P.:

[1] Finite projective spaces of three dimensions. Clarendon Press, Oxford, 1991.

HJELMSLEV, J.:

[1] Einleitung in die allgemeine Kongruenzlehre. 1.–6. Mitt. Danske Vid. Selsk. Mat.-Fys. Medd. 8 (1929), 10 (1929), 19 (1942), 22 (1945), 22 (1945), 25 (1949).

HOTJE, H.:

[1] Einbettung gewisser Kettengeometrien in projektive Räume. Journ. Geom. 5 (1974) 85–94.

[2] Zur Einbettung von Kettengeometrien in projektive Räume. Math. Zeitschr. 151 (1976) 5–17.

[3] Die Algebren einbettbarer Berührstrukturen. Geom. Ded. 7 (1978) 355–362.

HUANG, W.:

[1] Geradenbildungen, die den Flächeninhalt 1 von Dreiecken erhalten. Hamburger Beiträge zur Math. aus dem Math. Seminar, Heft 22 (1993).

[2] Punkte– und Geradenbildungen, die das Volumen 1 von n–dimensionalen Simplices im $\mathbb{R}^n$ erhalten. Hamburger Beiträge zur Math. aus dem Math. Seminar, Heft 26 (1993).

HUGHES, D.R. and PIPER, F.C.:

[1] Projective Planes. New York 1973.

KARZEL, H. and KROLL, H.J.:

[1] Geschichte der Geometrie seit Hilbert. Wissenschaftliche Buchgesellschaft, Darmstadt, 1988.

KARZEL, H. and SÖRENSEN, K. and WINDELBERG, D.:

[1] Einführung in die Geometrie. UTB Vandenhoeck, Göttingen, 1973.

KARZEL, H. and WEFELSCHEID, H.:

[1] Groups with an involutory antiautomorphism and K–loops; application to space–time-world and hyperbolic geometry I. Results Math. 23 (1993) 338–354.

KLEIN, F.:

[1] Vorlesungen über höhere Geometrie. 3. Aufl. Bearbeitet und herausgegeben von W. Blaschke. Grundlehren der math. Wiss. in Einzeldarstellungen, Bd. 22, Springer-Verlag, Berlin 1926 (Nachdruck 1968).

[2] Über die Integralform der Erhaltungssätze und die Theorie der räumlich–geschlossenen Welt. Gesammelte Math. Abhdlgn., Bd. 1 (1973) 586–612.

KLOTZEK, B.:

[1] Geometrie. Deutscher Verlag der Wissenschaften, Berlin, 1971.

KLOTZEK, B. and QUAISSER, E.:

[1] Nichteuklidische Geometrie. Deutscher Verlag der Wissenschaften, Berlin, 1978.

KROLL, H.J.:

[1] Unterräume von Kettengeometrien und Kettengeometrien mit Quadrikenmodell. Results Math. 19 (1991) 327–334.

KUZ'MINYH, A.V.:

[1] Mappings preserving a unit distance. Sibirsk. Mat. Ž. 20 (1979) 597–602.

[2] On a Characteristic Property of Isometric Mappings. Dokl. Akad. Nauk, SSSR, 226 (1976) Nr. 1.

[3] A Minimal Condition that determines a Lorentz–Transformation. Sibirsk Mat. Ž. 17 (1976) 13212–1326.

[4] On the characterization of isometric and similarity mappings. Dokl. Akad. Nauk. SSSR 244 (1979) 526–528.

LAUGWITZ, D.:

[1] Regular hexagons in normed spaces and a theorem of Walter Benz. Aequat. Math. 45 (1993) 163–166.

LEISSNER, W.:

[1] Büschelhomogene Lie–Ebenen. Journ. Reine Angew. Math. 246 (1971) 76–116.

LENZ, H.:

[1] Vorlesungen über Projektive Geometrie. Leipzig, 1965.

[2] Über einen Satz von June Lester zur Charakterisierung euklidischer Bewegungen. Journ. Geom. 28 (1987) 197–201.

LESTER, J.A.:

[1] Alexandrov–Type Transformations on Einstein's Cylinder Universe. C.R. Math. Rep. Acad. Sci. Canada IV (1982) 175–178.

[2] On Distance Preserving Transformations of Lines in Euclidean Three–Space. Aequat. Math. 28 (1985) 69–72.

[3] The Beckman–Quarles theorem in Minkowski space for a spacelike squaredistance. Archiv d. Math. 37 (1981) 561–568.

[4] Separation–Preserving Tranformations of De Sitter Spacetime. Abhdlgn. Math. Sem. Hamburg 53 (1983) 217–224.

[5] Martin's theorem for Euclidean n–space and a generalization to the perimeter case. Journ. Geom. 27 (1986) 29–35.

[6] On line mappings which preserve unit triangles. Utilitas Math. 31 (1987) 81–84.

[7] Transformations of Robertson–Walker spacetimes preserving separation zero. Aequat. Math. 25 (1982) 216–232.

[8] A Physical Characterization of Conformal Transformations of Minkowski Spacetime. Ann. Discrete Math. 18 (1983) 567–574.

[9] The Causal Automorphisms of de Sitter and Einstein Cylinder Spacetimes. J. Math. Phys. 25 (1984) 113–116.

[10] Transformations Preserving Null Line Sections of a Domain. Resultate Math. 9 (1986) 107–118.

[11] Distance–preserving transformations. In Handbook of Geometry (ed. F. Buekenhout), North–Holland, to appear.

[12] Cone preserving mappings for quadratic cones over arbitrary fields. Canad. J. Math. 29 (1977) 1247–1253.

LIMAYE, B.V. and LIMAYE, N.B.:

[1] The fundamental theorem for the projective line over commutative rings. Aequat. Math. 16 (1977) 275–281.

LINGENBERG, R.

[1] Grundlagen der Geometrie. BI–Wissenschaftsverlag, Mannheim, Wien, Zürich, 1976.

MÄURER, H.:

[1] Ein spiegelungsgeometrischer Aufbau der Laguerregeometrie I, II. Math. Zeitschr. 87 (1965) 78–100, 263–282.

[2] Die Automorphismengruppe der ebenen reellen Polynomgeometrie. Results Math. 19 (1991) 335–340.

MAZUR, S. and ULAM, S.:

[1] Sur les transformations isométriques vectoriels normés. C.R. Acad. Sci. Paris 194 (1932) 946–948.

MISFELD, J.:

[1] Topologische projektive Räume. Abhdlgn. Math. Sem. Hamburg 32 (1968) 232–263.

MOSZNER, Z.:

[1] Remark P 272 S 2. Aequat. Math. 29 (1985) 102–104.

MOSZNER, Z. and NAWOLSKA, B.:

[1] On the rectangle proportion. Wyz. Szkola Ped. Krakow. Rocznik Nauk.–Dydakt. Prace Mat. 12 (1987) 115–127.

PAGANONI, L.:

[1] On a functional equation concerning affine transformations. Journ. Math. Anal. Appl. 127 (1987) 475–491.

PICKERT, G.:

[1] Projektive Ebenen. Berlin, Göttingen, Heidelberg, 1975.

RADÓ, F.:

[1] Non–injective collineations on some sets in Desarguesian projective planes and extension of non–commutative valuations. Aequat. Math. 4 (1970) 307–321.

[2] Characterization of semi–isometries of the Minkowskian plane over a field K. Journ. Geom. 21 (1983) 164–183.

[3] Mappings of Galois planes preserving the unit Euclidean distance. Aequat. Math. 29 (1985) 1–6.

[4] On mappings of the Galois space. Israel J. Math. 53 (1986) 217–230.

[5] Extension of Collineations defined on subsets of a Translation Plane. Journ. Geom. 1 (1971) 1–17.

RÄTZ, J.:

[1] The orthogonally additive mappings. Aequat. Math. 28 (1985) 35–49.

[2] Zur Charakterisierung des Skalarproduktes. Elem. Math. 36 (1981) 94–97.

RIGBY, J.F.:

[1] Collineations on quadrilaterals in projective planes. Mathematica 10 (1968) 369–383.

SAMAGA, H.-J.:

[1] Dreidimensionale Kettengeometrien über $\mathbb{R}$. Journ. Geom. 8 (1976) 61–73.

[2] $(B_n^* G_n S_n)$–Geometrien. Journ. Geom. 12 (1979) 69–87.

[3] Zur Kennzeichnung von Lorentztransformationen in endlichen Ebenen. Journ. Geom. 18 (1982) 169–184.

[4] Über fraktale Strukturen in Kreisgeometrien, to appear.

SCHAEFFER, H.:

[1] Das von Staudtsche Theorem in der Geometrie der Algebren. Journ. reine angew. Math. 267 (1974) 133–142.

[2] Eine Kennzeichnung der Dilatationen endlicher Desarguesscher Ebenen der Charakteristik $\neq 2, 3, 5$. Jorn. Geom. 22 (1984) 51–56.

[3] Der Satz von Benz–Radó. Aequat. Math. 31 (1986) 300–309.

[4] Automorphisms of Laguerre geometry and cone–preserving mappings of metric vector spaces. Lecture Notes in Math. 792 (1980) 143–147.

SCHERK, P. and LINGENBERG, R.:

[1] Rudiments of plane affine geometry. Toronto, Buffalo, 1975.

SCHRÖDER, E.M.:

[1] Vorlesungen über Geometrie I, II, III. BI–Wissenschaftsverlag, Mannheim, Wien, Zürich, 1991, 1991, 1992.

[2] On 0–distance preserving permutations of affine and projective quadrics. Journ. Geom. 46 (1993) 177–185.

[3] Modelle ebener metrischer Ringgeometrien. Abhdlgn. Math. Sem. Hamburg 48 (1979) 139–170.

368

[4] Metric Geometry. In: Handbook of Incidence Geometry (ed. F. Buekenhout), North–Holland, to appear.

[5] Eine Ergänzung zum Satz von Beckman und Quarles. Aequat. Math. 19 (1979) 89–92.

[6] Geometrie euklidischer Ebenen. Ferdinand Schöningh, Paderborn, 1985.

[7] Zur Kennzeichnung distanztreuer Abbildungen in nichteuklidischen Räumen. Journ. Geom. 15 (1980) 108–118.

[8] Ein einfacher Beweis des Satzes von Alexandrov–Lester. Journ. Geom. 37 (1990) 153–158.

[9] Zur Kennzeichnung der Lorentztransformationen. Aequat. Math. 19 (1979) 134–144.

[10] On permutations of central quadrics which preserve an inner distance, to appear.

SCHWERDTFEGER, H.:

[1] Geometry of Complex Numbers. Circle Geometry, Moebius Transformation, Non-euclidean Geometry. Dover Publications, New York, 1979.

SEIER, W.:

[1] Kettengeometrie über Hjelmslevringen. In: Beiträge zur Geom. Algebr., H.J. Arnold, W. Benz, H. Wefelscheid (edts.), 1977, 299–303.

TALLINI, G.:

[1] On a theorem by W. Benz characterizing plane Lorentz transformations in Järnefelt's world. Journ. Geom. 17 (1981) 171–173.

WERNER, M.:

[1] Quadrikenmodell einer Kettengeometrie. Journ. Geom. 18 (1982) 161–168.

[2] Zur Darstellung der Automorphismengruppe einer kinematischen Kettengeometrie im Quadrikenmodell. Journ. Geom. 19 (1982) 146–153.

[3] Einbettung von Kettengeometrien durch Quadroide. Journ. Geom. 24 (1985) 74–76.

WEYL, H.:

[1] Über die Gleichverteilung von Zahlen mod. Eins. Math. Ann. 77 (1916) 313–352.

[2] Elementary Theory of Invariants. Princeton, 1936.

Notation and symbols

Theorems, propositions, and lemmata are numbered consecutively in each chapter, so that Lemma 1 may be followed by Proposition 2 and that by Theorem 3. Chapters are subdivided into sections (some sections furthermore into subsections) but numbering of formulas, etc., is within chapters, not sections. As usual, easier theorems are called *Propositions*. The end of a proof is always indicated by a □. The symbols := or =: mean that the side of the equation, where he colon is, is defined by the other side. Sometimes *iff* is used as an abbreviation for *if and only if*.

$A \Rightarrow B$	A implies B
$A \Leftrightarrow B$	$(A \Rightarrow B)$ and $(B \Rightarrow A)$
$\forall$	for all
$\forall_{x \in S} \quad A(x) \Rightarrow B(x)$	$A(x)$ implies $B(x)$ for all x in S
$\exists$	there exist(s)

If f is a mapping from B into C and if g is a mapping from A into B, then $fg : A \to C$ is defined by $(fg)(x) := f[g(x)]$ for all $x \in A$.

If f is a mapping from M into N and if H is a subset of M, then $f \mid H$ (the so–called restriction of f on H) denotes the mapping $\varphi : H \to N$ with $\varphi(x) := f(x)$ for all x in H.

If M is a set, then id : $M \to M$ is the mapping defined by id $(x) = x$ for all $x \in M$.

If S is a set, then $\{x \in S \mid P(x)\}$ denotes the set of all x in S which satisfy property P.

If A, B are sets, then $A \backslash B := \{x \in A \mid x \notin B\}$.

As usual, the set of integers is denoted by $\mathbb{Z}$, that of rationals by $\mathbb{Q}$, that of real numbers by $\mathbb{R}$ and that of complex numbers by $\mathbb{C}$. Furthermore,

$$\mathbb{R}_{>0} := \{x \in \mathbb{R} \mid x > 0\},$$
$$\mathbb{R}_{\geq 0} := \{x \in \mathbb{R} \mid x \geq 0\}.$$

If $a \leq b$ are real numbers, then so–called intervals are defined:

$$[a, b] := \{x \in \mathbb{R} \mid a \leq x \leq b\},$$
$$[a, b[:= \{x \in \mathbb{R} \mid a \leq x < b\},$$
$$]a, b] := \{x \in \mathbb{R} \mid a < x \leq b\},$$
$$]a, b[:= \{x \in \mathbb{R} \mid a < x < b\}.$$

Furthermore,

$$]-\infty, a] := \{x \in \mathbb{R} \mid x \leq a\},$$
$$]-\infty, a[:= \{x \in \mathbb{R} \mid x < a\},$$
$$[a, +\infty[:= \{x \in \mathbb{R} \mid a \leq x\},$$
$$]a, +\infty[:= \{x \in \mathbb{R} \mid a < x\}.$$

If $S_1, S_2, \ldots, S_n$ are sets, then their *cartesian product* is

$$S_1 \times S_2 \times \ldots \times S_n := \{(x_1, \ldots, x_n) \mid x_i \in S_i \text{ for } i = 1, \ldots, n\}.$$

If M is a set, then $\#M$ denotes its *cardinality*. The diagram

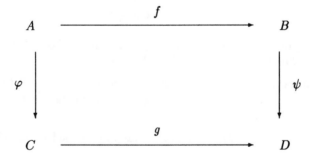

expresses the fact that A, B, C, D are sets and that

$$f : A \to B \quad g : C \to D$$
$$\varphi : A \to C \quad \psi : B \to D$$

are mappings. The diagram is said to be *commutative* iff $\psi f = g\varphi$.

δ_{ij} denotes the so–called Kronecker delta,

$$\delta_{ij} := \begin{cases} 1 & i = j \\ & \text{for} \\ 0 & i \neq j \end{cases} .$$

If a is a complex number, then $|a|$ denotes the absolute value of a.

If a is a non–negative real number, then $\sqrt{a}$ denotes the real number $b \geq 0$ satisfying $b^2 = a$.

If A is a matrix, then A^T denotes the transpose of A. If A is a quadratic matrix, then $\det A = |A|$ is the determinant of A.

C^n	set of points of n–dimensional Einstein's cylinder universe
M^n	group of motions of C^n
S^n	set of points of n–dimensional de Sitter's world
Δ^n	group of motions of S^n
L_0, L_c, L_∞	set of null–lines, closed lines, open lines of S^n, respectively
L^n	Lie quadric (see section 3.8)
$L(k,a), (\alpha, i, j), [\alpha, i, j]$	(see section 4.9)
$V(a_1, \ldots, a_{n+1})$	(see section 5.3.2)
$R(a, b, c)$	affine ratio
$\Pi(V)$	projective space over the vector space V
$G(V)$	projective group of $\Pi(V)$
$\begin{bmatrix} A & B \\ D & C \end{bmatrix}$	cross ratio
$G \geq H$	H is a subgroup of the group G

$A \oslash B$	(see section 5.6.5)
$A \, N \, G$	(see section 5.2.3)
$A \, N \, H$	(see section 5.7.2)
$l_1 \parallel l_2$	the lines l_1, l_2 are parallel
$P \parallel Q$	the points P, Q are parallel
$a \, P \, b$	a is in contact with b in P
$A - z$	A is in contact with z
$\mathbb{D}$	ring of dual numbers
$\mathbb{A}$	ring of double numbers
H_{abc}	(see section 6.4.2)
$(S^n, \sim)$	proportion relation
$\Sigma^{n,m}$	set of n–dimensional boxes of $\mathbb{R}^m$
$p(x, y)$	rectangle proportion
D, I	(see section 6.5.2)
H	(see section 6.5.4)
$f(\varphi)$	proportion function with $f(\varphi) \mid D = \varphi$
Π	rectangle pattern (as a finite subset of $\Sigma^{2,2}$)

Index

A

B

C

374

congruent mappings   182

contact relation   98, 282, 294

continuous proportion

function   342

continuous proportion

relation   357

cosine theorem   253

Cremona geometry   263, 271, 309

Cremona group   271

cross ratio   227, 230

cycle coordinates   294

D

defining function   23

defining invariant of equiaffine

geometry   197

defining notion   23

definite 2–point–invariant   80, 84

de Sitter's plane   139, 144

de Sitter's world   119

de Sitter's world over a ring   132

dilatations   182

direct product of two geo-

metries   31

distance function   19, 22, 90,

103, 139

distance spaces   22

dual numbers   289

E

Einstein's cylinder universe   35, 77

Einstein's cylinder universe over

a ring   105

Einstein's plane   108

elliptic distance   259

elliptic geometry   258, 259

elliptic metric space   259

equiaffine geometry   193, 196

equiaffine mapping   196

equivalence of invariants   45

euclidean geometry   28, 30, 168, 211

euclidean geometry of normed

spaces   210

euclidean parallel axiom   92

Further Reading in Mathematics by B. I.-Wissenschaftsverlag

A. Kerber
Algebraic Combinatorics via Finite Group Actions
440 pages. 1991. Hardcover.
This book contains an introduction to the theory of enumeration, classification, construction and generation of discrete structures in mathematics and sciences that can be defined as equivalence classes on finites sets, and in particular on finite sets of mappings. Prominent examples are graphs, switching functions, physical states and chemical isomers.

ADALBERT KERBER

ALGEBRAIC
COMBINATORICS
VIA FINITE
GROUP ACTIONS

BI
Wissenschaftsverlag

H. Lüneburg
Tools and Fundamental Constructions of Combinatorial Mathematics
525 pages. 1989. Hardcover.
The book is intended to give the reader a feeling of what combinatorics is about. It therefore starts with the investigation of Dedekind triples which are at the basis of induction and recursion. They are also needed for the definition of finite sets. Combinatorial theory is certainly also concerned with the countable and even with the uncountable. Also algorithms play a central role in the book.

M. Reimer
Constructive Theory of Multivariate Functions with an Application to Tomography
288 pages. 1990. Soft cover.
This book is concerned with a constructive theory of approximations to multivariate functions, preferably by polynomial restrictions. The first part is devoted to multivariate polynomials, their properties and the relations between the various polynomials spaces. The second part deals with multivariate approximations by the use of linear operators. Finally the use of theory and methods presented is checked by their application in the reconstruction problem of tomography.

B·I·

Wissenschaftsverlag
Mannheim · Leipzig · Wien · Zürich

Further Reading
in Theoretical Physics
by B.I.-Wissenschaftsverlag

Steeb, W.-H./A. Kunick

Chaos in dynamischen Systemen

Introduction to non-linear dynamic systems with chaotic behaviour.
255 pp. 2nd revised and enlarged edition 1989.

Steeb, W.-H.

Problems in Theoretical Physics

Volume I: Introductory Problems
207 pp. 1990.
Volume II: Advanced Problems
300 pp. 1990.
This work offers advanced undergraduate and gratuate students of mathematics, physics and engineering problems and solutions in modern mathematical and theoretical physics.

Steeb, W.-H.

Kronecker product of matrices and applications

Introduction to the fundamentals of the Kronecker product and its applications in mathematics and theoretical physics.
144 pp. 1991.

Steeb, W.-H.

A Handbook of Terms Used in Chaos and Quantum Chaos

This handbook helps to familiarize the reader with terms, definitions and theorems in the research field of chaos and quantum chaos.
208 pp. 1991.

Steeb, W.-H.

Hilbert Spaces, Generalized Functions and Quantum Mechanics

This book provides the basic mathematical tools for quantum mechanics: the Hilbert space theory and generalized functions and gives an introduction to quantum mechanics.
198 pp. 1991.

Sundermeyer, K.

Knowledge-Based Systems

Terminology and References
This book contains definitions of catchwords from the field of knowledge-based systems.
222 pp. 1991.

Wissenschaftsverlag
Mannheim · Leipzig · Wien · Zürich

Knowledge–based systems are a new way of thinking about problem solving by computers.

This book contains definitions of catchwords from the field of knowledge-based systems. Most of the entries are provided with references to the literature (either original articles or selected reviews). The material addresses engineering-oriented researchers and research-oriented engineers who observe the knowledge-based system scene or are already involved in work relating to knowledge-based systems.

Most of the entries are concerned with the problem solving aspects of knowledge-based techniques. The field is approached essentially from its applications to engineering problem solving and only mentions aspects of cognitive science in passing. In addition the book covers some commercial products (e. g. specific software and hardware tools). Implemented systems which have been important to the development of the field are discussed, as are the organizations and research initiatives

which were launched to establish knowledge-based systems as an important component of advanced information technology. From this scope, the book presents a balanced treatment of theoretical and practical aspects of knowledge-based systems.

Sundermeyer, K.
Knowledge-Based Systems
Terminology and References
222 pages. 1991. Softcover.
ISBN 3-411-14941-8

Wissenschaftsverlag
Mannheim · Leipzig · Wien · Zürich